ART PAK TO ACCOMPANY

Anatomy & Physiology
THIRD EDITION

Rod R. Seeley, Ph.D.
Trent D. Stephens, Ph.D.
Philip Tate, D.A. (Biological Education)

 Mosby

St. Louis Baltimore Boston Carlsbad Chicago Naples New York Philadelphia Portland
London Madrid Mexico City Singapore Sydney Tokyo Toronto Wiesbaden

Mosby

Dedicated to Publishing Excellence

**A Times Mirror
Company**

Editor-in-Chief: James M. Smith
Editor: Robert J. Callanan
Developmental Editor: Jean Babrick

Printed in the United States of America

Printing/binding by Plus Communications

Mosby–Year Book, Inc.
11830 Westline Industrial Drive
St. Louis, Missouri 63146

26055

95 96 97 98 99 / 9 8 7 6 5 4 3 2 1

TRANSPARENCY ACETATES

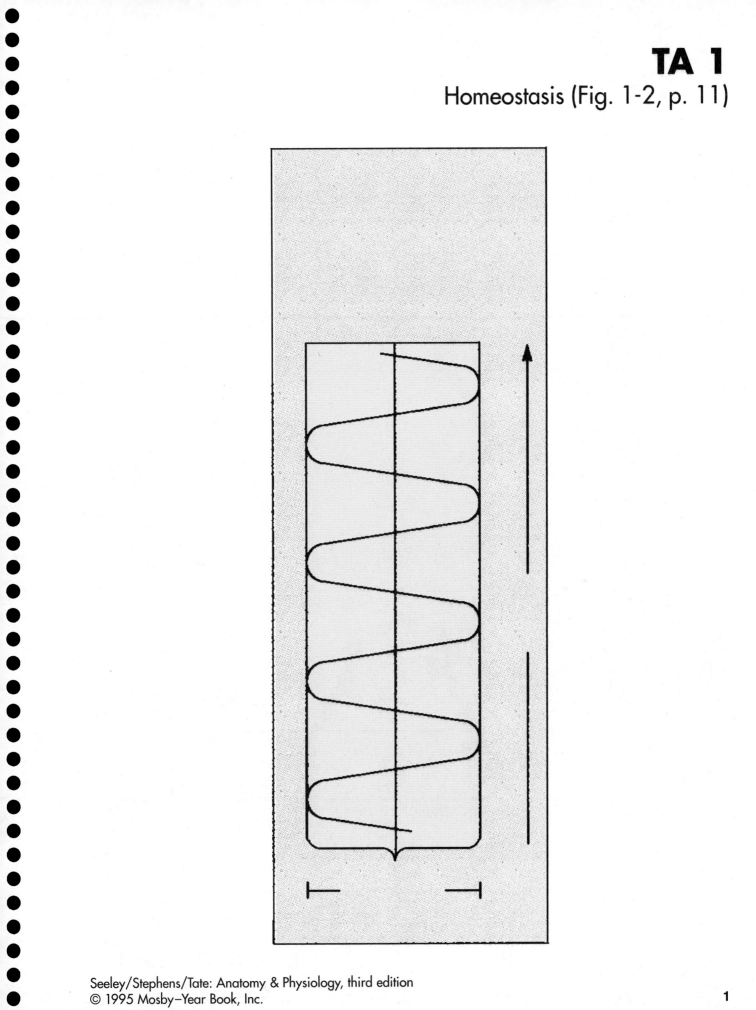

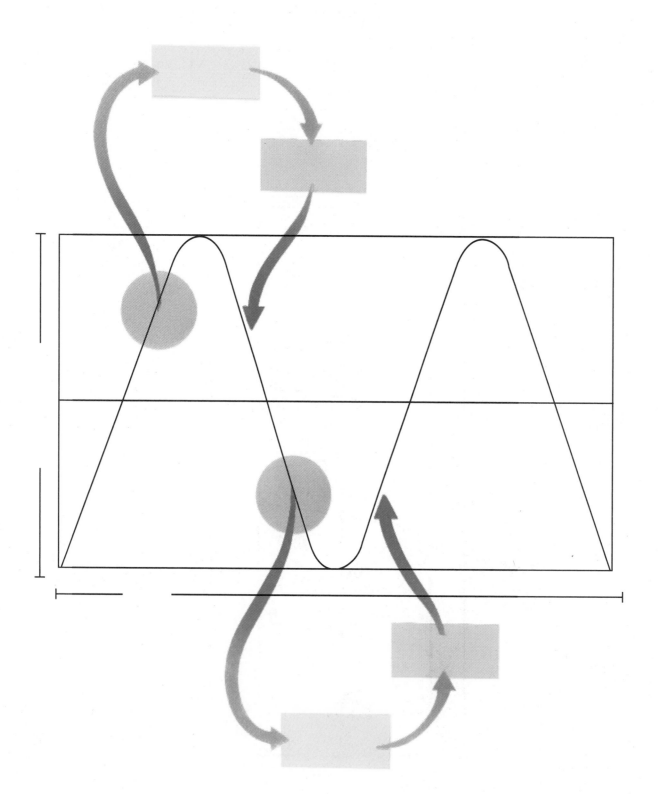

Seeley/Stephens/Tate: Anatomy & Physiology, third edition
© 1995 Mosby–Year Book, Inc.

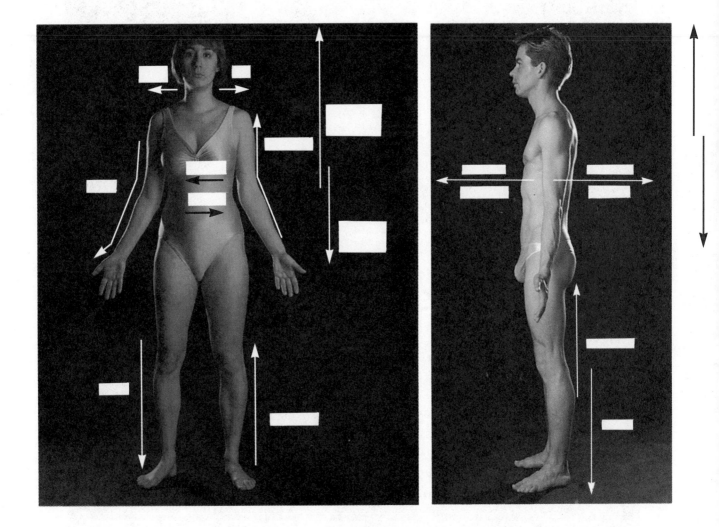

Planes of Section of the Body (Fig. 1-9 A, p. 18)

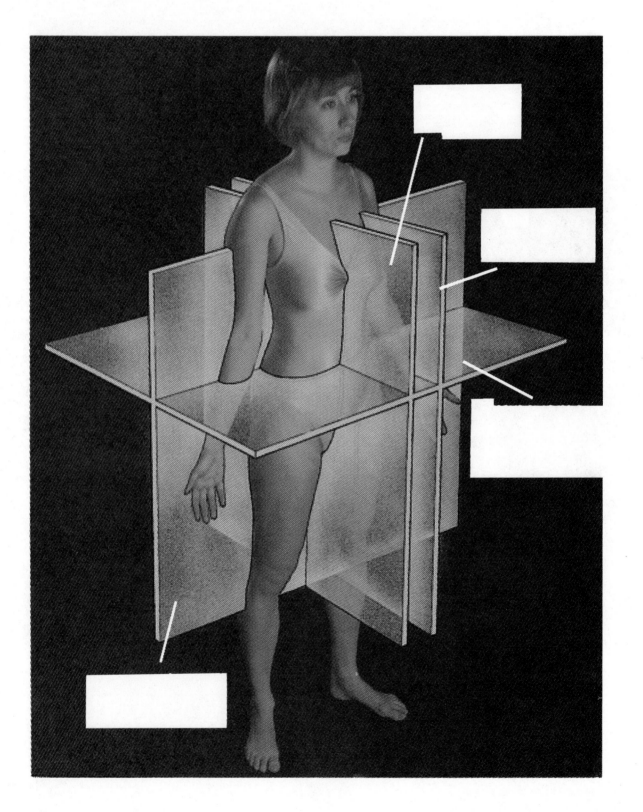

Seeley/Stephens/Tate: Anatomy & Physiology, third edition
© 1995 Mosby–Year Book, Inc.

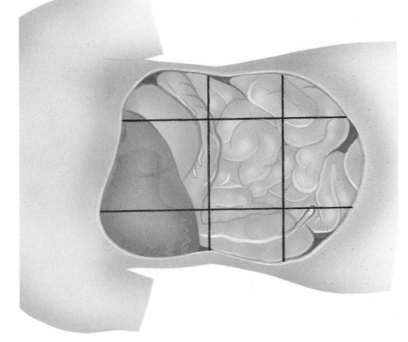

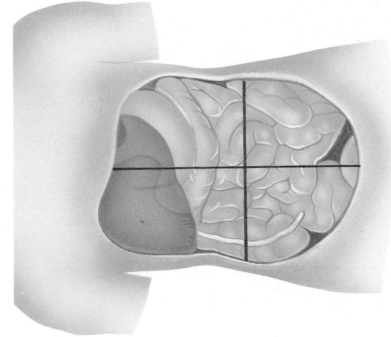

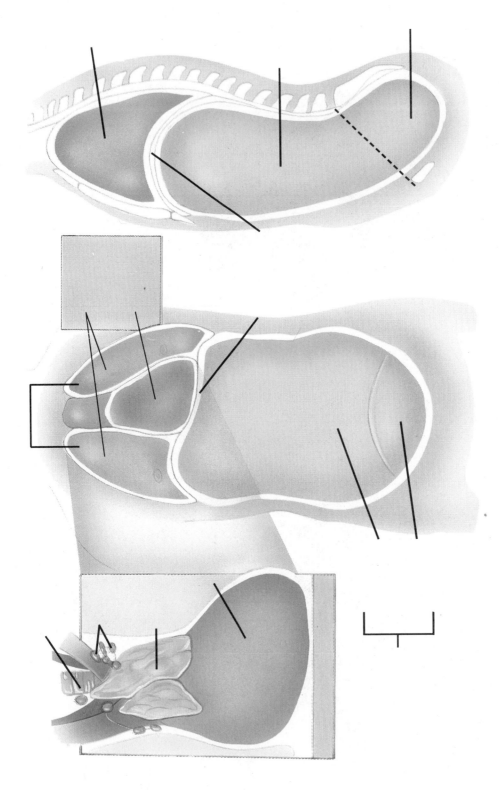

Seeley/Stephens/Tate: Anatomy & Physiology, third edition
© 1995 Mosby–Year Book, Inc.

Serous Membranes (Fig. 1-14 A & B, p. 21)

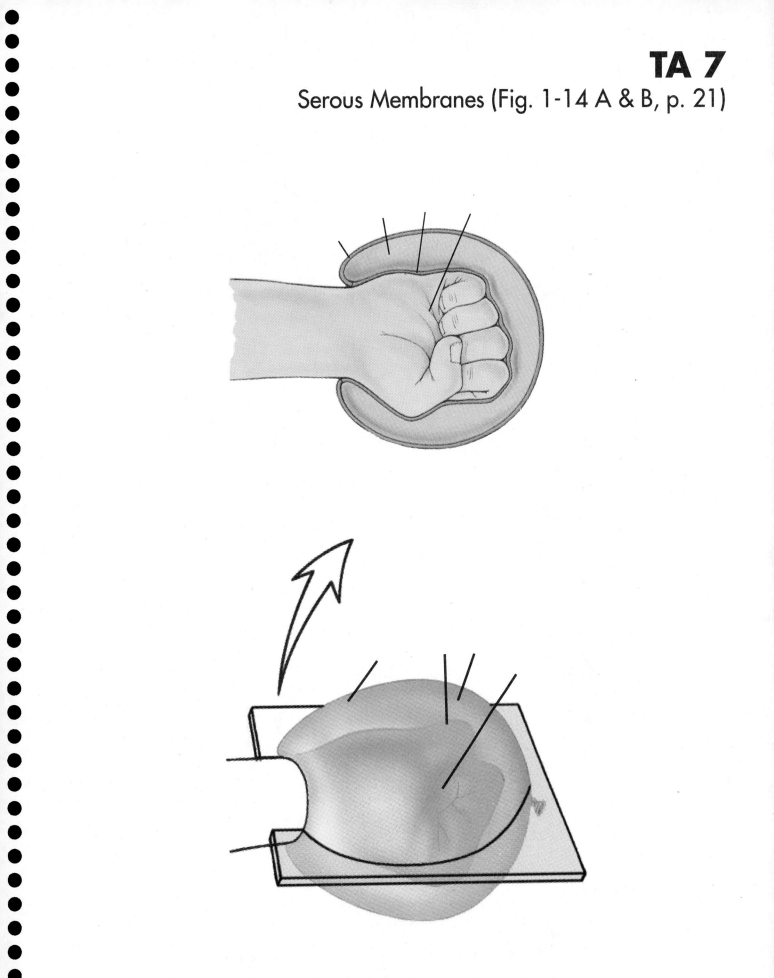

TA 8
Location of Serous Membranes (Fig. 1-15 A-C, p. 24)

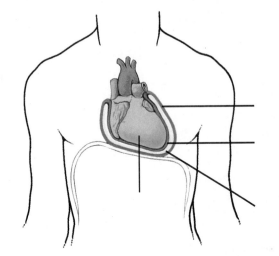

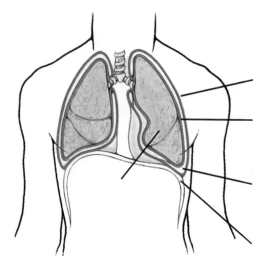

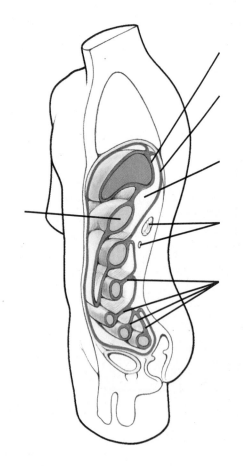

Seeley/Stephens/Tate: Anatomy & Physiology, third edition
© 1995 Mosby–Year Book, Inc.

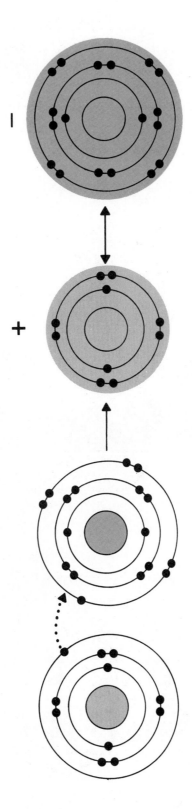

TA 10
Covalent Bonds (Fig. 2-4, p. 34)

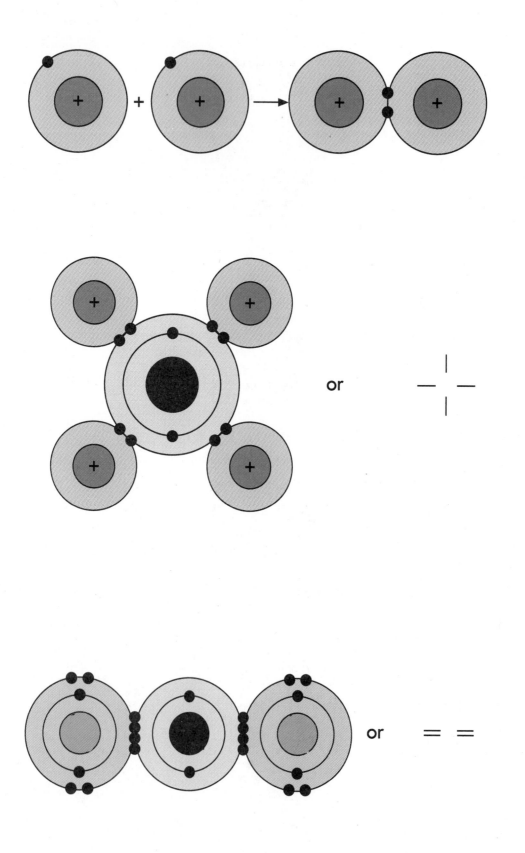

or

—|—
— —
—|—

or = =

Seeley/Stephens/Tate: Anatomy & Physiology, third edition
© 1995 Mosby–Year Book, Inc.

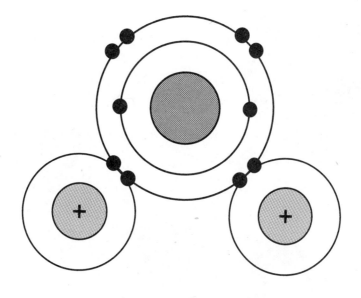

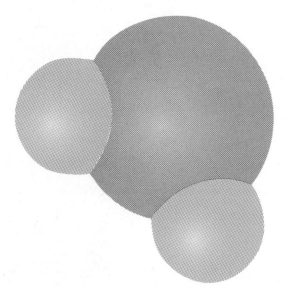

Dissociation (Fig. 2-6, p. 36)

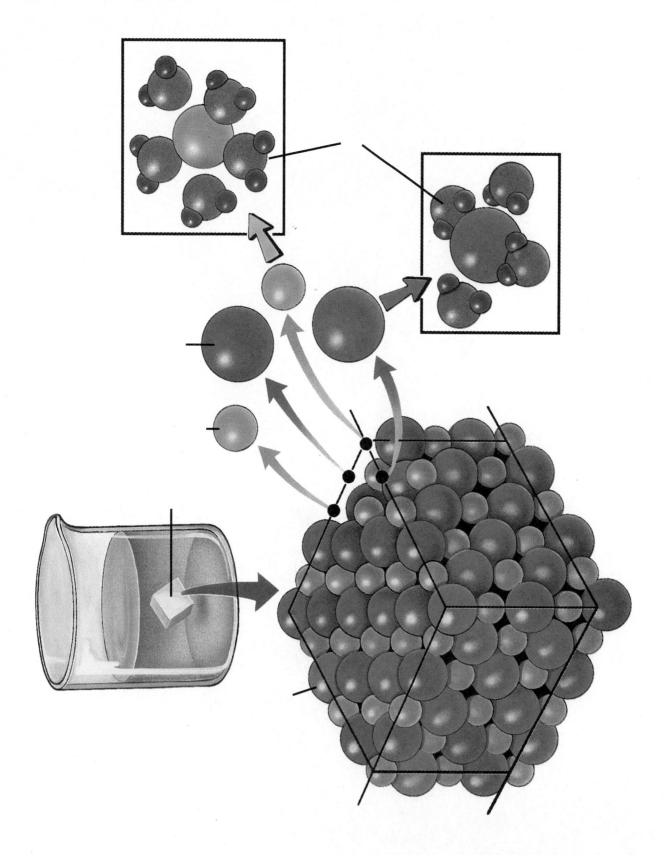

Seeley/Stephens/Tate: Anatomy & Physiology, third edition
© 1995 Mosby–Year Book, Inc.

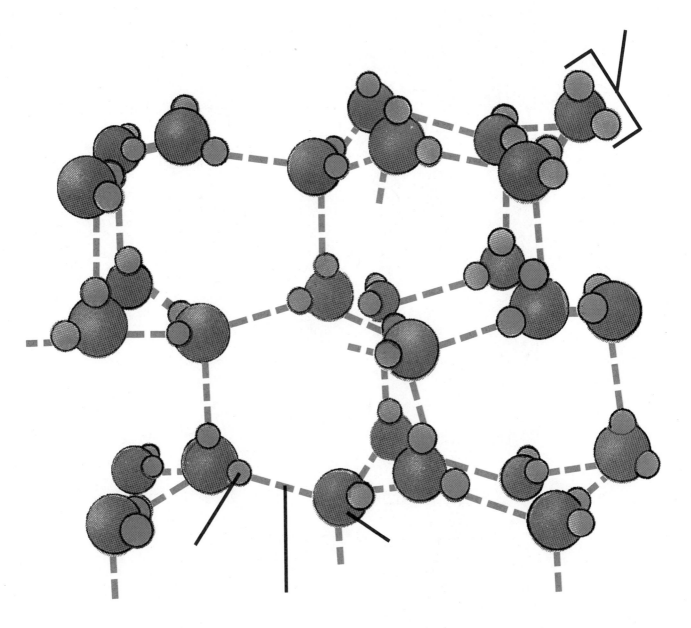

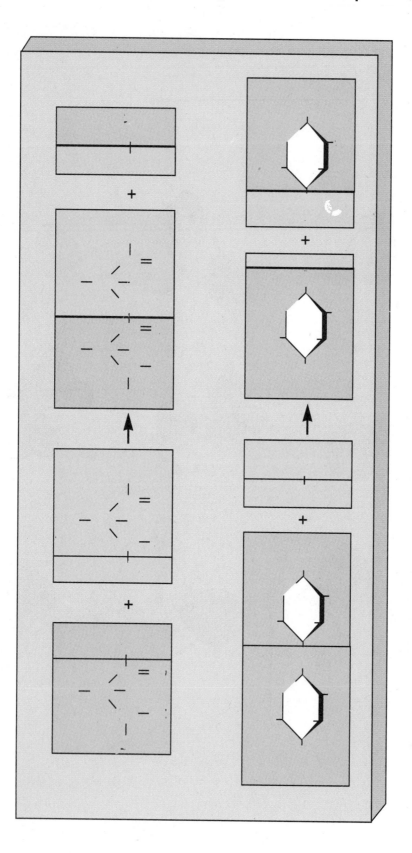

Seeley/Stephens/Tate: Anatomy & Physiology, third edition
© 1995 Mosby–Year Book, Inc.

Energy and Chemical Reactions (Fig. 2-10 A & B, p. 41)

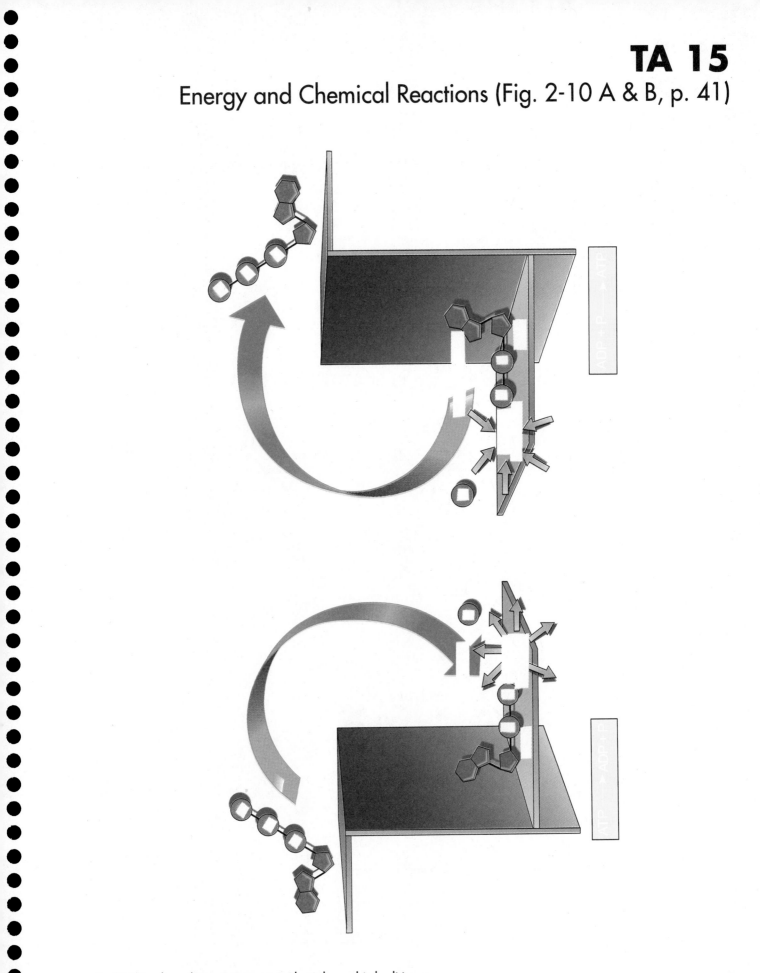

TA 16
Monosaccharides; Disaccharide and Polysaccharide
(Fig. 2-12, 2-13 A & B, p. 46)

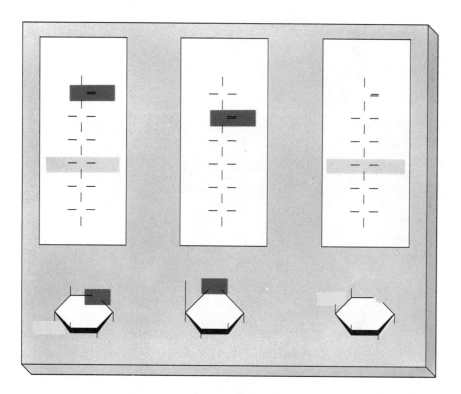

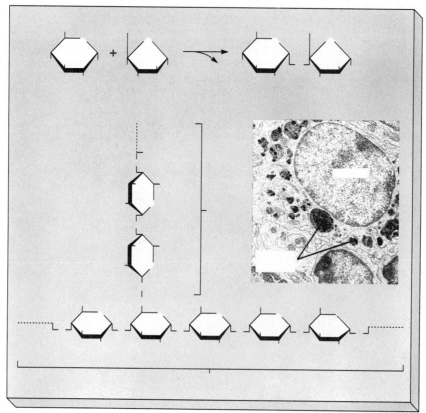

Seeley/Stephens/Tate: Anatomy & Physiology, third edition
© 1995 Mosby–Year Book, Inc.

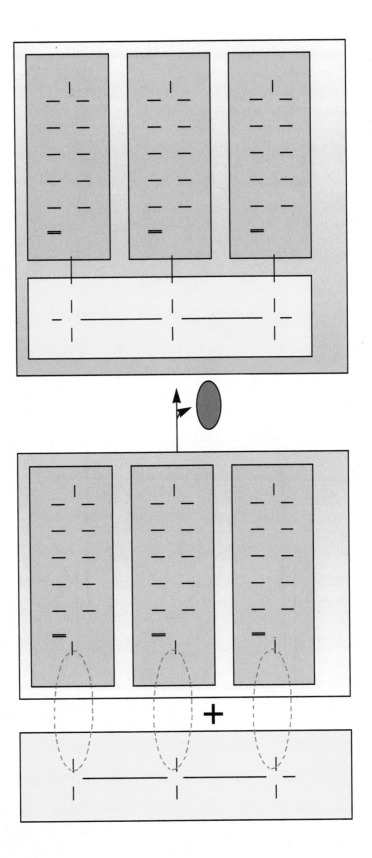

Seeley/Stephens/Tate: Anatomy & Physiology, third edition
© 1995 Mosby–Year Book, Inc.

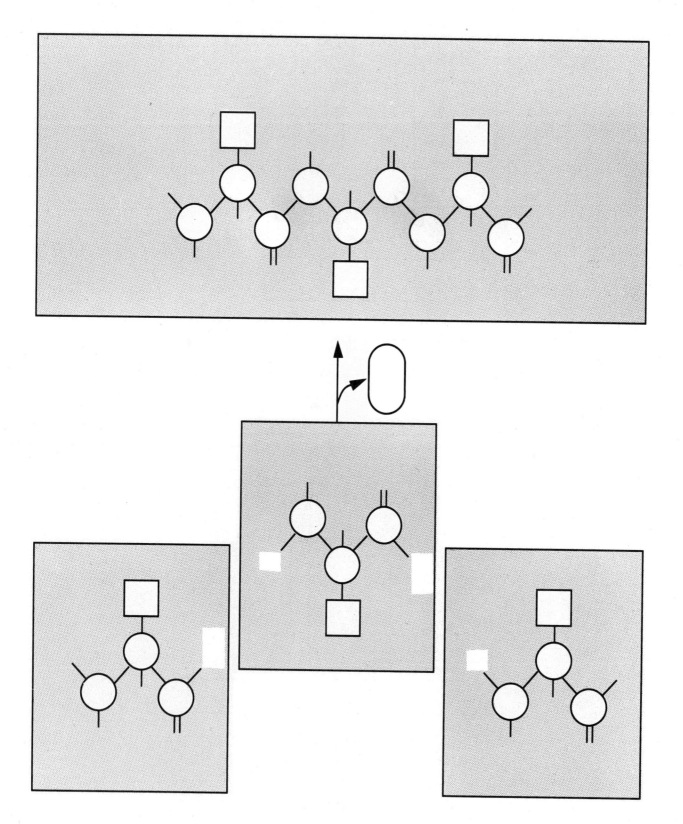

Seeley/Stephens/Tate: Anatomy & Physiology, third edition
© 1995 Mosby–Year Book, Inc.

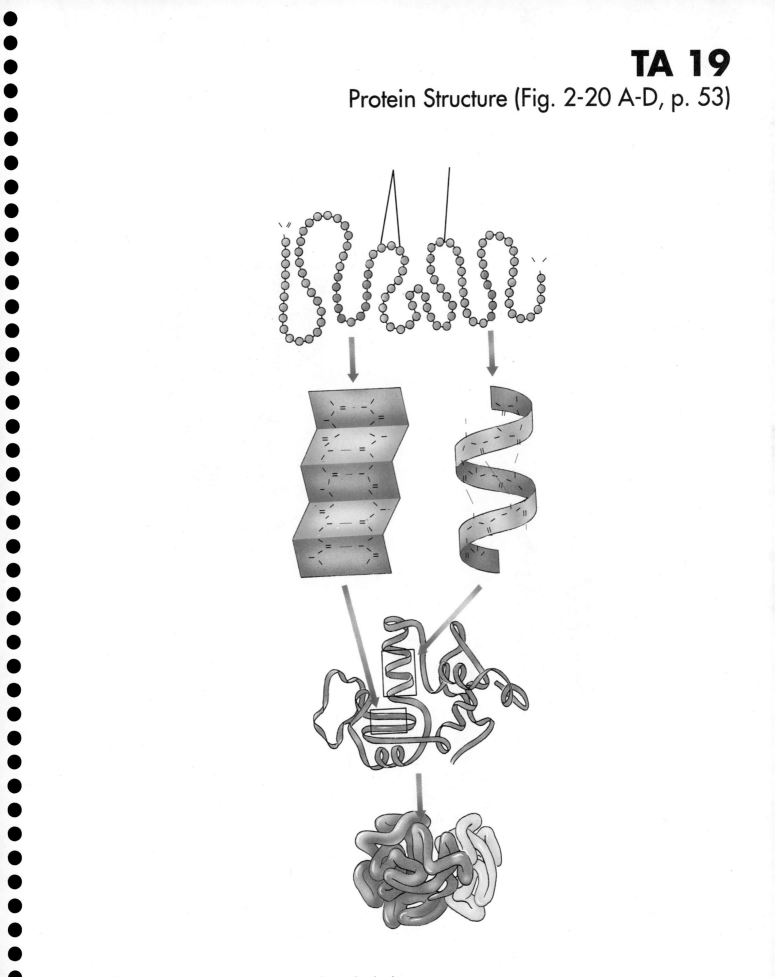

Activation Energy and Enzymes (Fig. 2-21 A & B, p. 54)

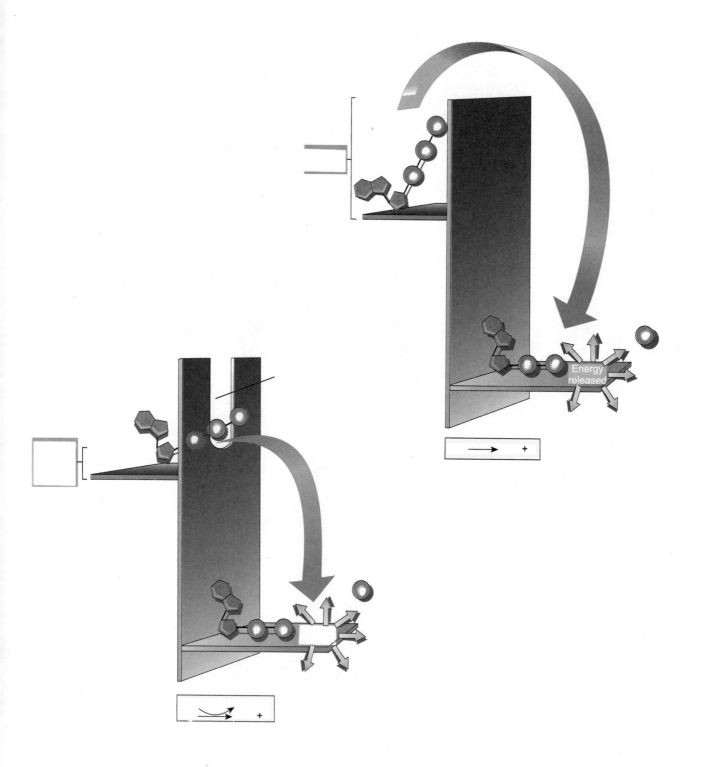

Seeley/Stephens/Tate: Anatomy & Physiology, third edition
© 1995 Mosby–Year Book, Inc.

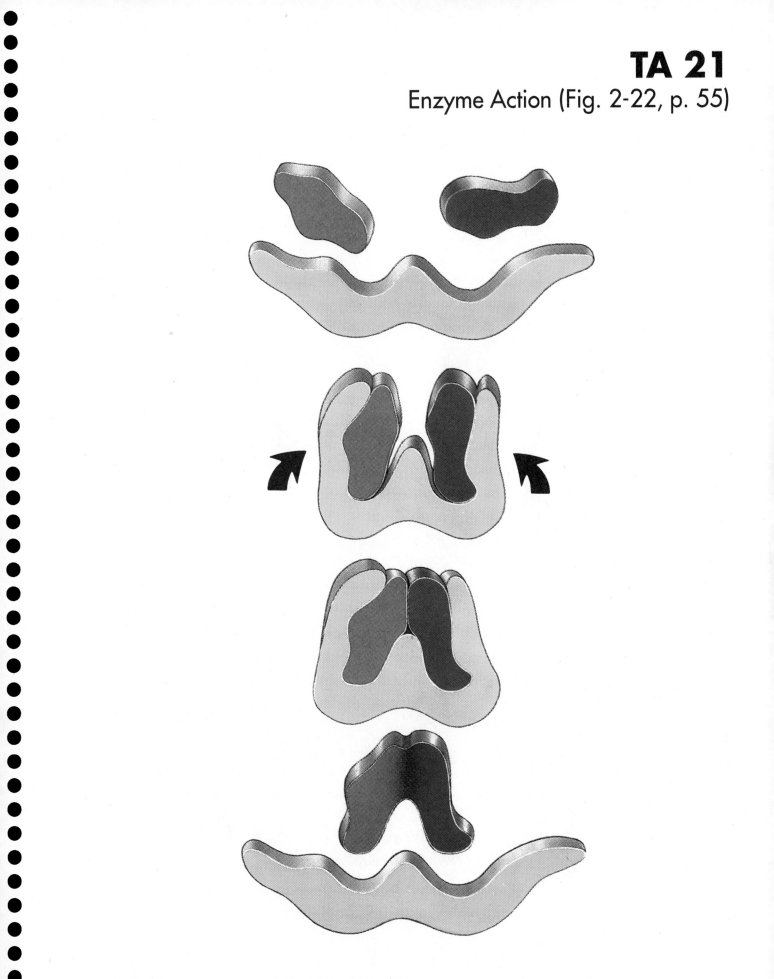

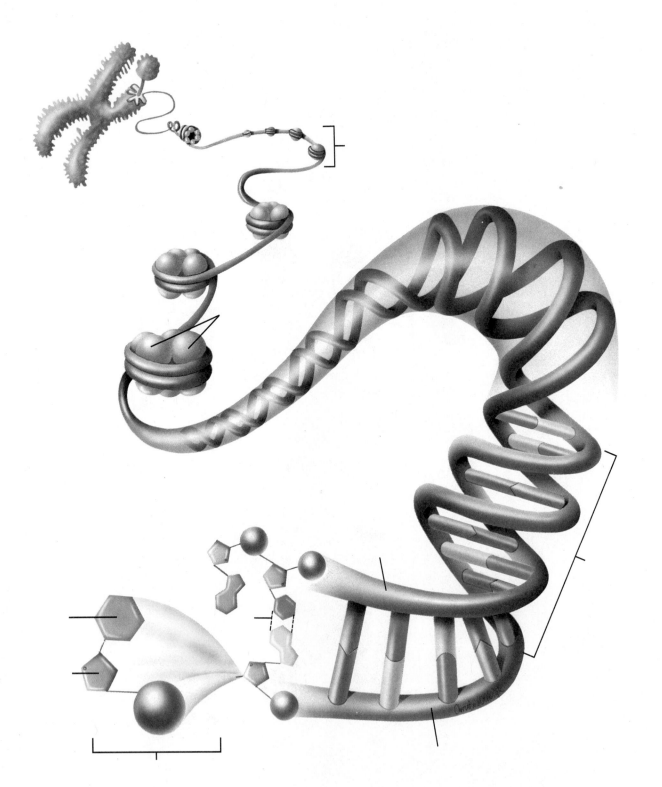

Seeley/Stephens/Tate: Anatomy & Physiology, third edition
© 1995 Mosby–Year Book, Inc.

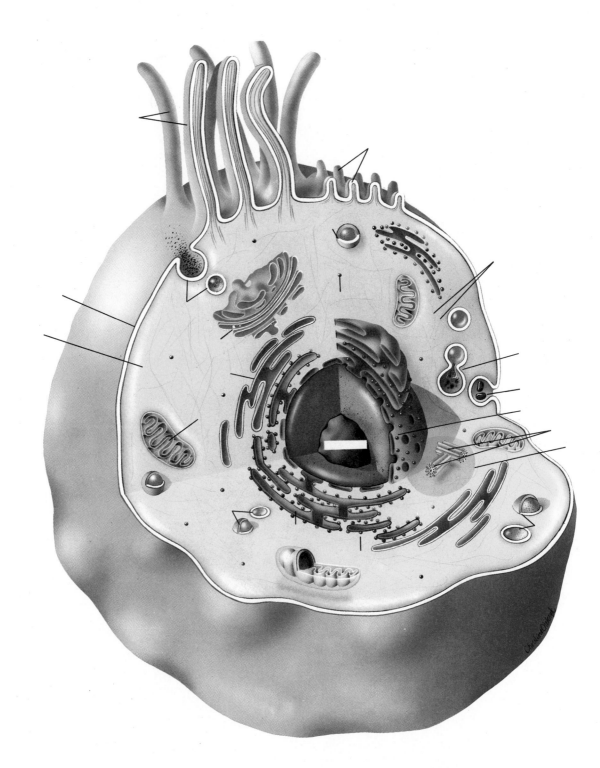

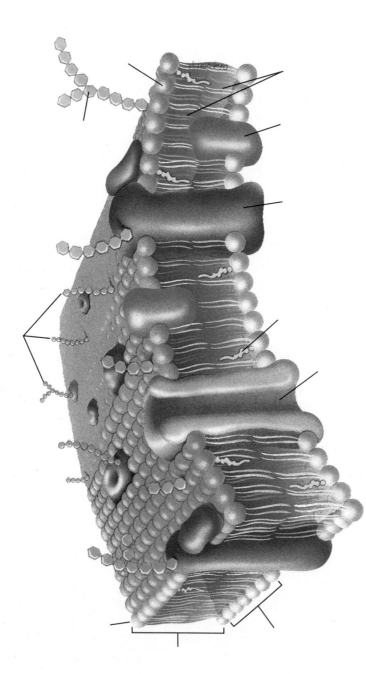

Seeley/Stephens/Tate: Anatomy & Physiology, third edition
© 1995 Mosby–Year Book, Inc.

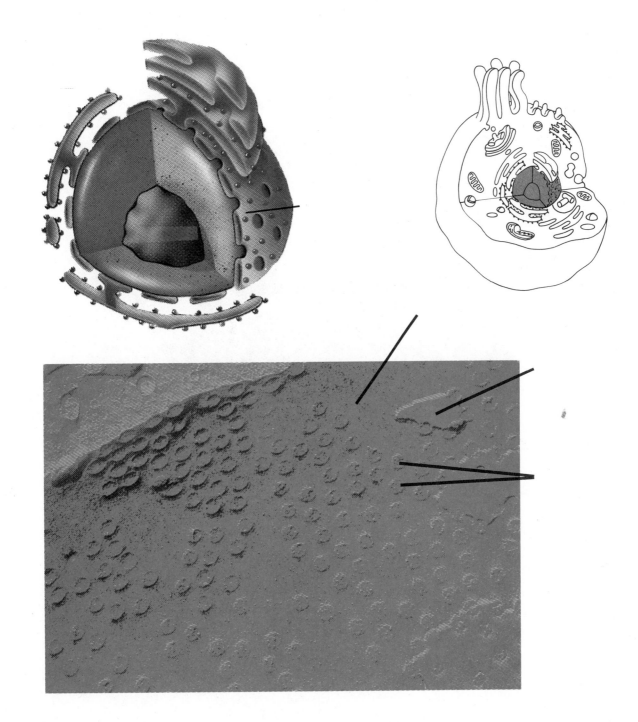

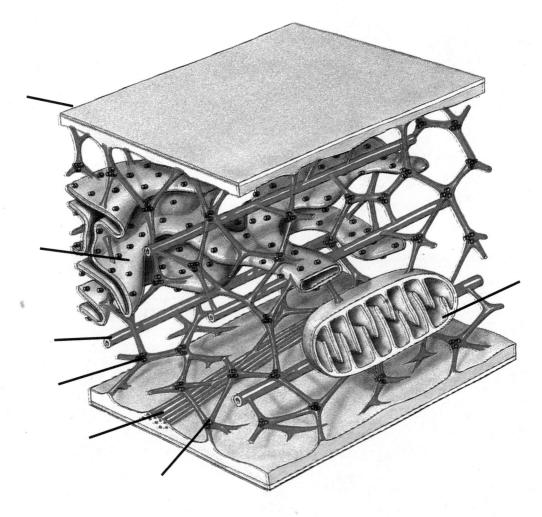

Seeley/Stephens/Tate: Anatomy & Physiology, third edition
© 1995 Mosby–Year Book, Inc.

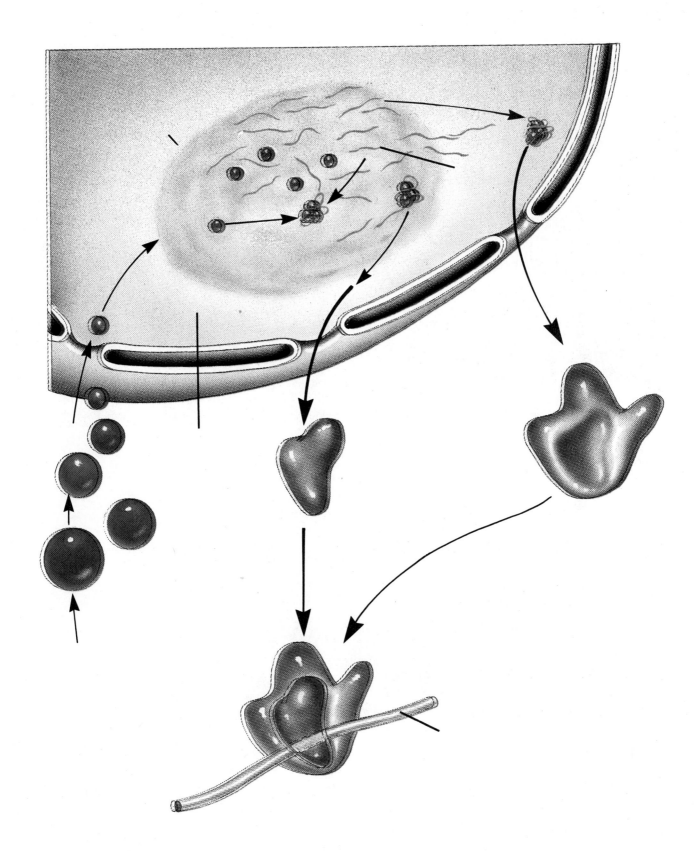

TA 28
The Endoplasmic Reticulum and Golgi Apparatus
(Fig. 3-7 A-C, p. 70)

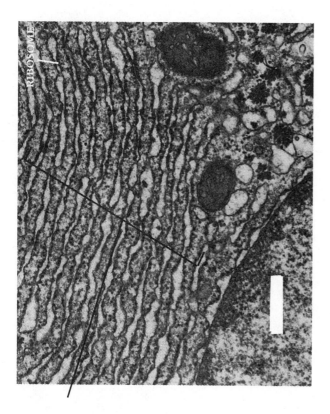

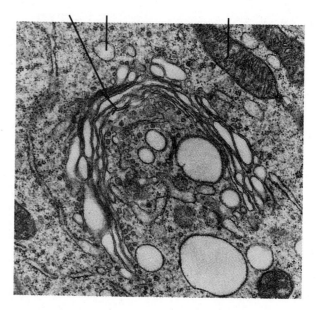

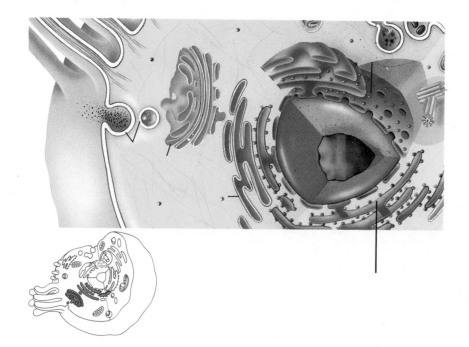

Seeley/Stephens/Tate: Anatomy & Physiology, third edition
© 1995 Mosby–Year Book, Inc.

Mitochondrion (Fig. 3-9 A & B, p. 73)

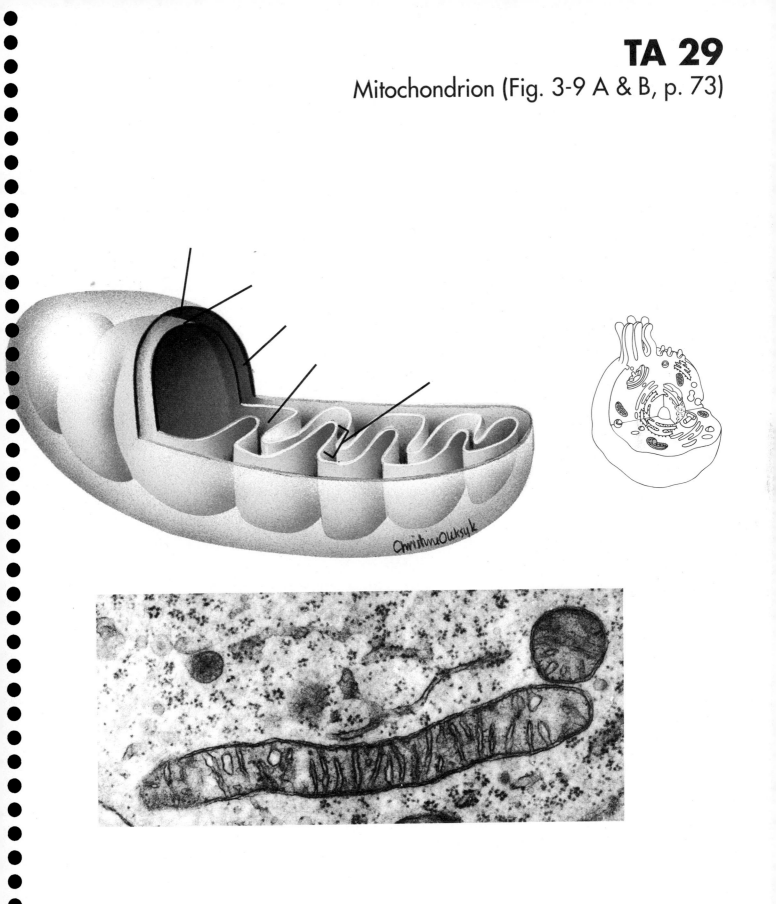

Seeley/Stephens/Tate: Anatomy & Physiology, third edition
© 1995 Mosby–Year Book, Inc.

TA 30
Cilia and Flagella (Fig. 3-11 A & B, p. 75)

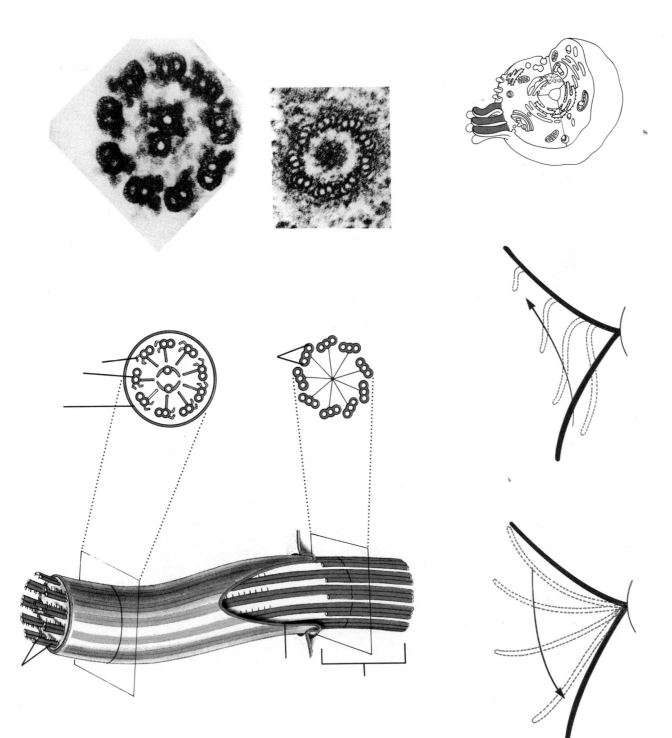

Seeley/Stephens/Tate: Anatomy & Physiology, third edition
© 1995 Mosby–Year Book, Inc.

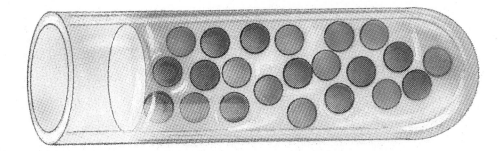

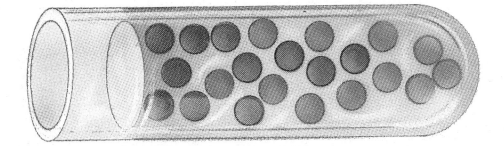

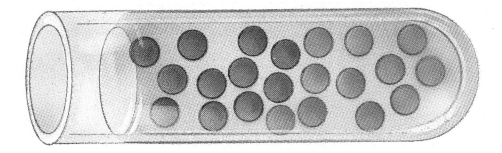

TA 32
Osmosis (Fig. 3-14 A-C, p. 80)

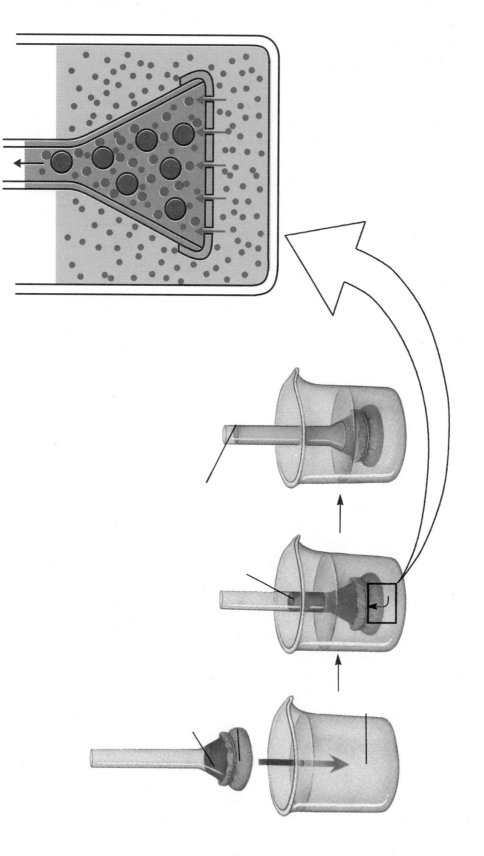

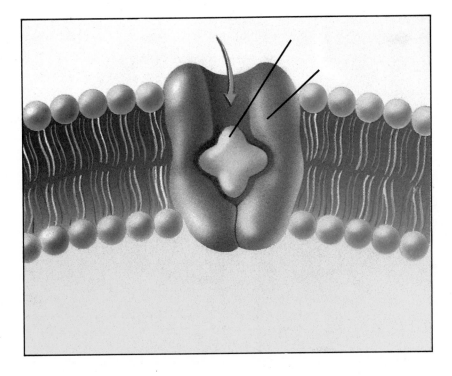

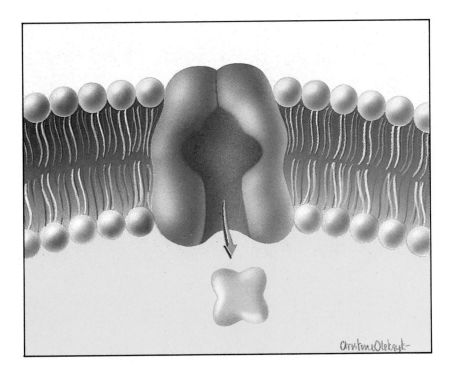

Sodium-Potassium Exchange Pump (Fig. 3-18 A-D, p. 84)

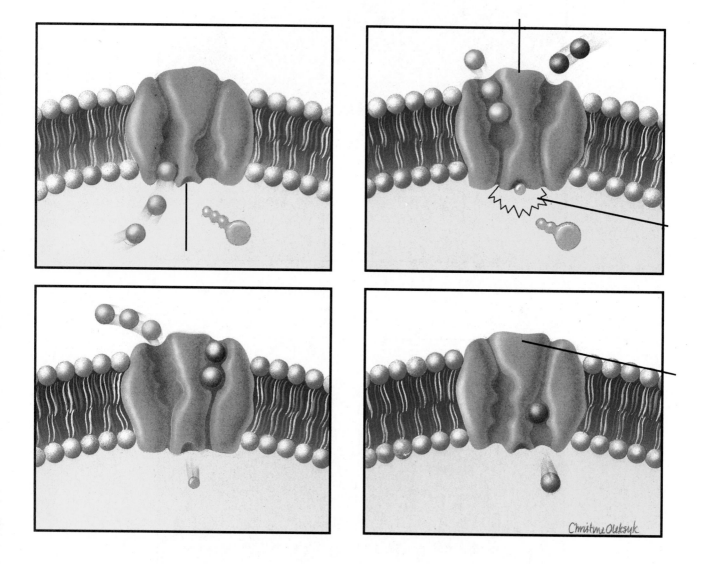

Seeley/Stephens/Tate: Anatomy & Physiology, third edition
© 1995 Mosby–Year Book, Inc.

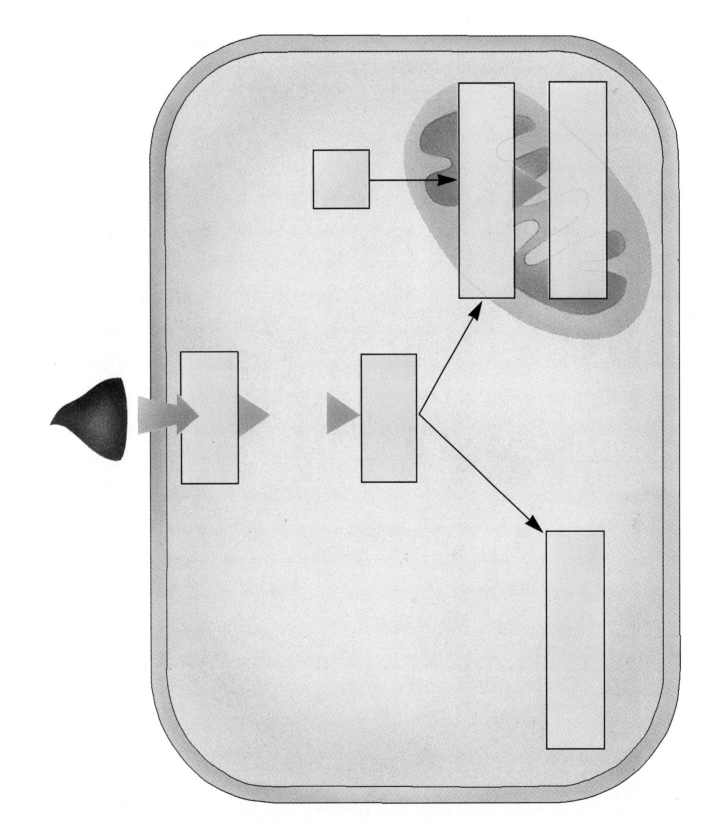

Seeley/Stephens/Tate: Anatomy & Physiology, third edition
© 1995 Mosby–Year Book, Inc.

Translation of mRNA to Produce a Protein (Fig. 3-26 A-D, p. 94)

Seeley/Stephens/Tate: Anatomy & Physiology, third edition
© 1995 Mosby–Year Book, Inc.

Replication of DNA (Fig. 3-27, p. 95)

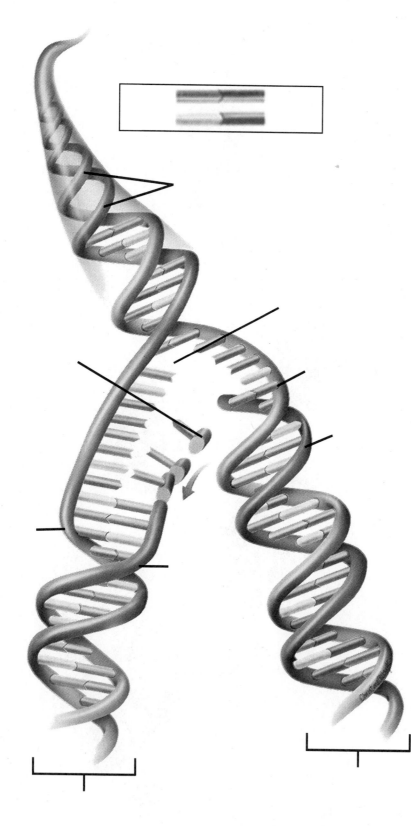

Seeley/Stephens/Tate: Anatomy & Physiology, third edition
© 1995 Mosby–Year Book, Inc.

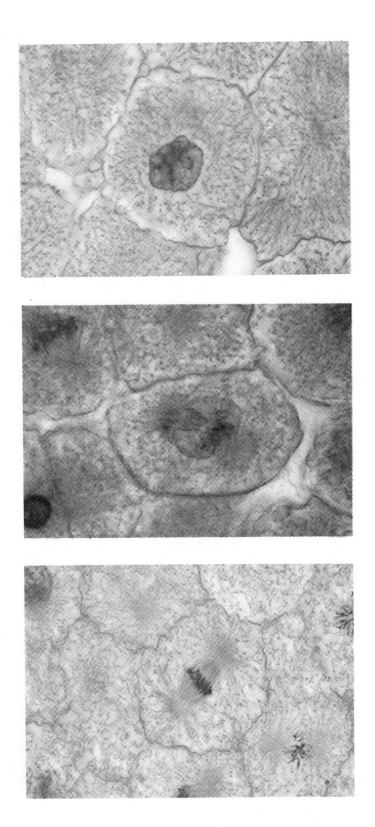

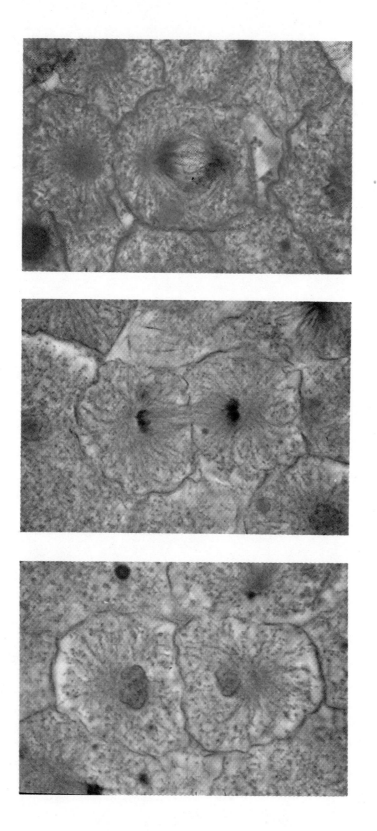

Seeley/Stephens/Tate: Anatomy & Physiology, third edition

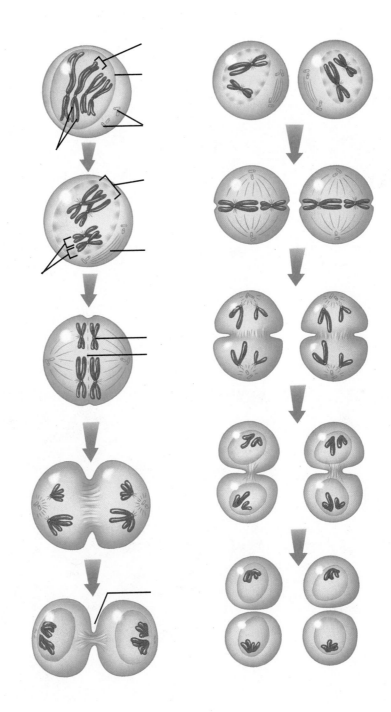

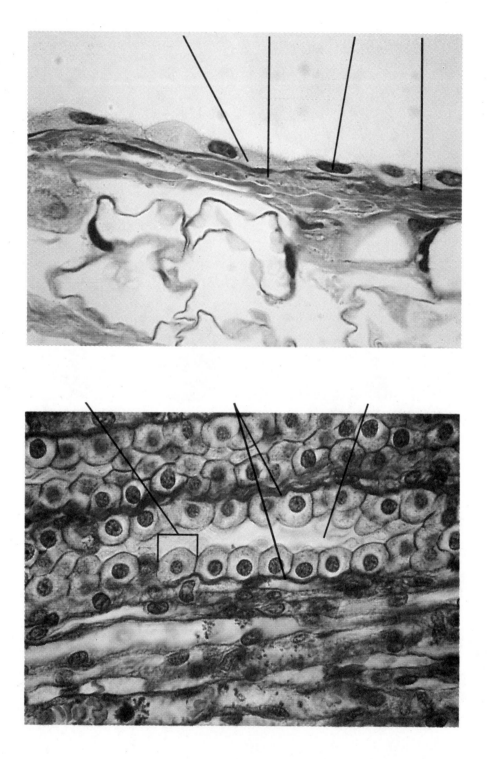

Seeley/Stephens/Tate: Anatomy & Physiology, third edition
© 1995 Mosby–Year Book, Inc.

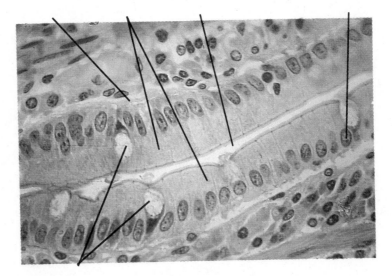

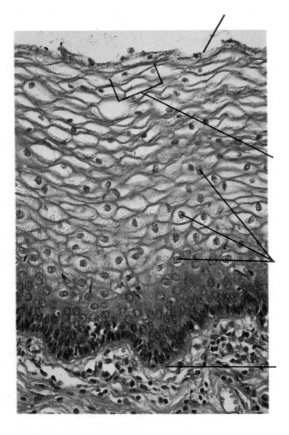

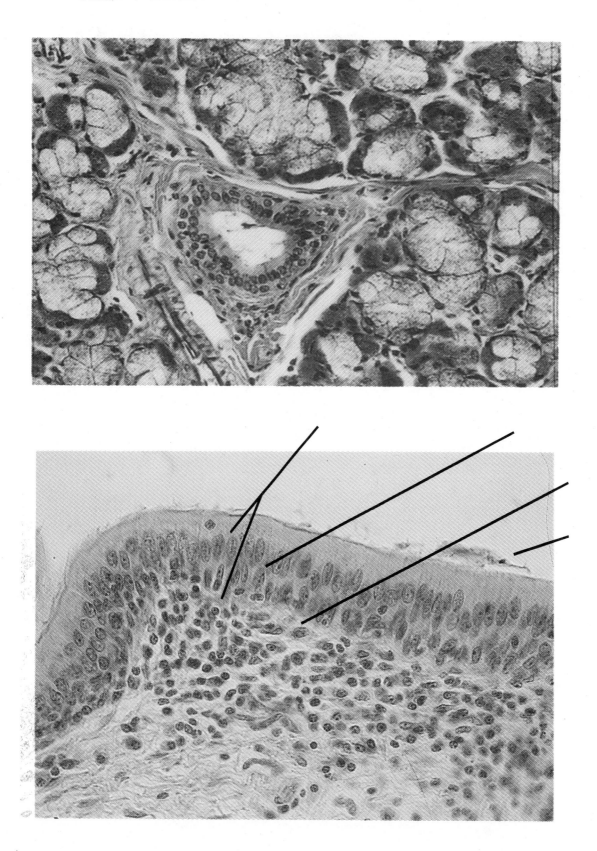

Seeley/Stephens/Tate: Anatomy & Physiology, third edition
© 1995 Mosby–Year Book, Inc.

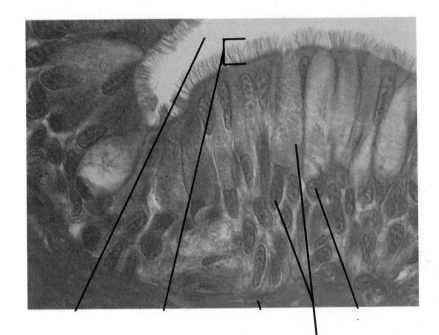

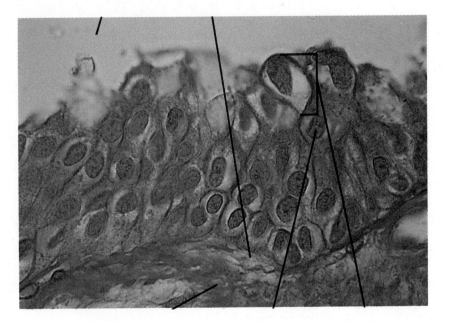

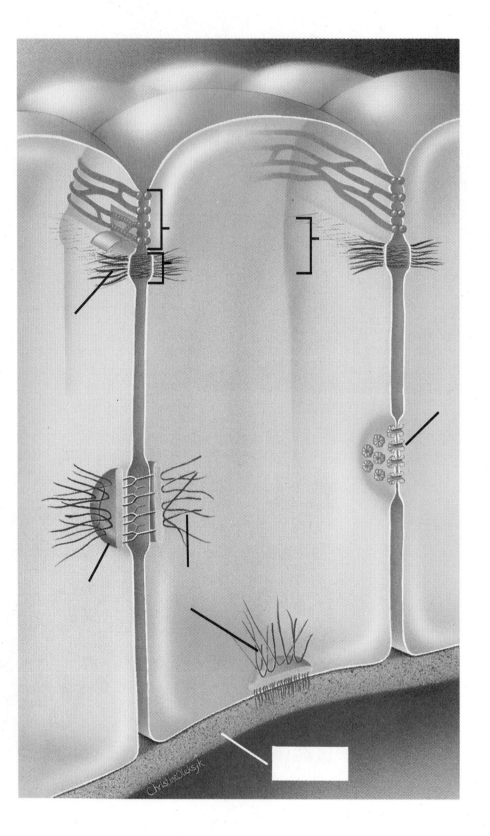

Seeley/Stephens/Tate: Anatomy & Physiology, third edition
© 1995 Mosby—Year Book, Inc.

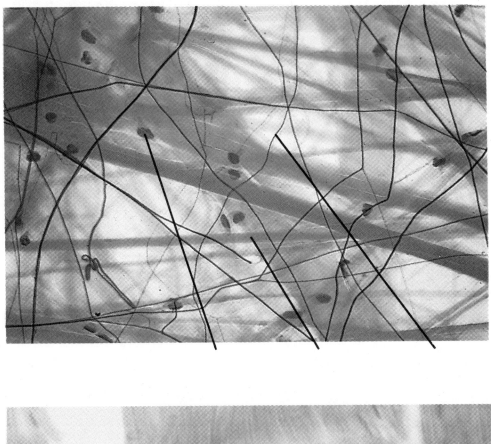

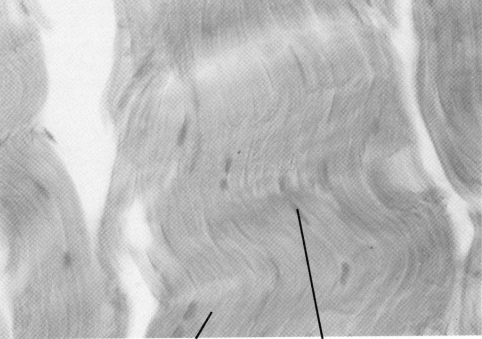

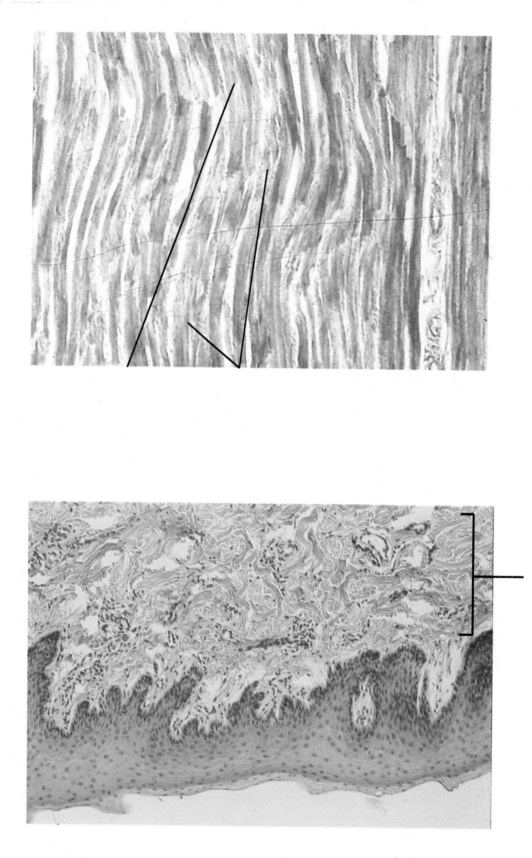

Seeley/Stephens/Tate: Anatomy & Physiology, third edition
© 1995 Mosby—Year Book, Inc.

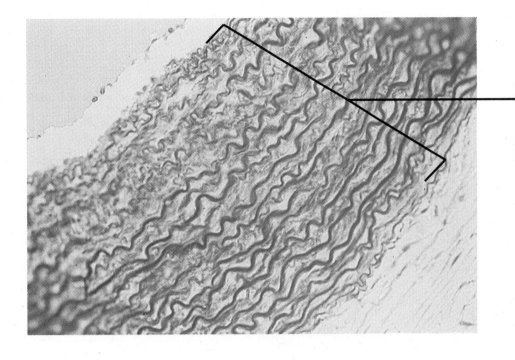

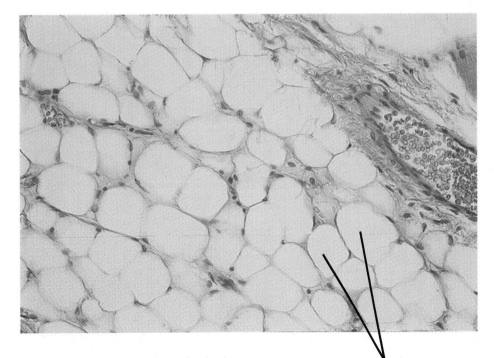

Seeley/Stephens/Tate: Anatomy & Physiology, third edition
© 1995 Mosby–Year Book, Inc.

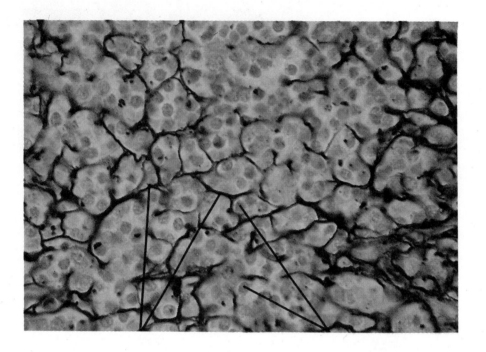

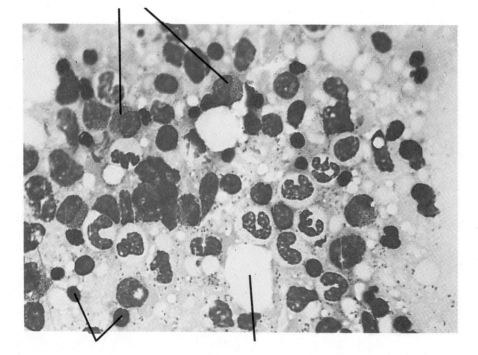

Seeley/Stephens/Tate: Anatomy & Physiology, third edition
© 1995 Mosby–Year Book, Inc.

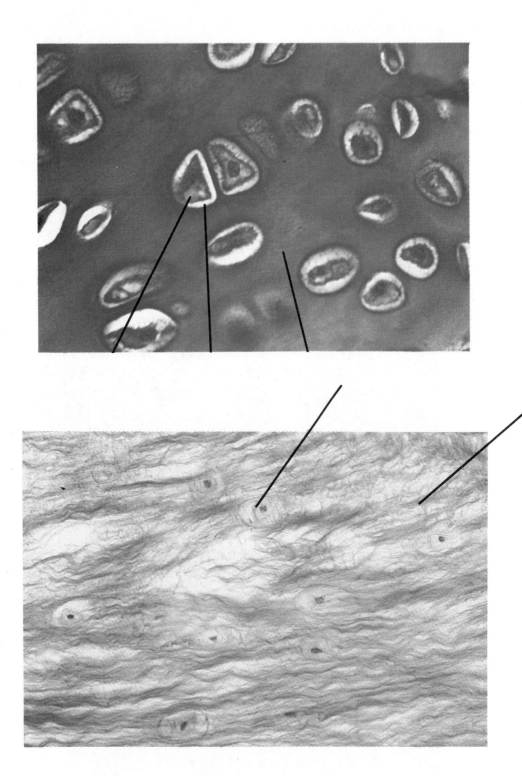

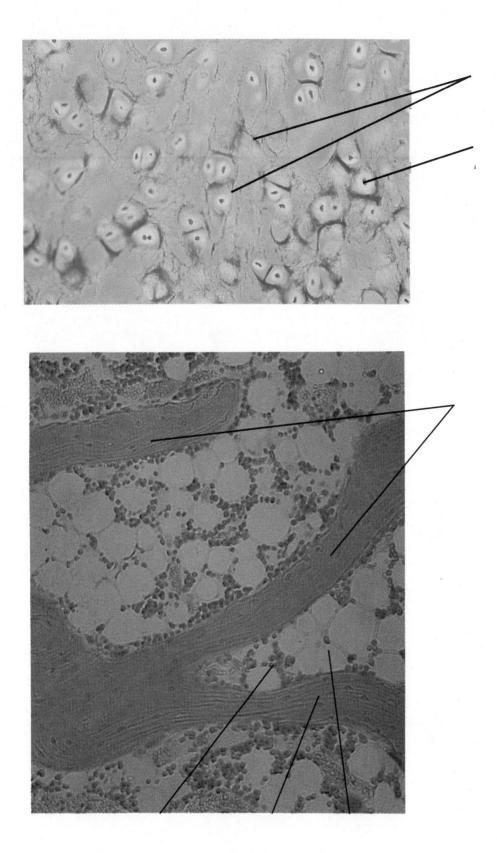

Seeley/Stephens/Tate: Anatomy & Physiology, third edition
© 1995 Mosby–Year Book, Inc.

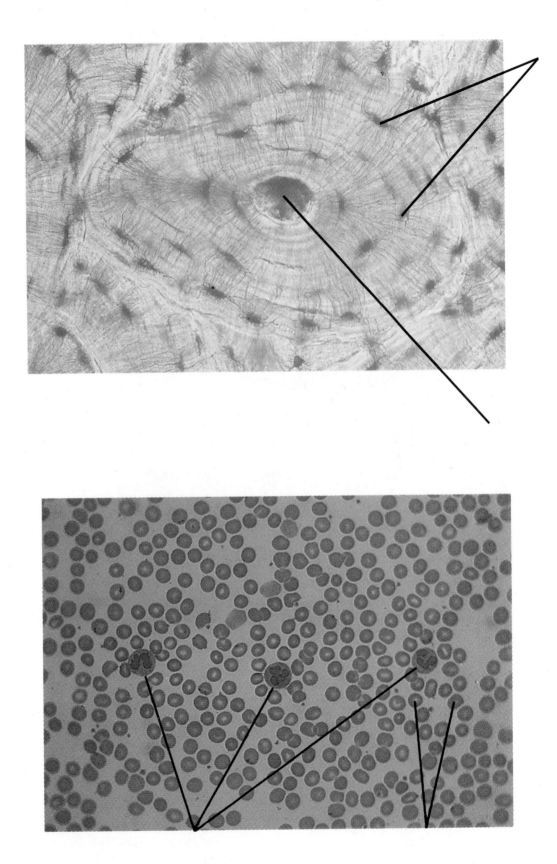

Seeley/Stephens/Tate: Anatomy & Physiology, third edition
© 1995 Mosby–Year Book, Inc.

TA 54
Muscular Tissue (Fig. 4-6 A-C, p. 127)

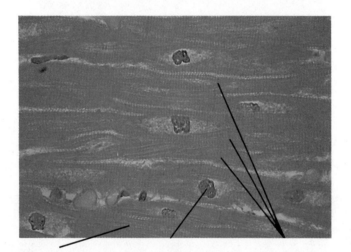

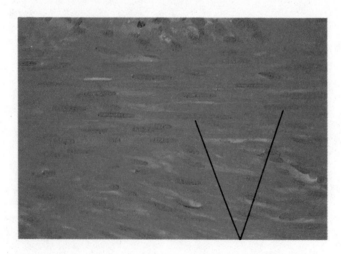

Seeley/Stephens/Tate: Anatomy & Physiology, third edition
© 1995 Mosby–Year Book, Inc.

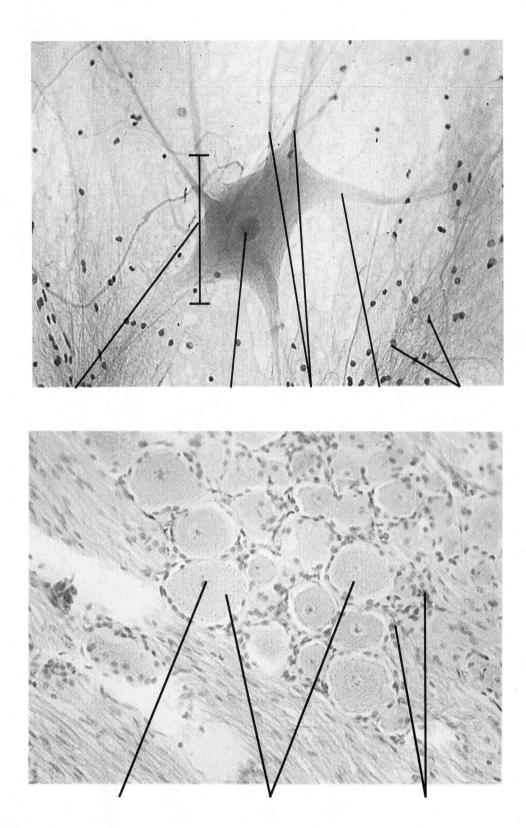

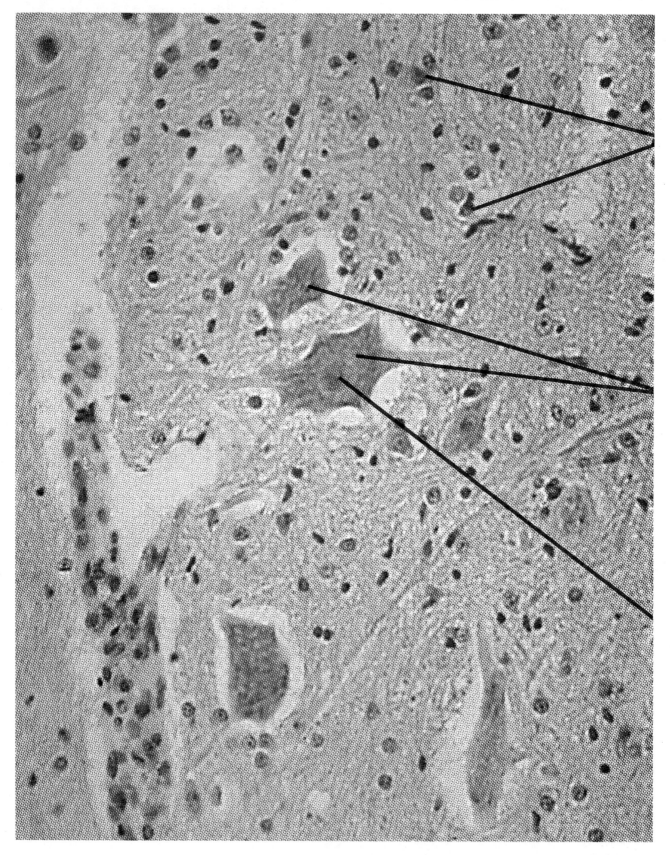

Seeley/Stephens/Tate: Anatomy & Physiology, third edition
© 1995 Mosby–Year Book, Inc.

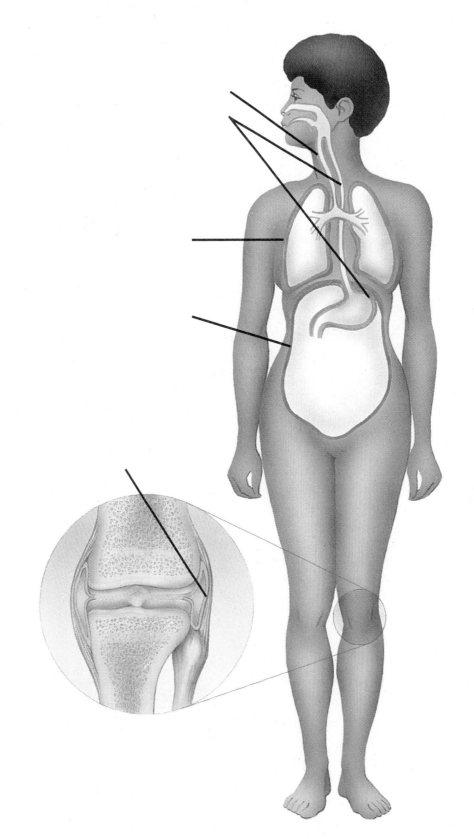

Seeley/Stephens/Tate: Anatomy & Physiology, third edition
© 1995 Mosby–Year Book, Inc.

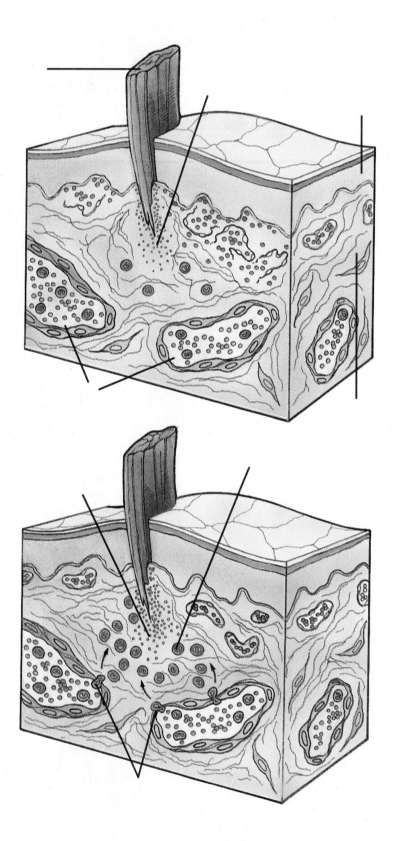

Seeley/Stephens/Tate: Anatomy & Physiology, third edition
© 1995 Mosby–Year Book, Inc.

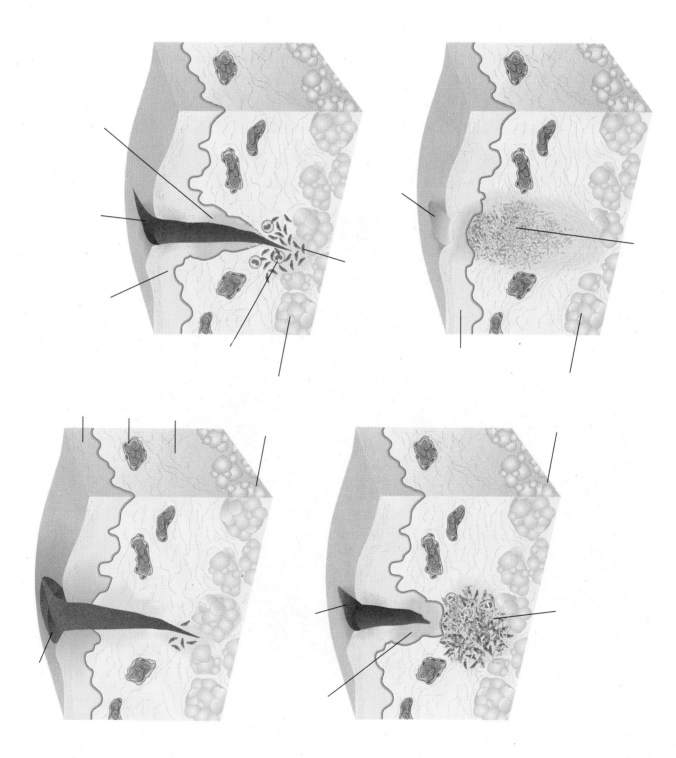

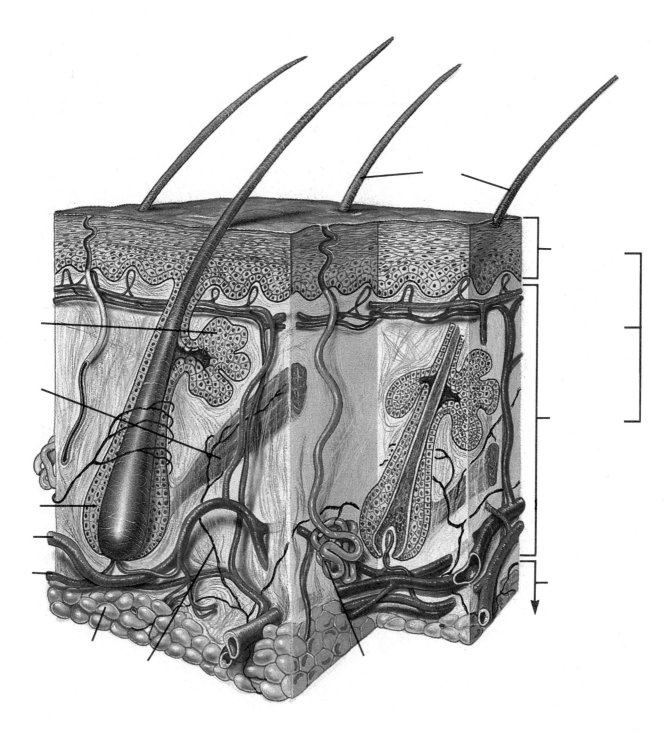

Seeley/Stephens/Tate: Anatomy & Physiology, third edition
© 1995 Mosby–Year Book, Inc.

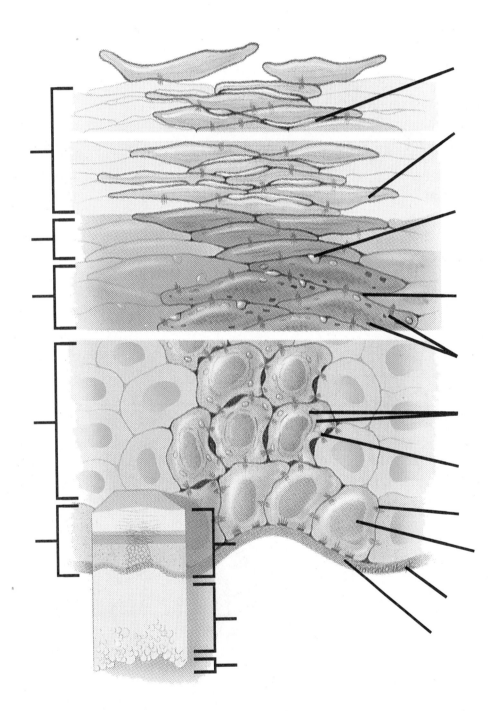

Seeley/Stephens/Tate: Anatomy & Physiology, third edition
© 1995 Mosby—Year Book, Inc.

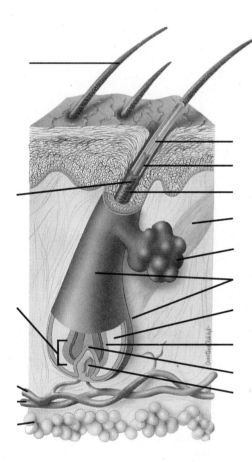

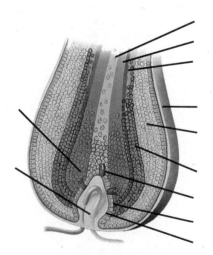

Seeley/Stephens/Tate: Anatomy & Physiology, third edition
© 1995 Mosby–Year Book, Inc.

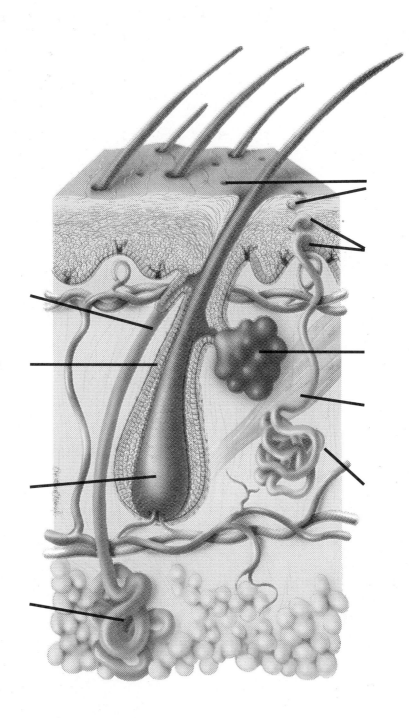

TA 64
Nail (Fig. 5-7 A-C, p. 154)

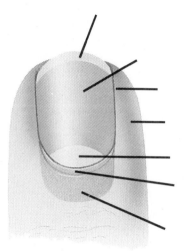

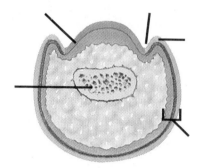

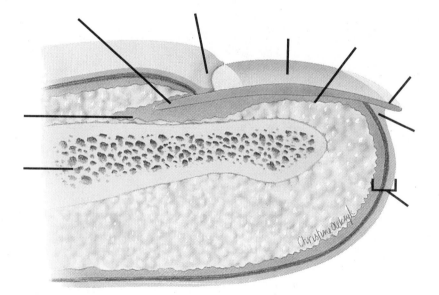

Seeley/Stephens/Tate: Anatomy & Physiology, third edition
© 1995 Mosby–Year Book, Inc.

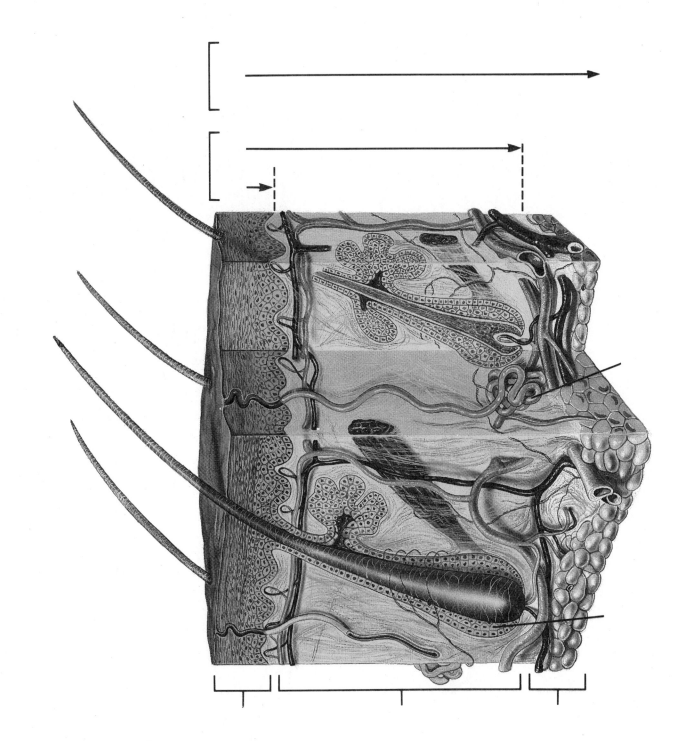

TA 66
Surface Area (Fig. 5-B, p. 151)

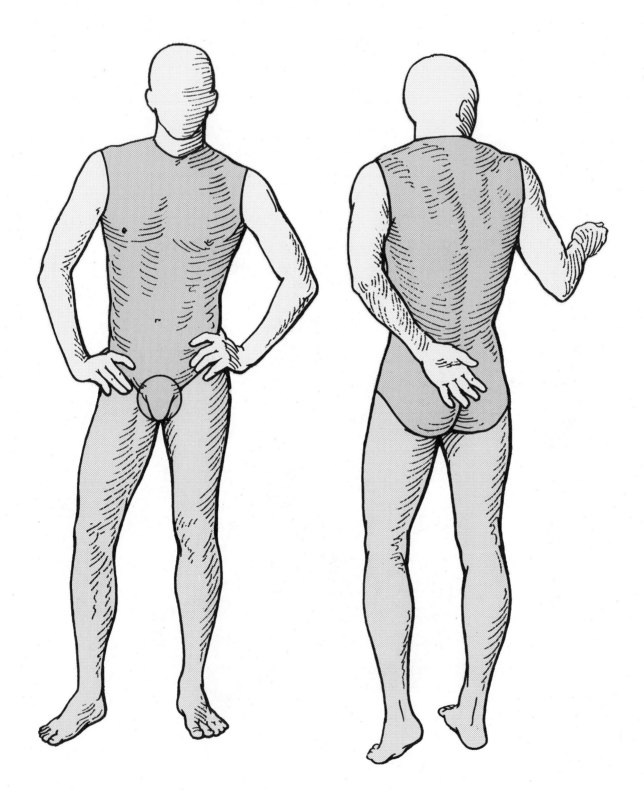

Seeley/Stephens/Tate: Anatomy & Physiology, third edition
© 1995 Mosby–Year Book, Inc.

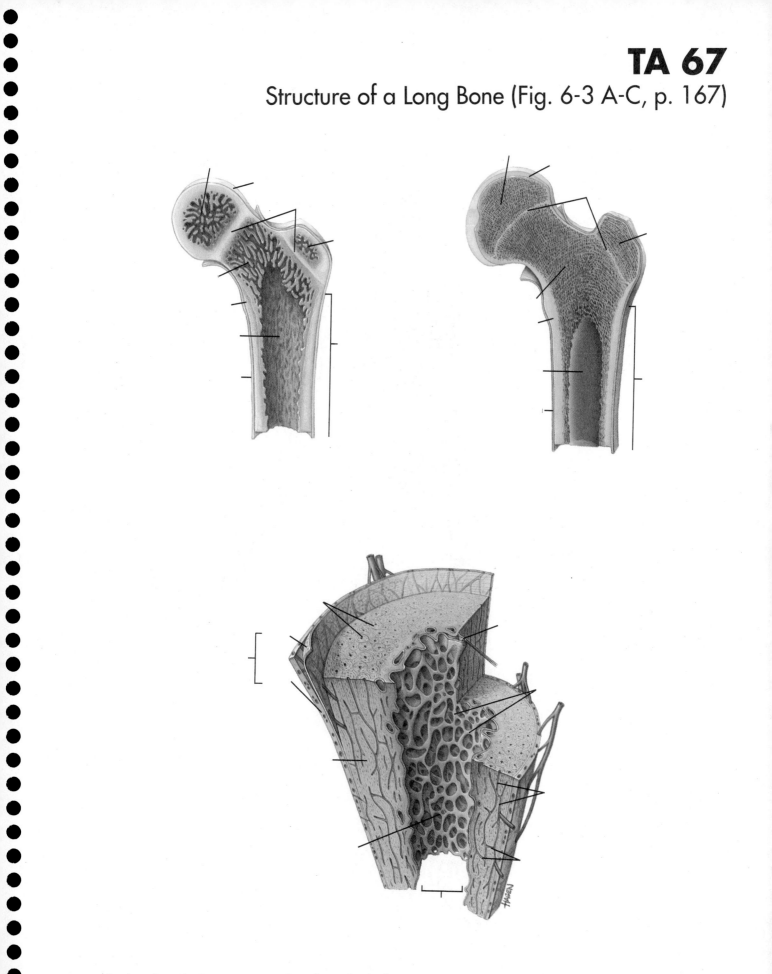

TA 68
Bone Marrow Distribution (Fig. 6-4, p. 168)

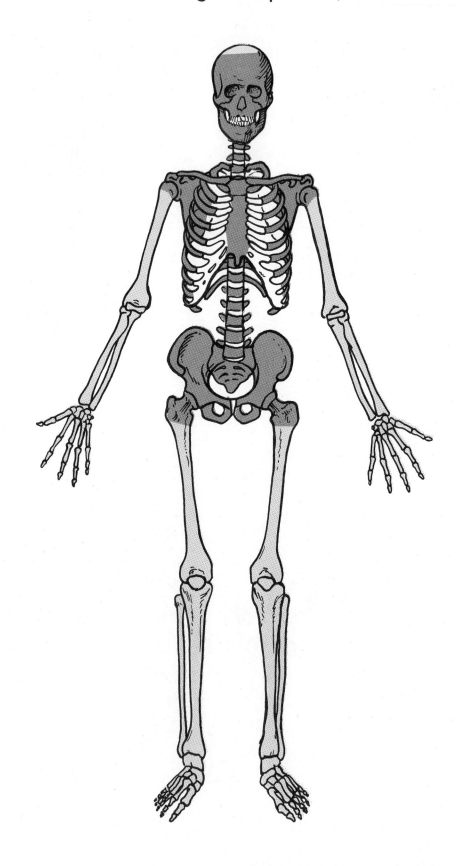

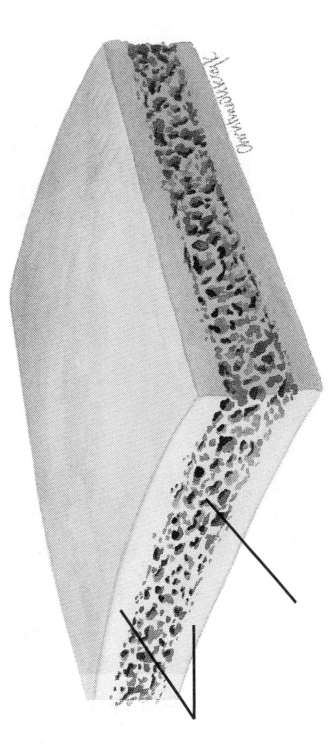

Seeley/Stephens/Tate: Anatomy & Physiology, third edition
© 1995 Mosby–Year Book, Inc.

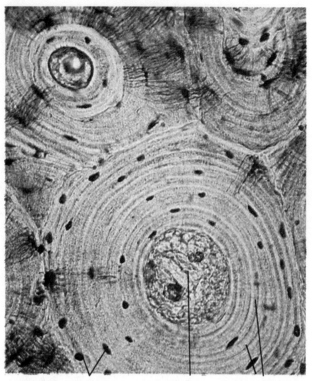

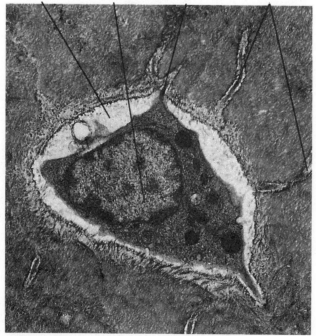

Seeley/Stephens/Tate: Anatomy & Physiology, third edition
© 1995 Mosby–Year Book, Inc.

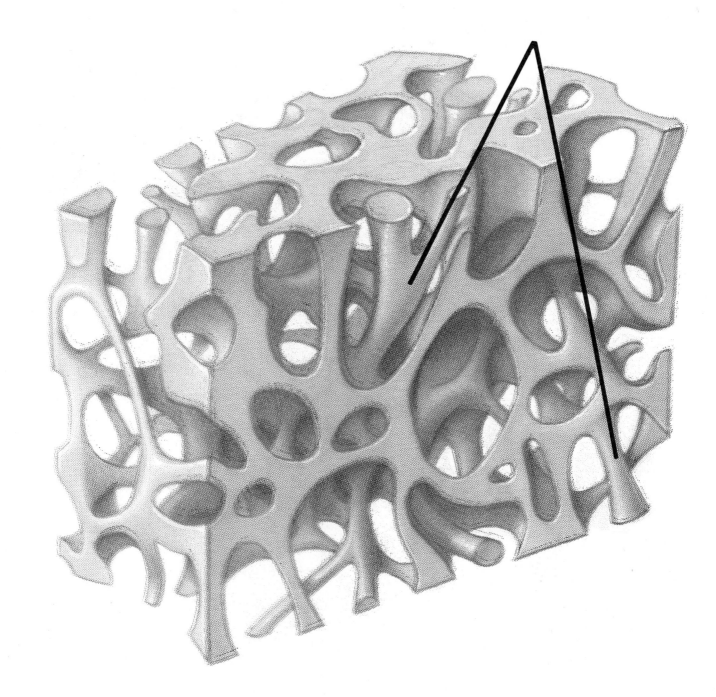

TA 72
Compact Bone (Fig. 6-10-A, p. 171)

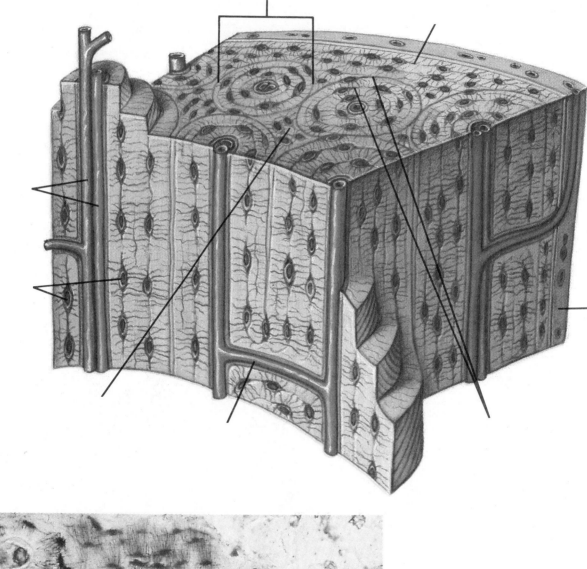

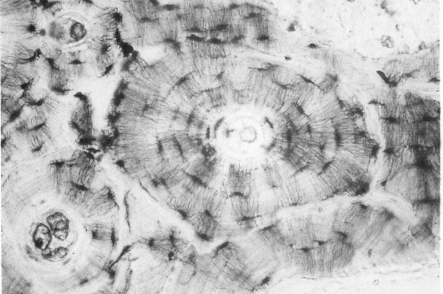

Seeley/Stephens/Tate: Anatomy & Physiology, third edition
© 1995 Mosby–Year Book, Inc.

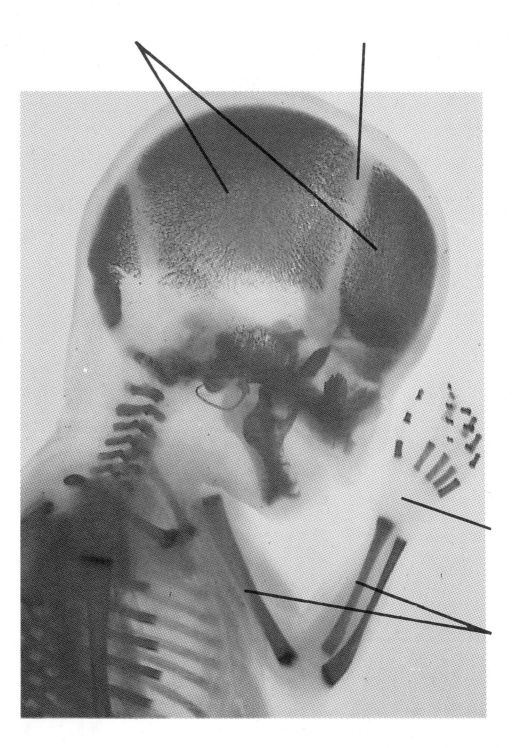

Endochondral Ossification (Fig. 6-12 A-E, p. 174)

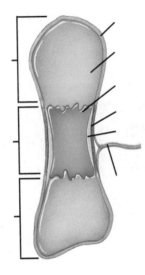

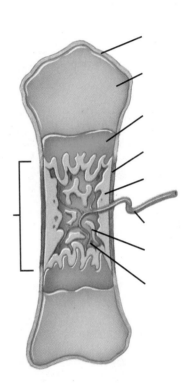

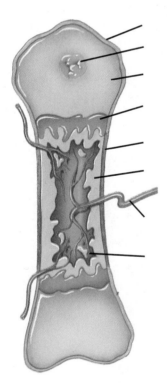

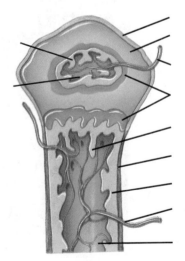

Seeley/Stephens/Tate: Anatomy & Physiology, third edition
© 1995 Mosby–Year Book, Inc.

Endochondral Ossification—cont'd (Fig. 6-12 F-G, p. 175)

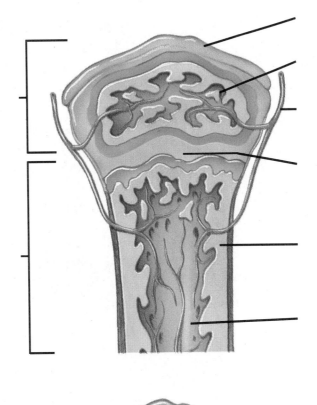

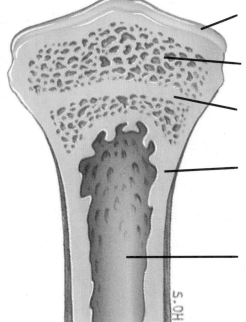

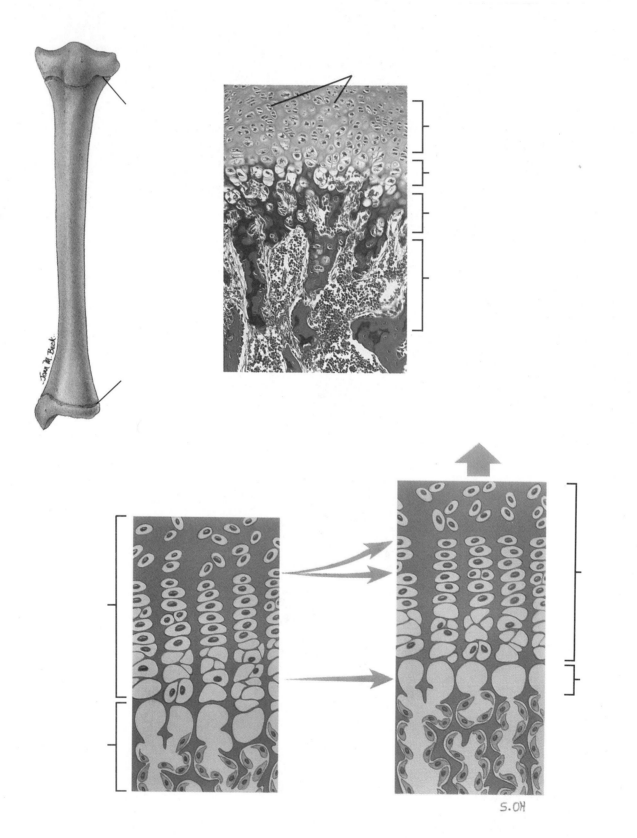

Seeley/Stephens/Tate: Anatomy & Physiology, third edition
© 1995 Mosby–Year Book, Inc.

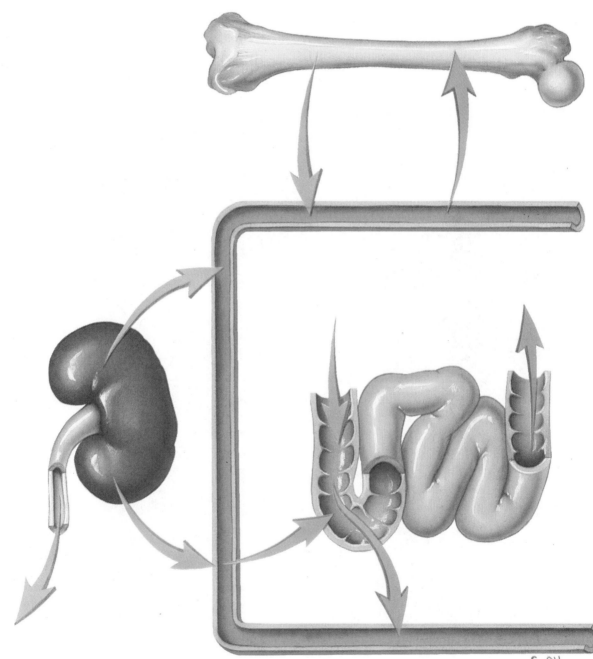

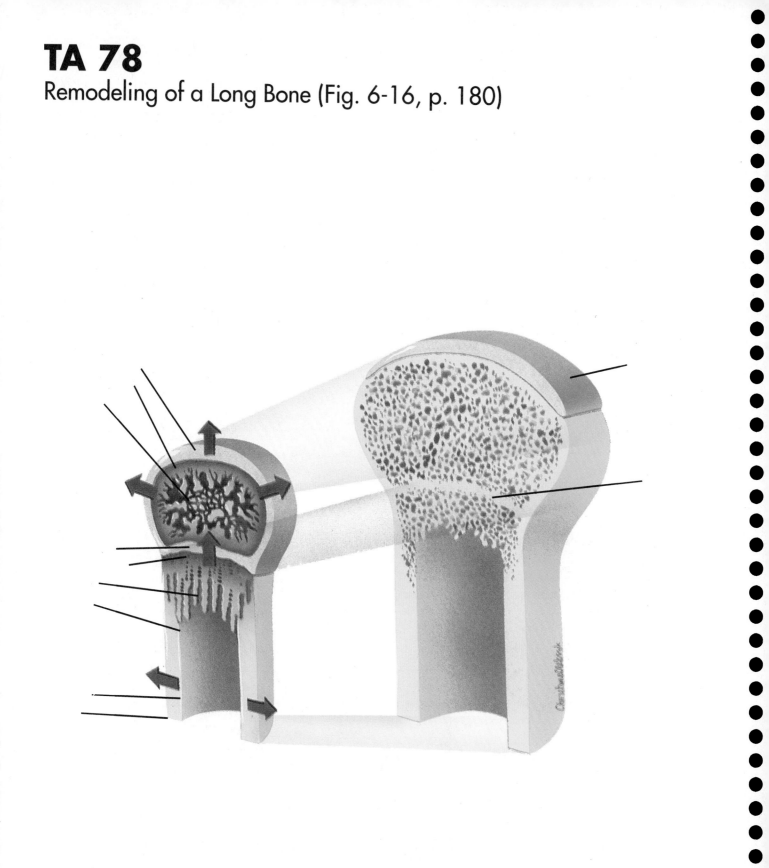

Seeley/Stephens/Tate: Anatomy & Physiology, third edition
© 1995 Mosby–Year Book, Inc.

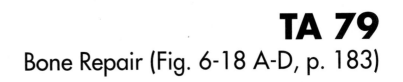

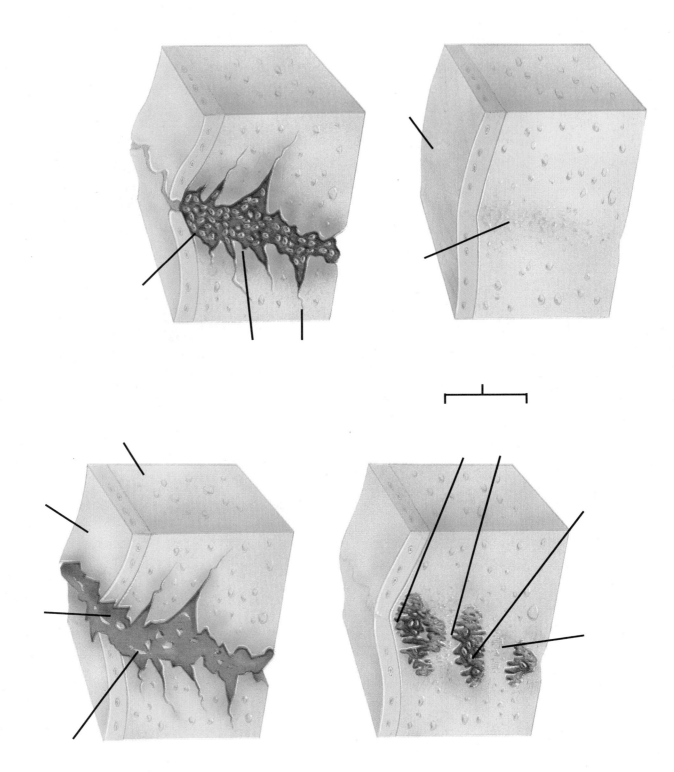

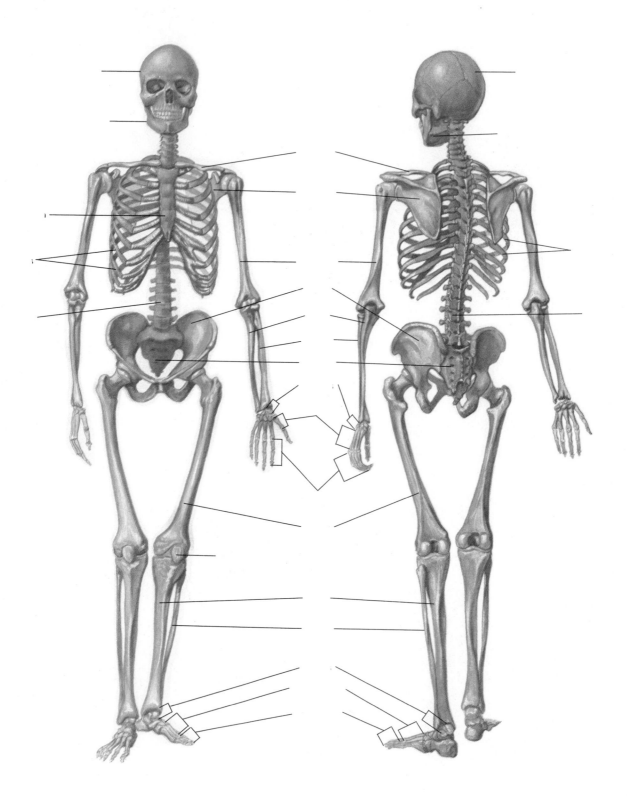

Seeley/Stephens/Tate: Anatomy & Physiology, third edition
© 1995 Mosby–Year Book, Inc.

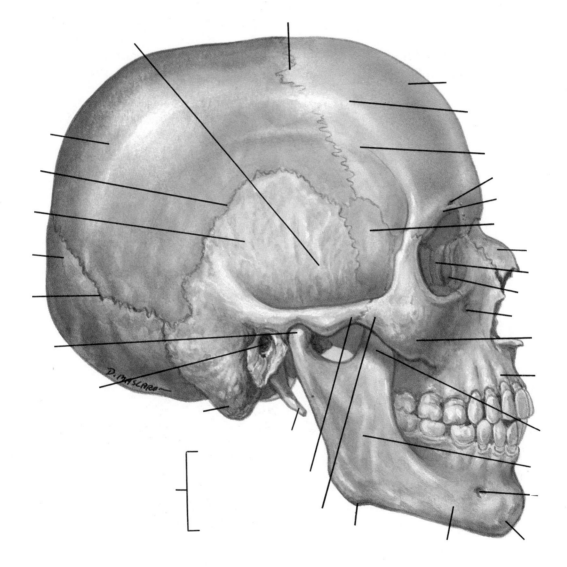

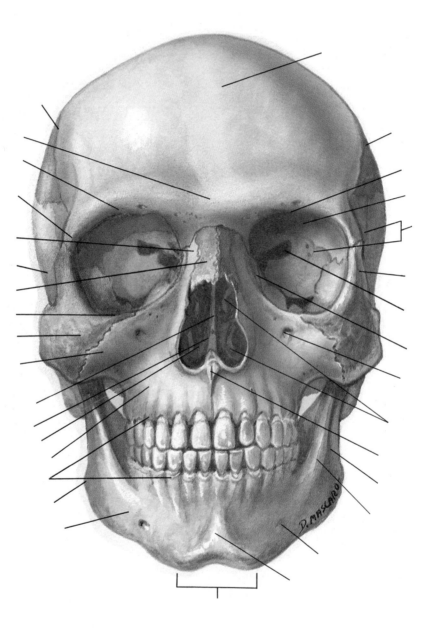

Seeley/Stephens/Tate: Anatomy & Physiology, third edition
© 1995 Mosby–Year Book, Inc.

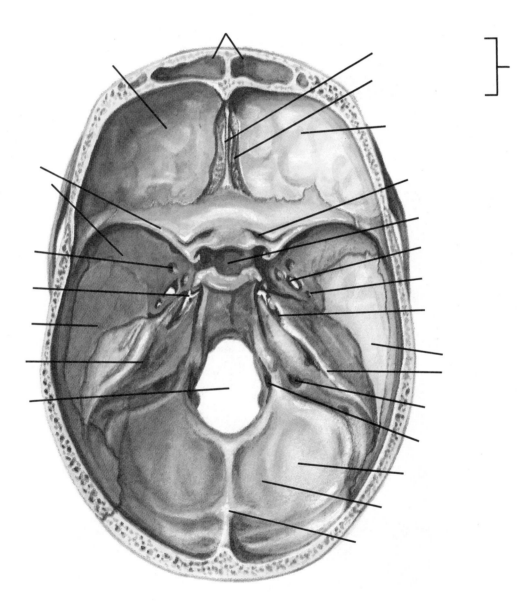

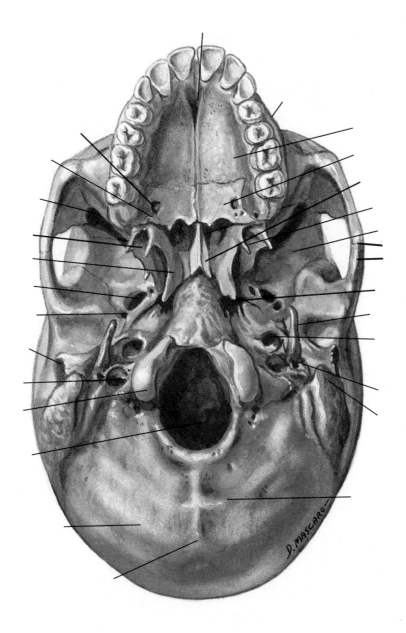

Seeley/Stephens/Tate: Anatomy & Physiology, third edition
© 1995 Mosby–Year Book, Inc.

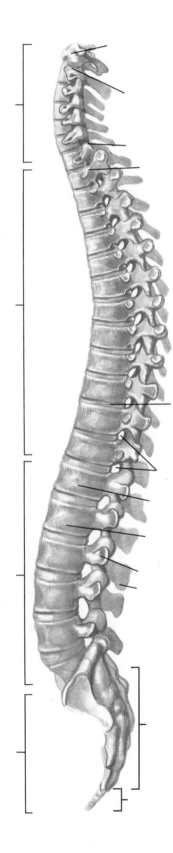

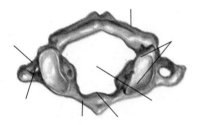

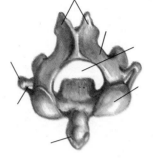

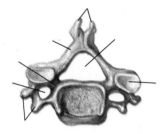

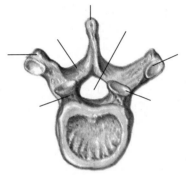

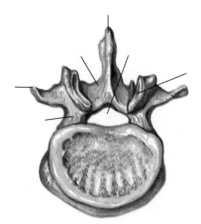

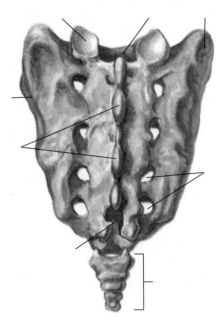

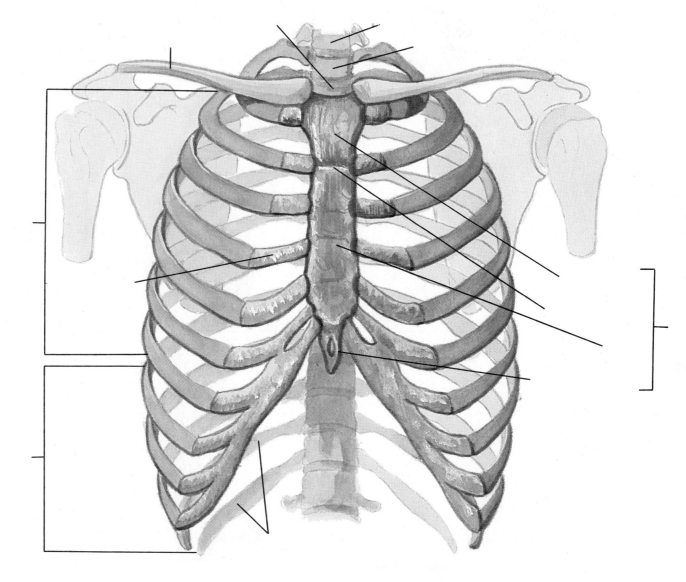

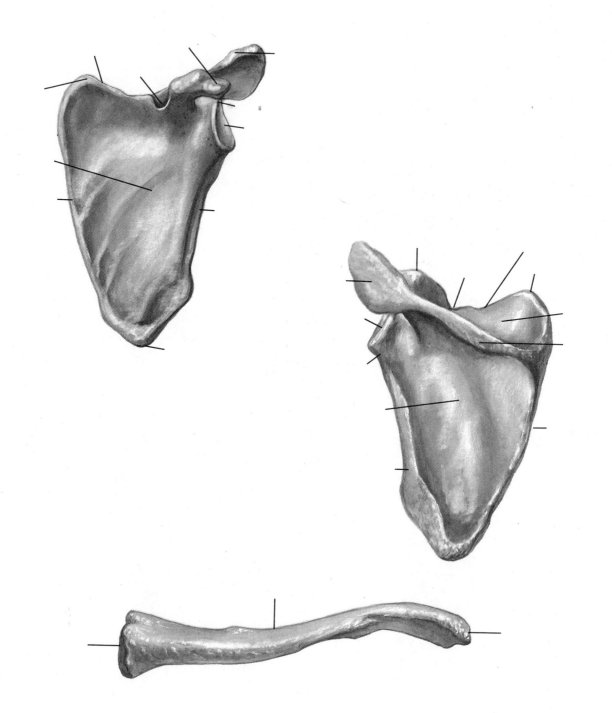

Seeley/Stephens/Tate: Anatomy & Physiology, third edition
© 1995 Mosby–Year Book, Inc.

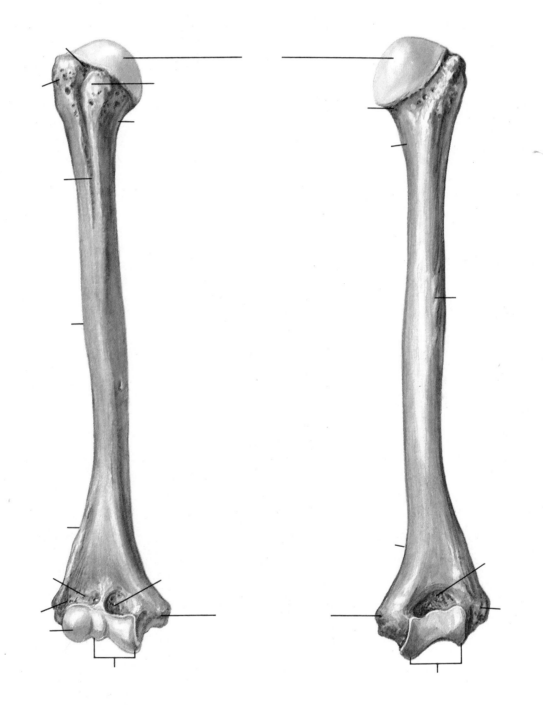

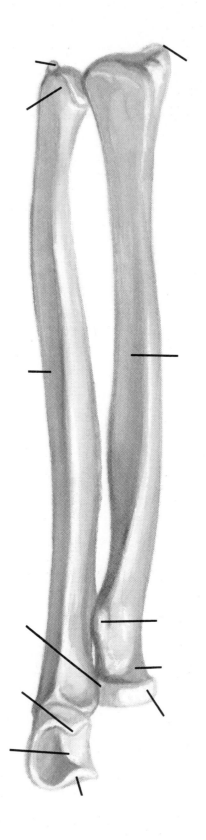

Seeley/Stephens/Tate: Anatomy & Physiology, third edition
© 1995 Mosby–Year Book, Inc.

Bones of the Right Wrist and Hand (Fig. 7-25, p. 223)

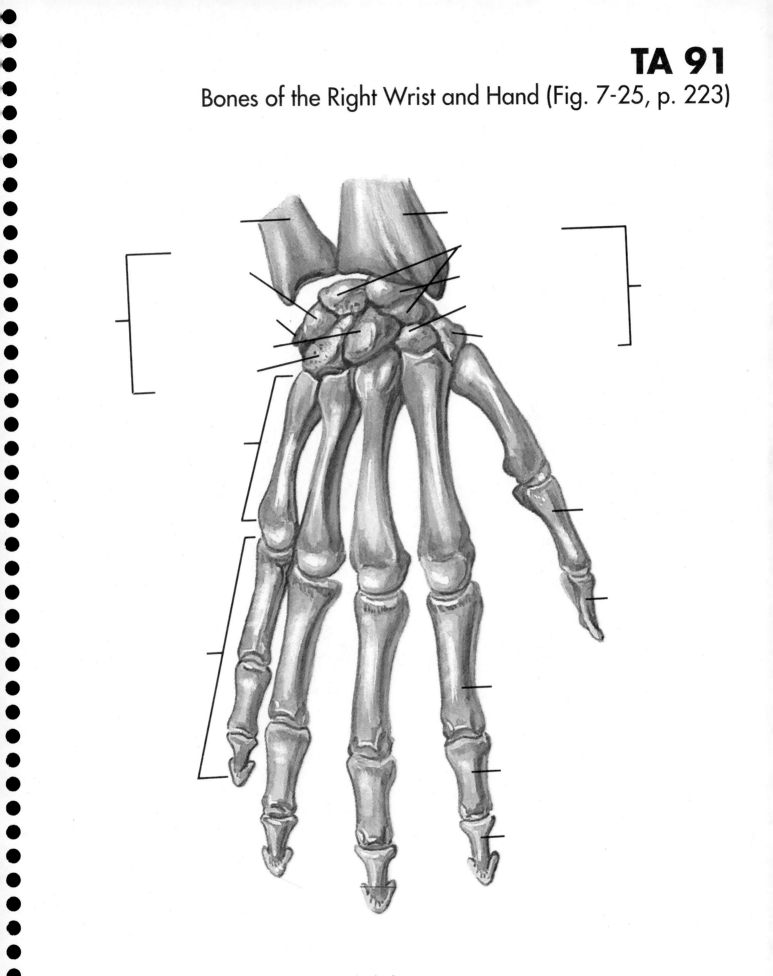

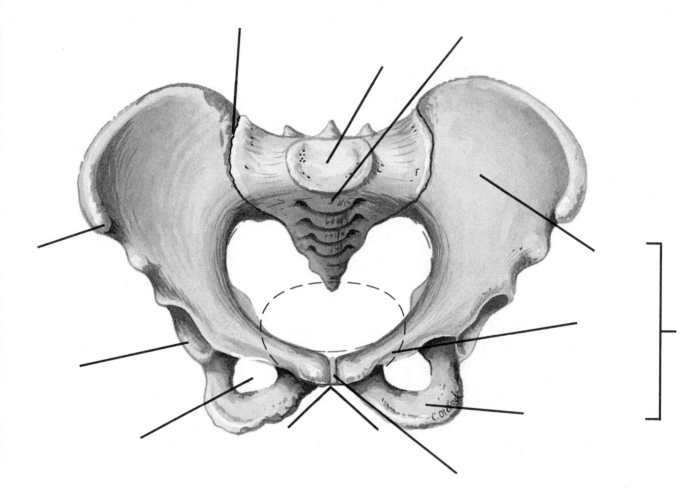

Seeley/Stephens/Tate: Anatomy & Physiology, third edition
© 1995 Mosby–Year Book, Inc.

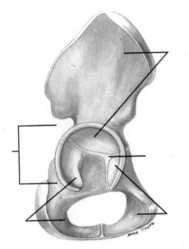

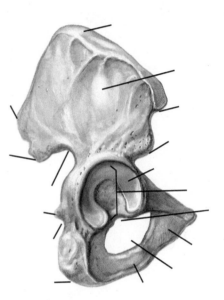

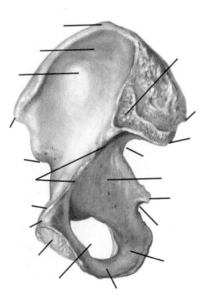

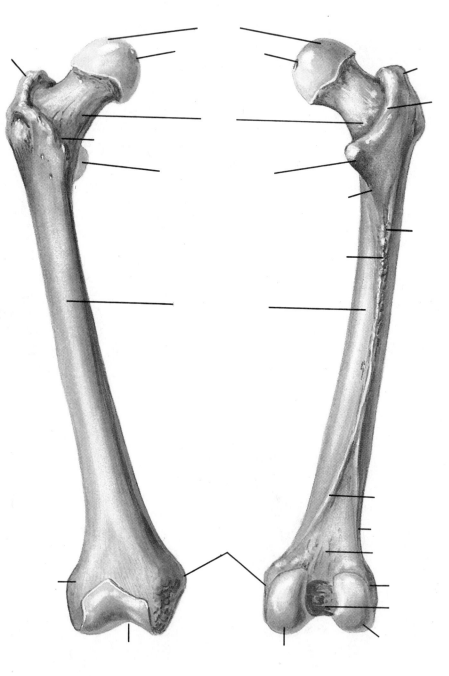

Seeley/Stephens/Tate: Anatomy & Physiology, third edition
© 1995 Mosby–Year Book, Inc.

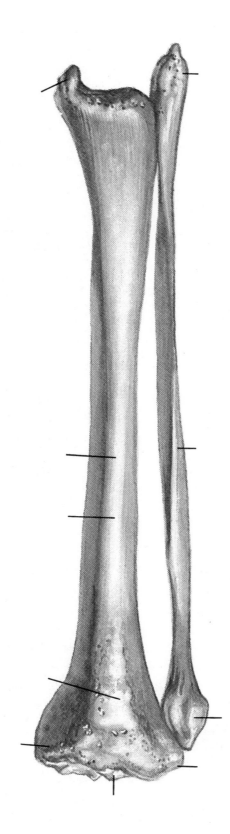

Bones of the Right Ankle and Foot (Fig. 7-34 A & B, p. 230)

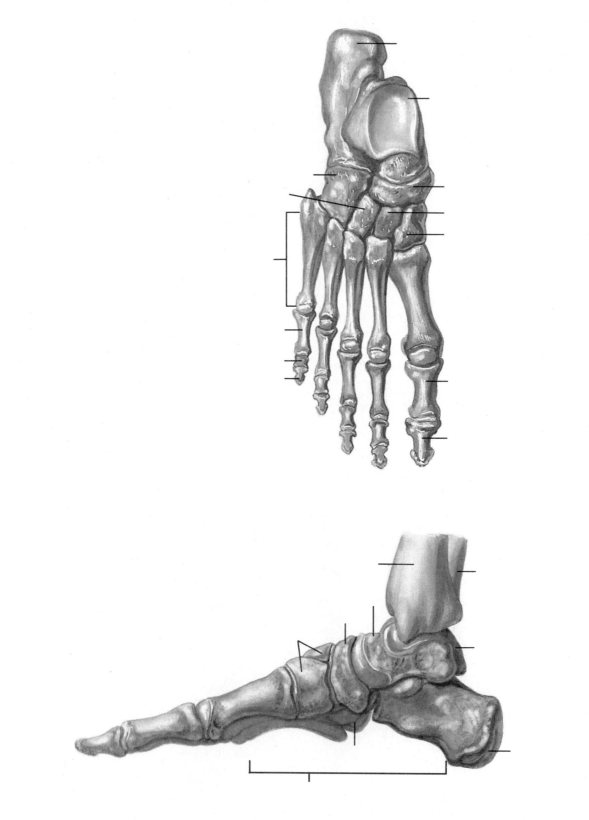

Seeley/Stephens/Tate: Anatomy & Physiology, third edition
© 1995 Mosby–Year Book, Inc.

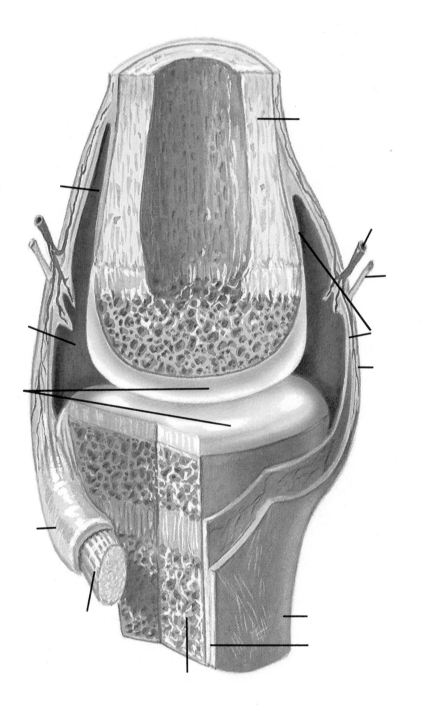

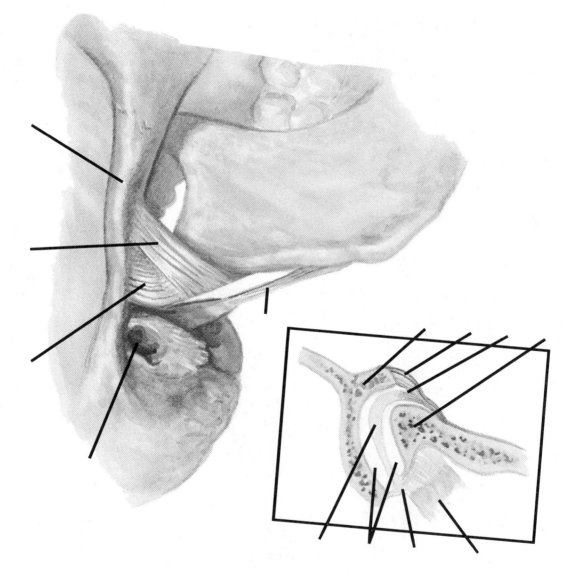

Seeley/Stephens/Tate: Anatomy & Physiology, third edition
© 1995 Mosby–Year Book, Inc.

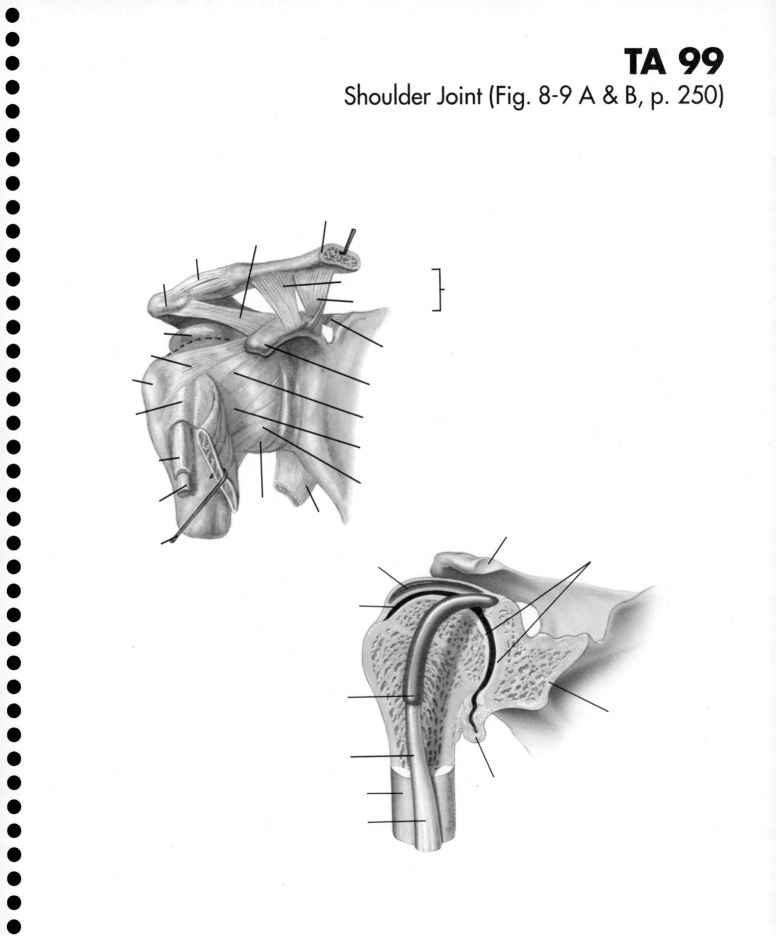

TA 100
Right Hip Joint (Fig. 8-10 A & B, p. 251)

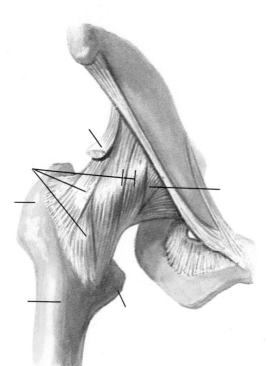

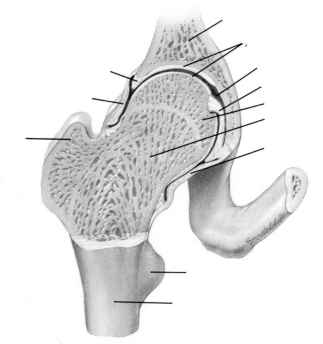

Seeley/Stephens/Tate: Anatomy & Physiology, third edition
© 1995 Mosby–Year Book, Inc.

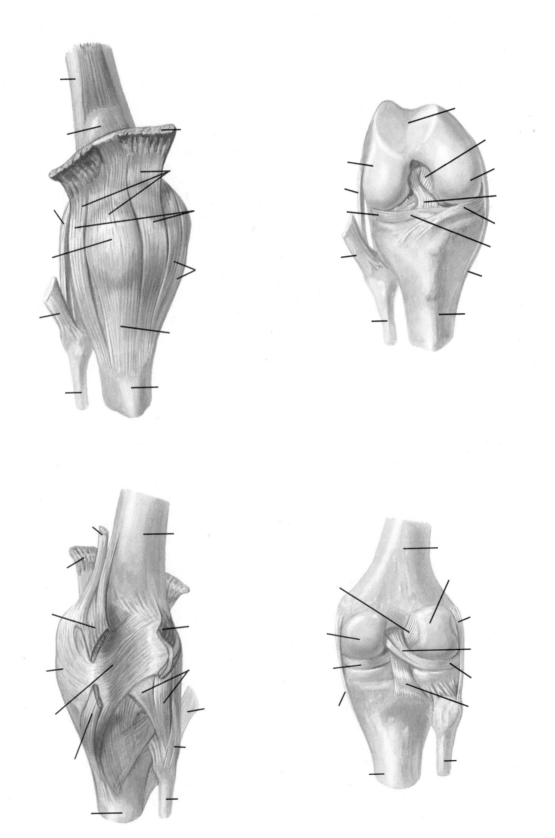

Seeley/Stephens/Tate: Anatomy & Physiology, third edition
© 1995 Mosby–Year Book, Inc.

Right Ankle Joint (Fig. 8-12 A & B, p. 255)

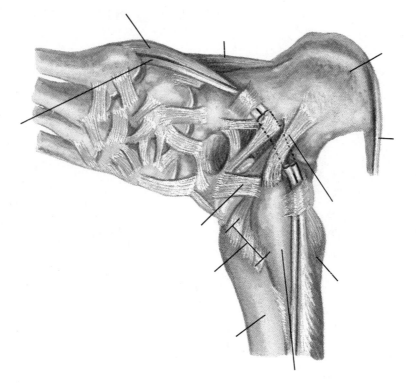

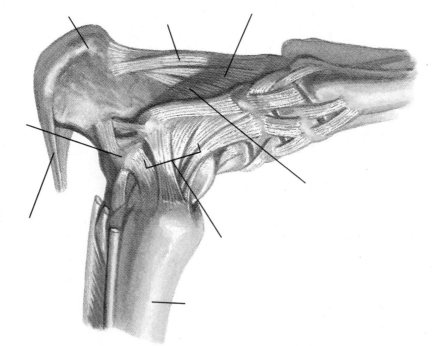

Seeley/Stephens/Tate: Anatomy & Physiology, third edition
© 1995 Mosby–Year Book, Inc.

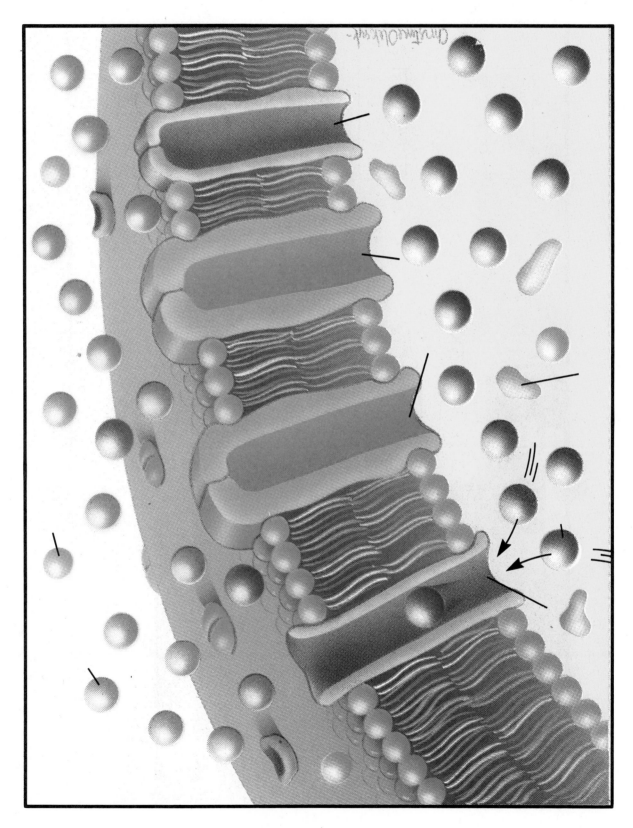

TA 104

Potassium Ions and the Resting Membrane Potential
(Fig. 9-3, p. 264)

Seeley/Stephens/Tate: Anatomy & Physiology, third edition
© 1995 Mosby–Year Book, Inc.

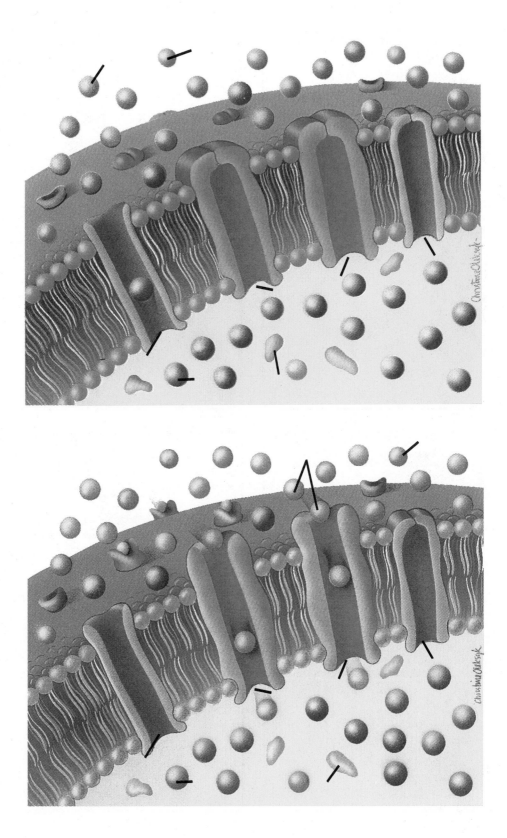

The Sodium-Potassium Exchange Pump (Fig. 9-6, p. 268)

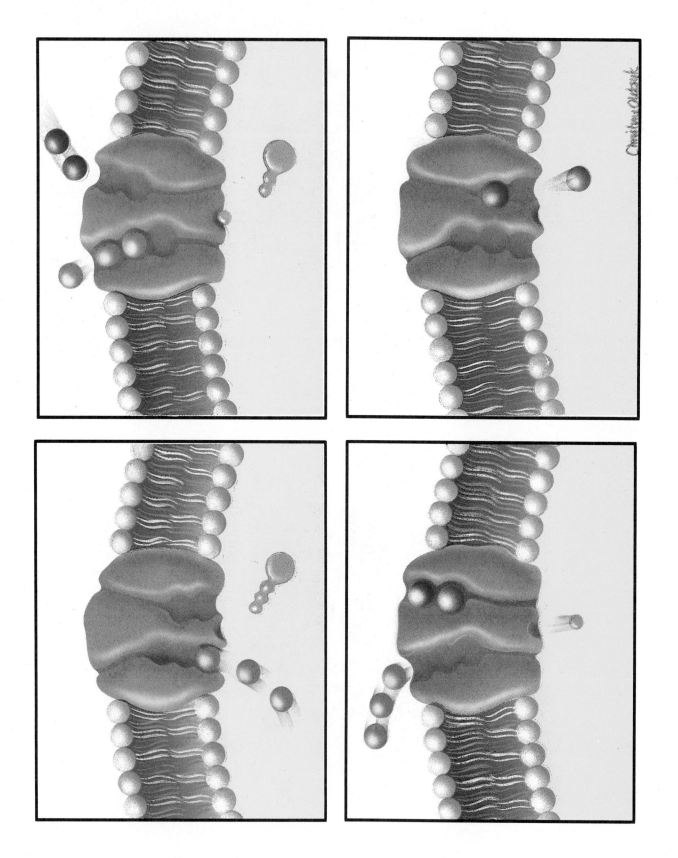

Seeley/Stephens/Tate: *Anatomy & Physiology, third edition*

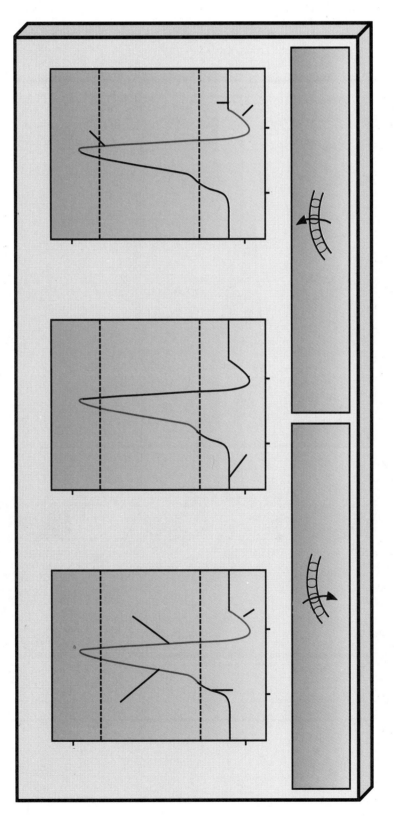

The Refractory Period (Fig. 9-9, p. 272)

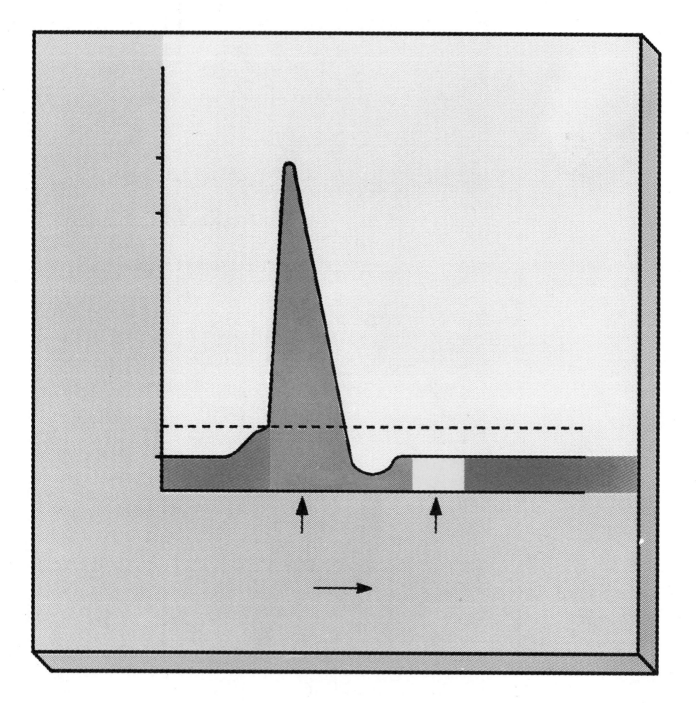

Stimuli, Local Potentials, and Action Potentials (Fig. 9-12, p. 273)

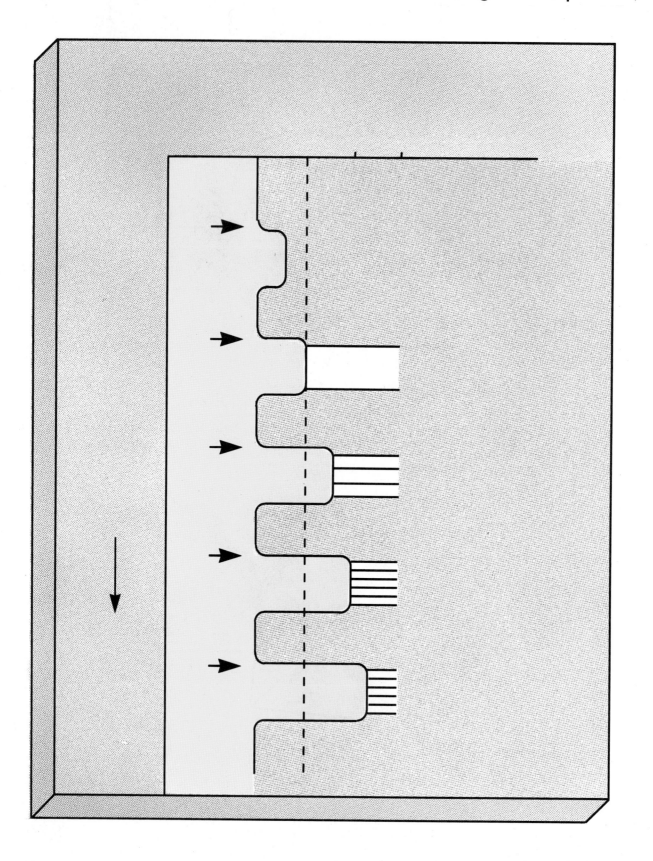

Seeley/Stephens/Tate: Anatomy & Physiology, third edition
© 1995 Mosby–Year Book, Inc.

Stimuli, Action Potential Frequency, and Accommodation
(Fig. 9-13 A & B, p. 274)

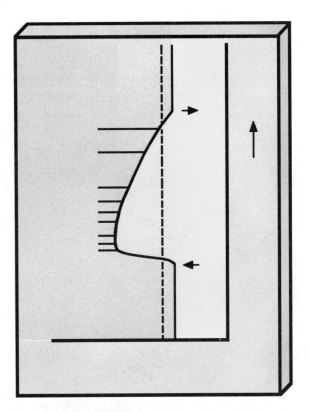

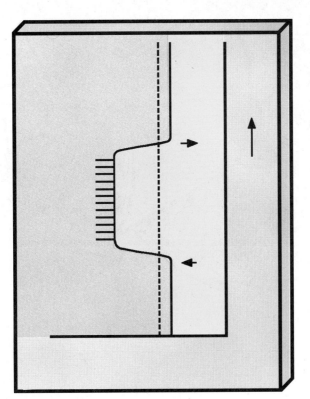

Seeley/Stephens/Tate: Anatomy & Physiology, third edition
© 1995 Mosby–Year Book, Inc.

TA 112
Skeletal Muscle Structure (Fig. 10-2, p. 282)

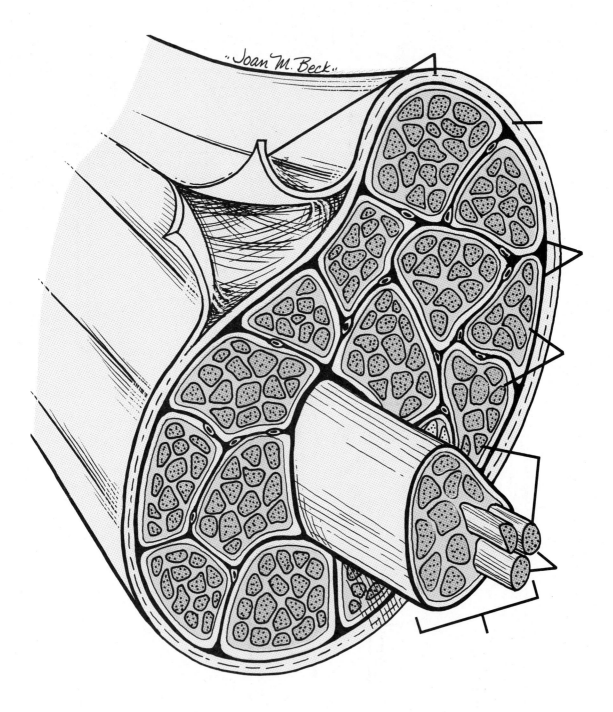

"Joan M. Beck"

Seeley/Stephens/Tate: Anatomy & Physiology, third edition
© 1995 Mosby–Year Book, Inc.

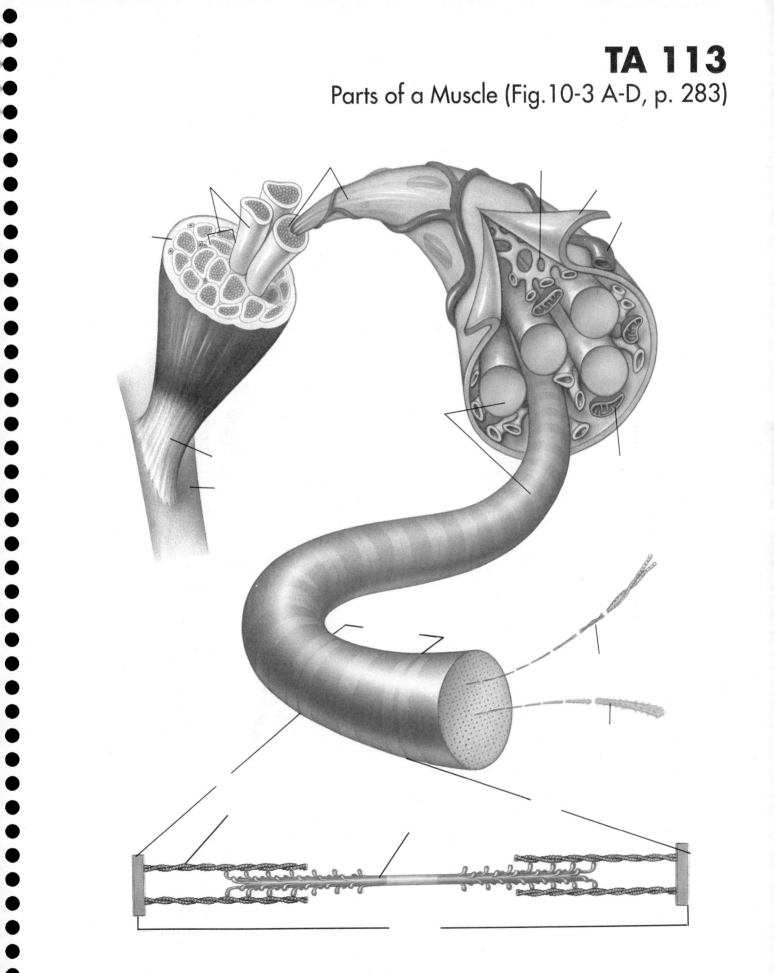

Seeley/Stephens/Tate: Anatomy & Physiology, third edition
© 1995 Mosby–Year Book, Inc.

TA 114
Structure of Actin and Myosin (Fig. 10-6 A & B, p. 285)

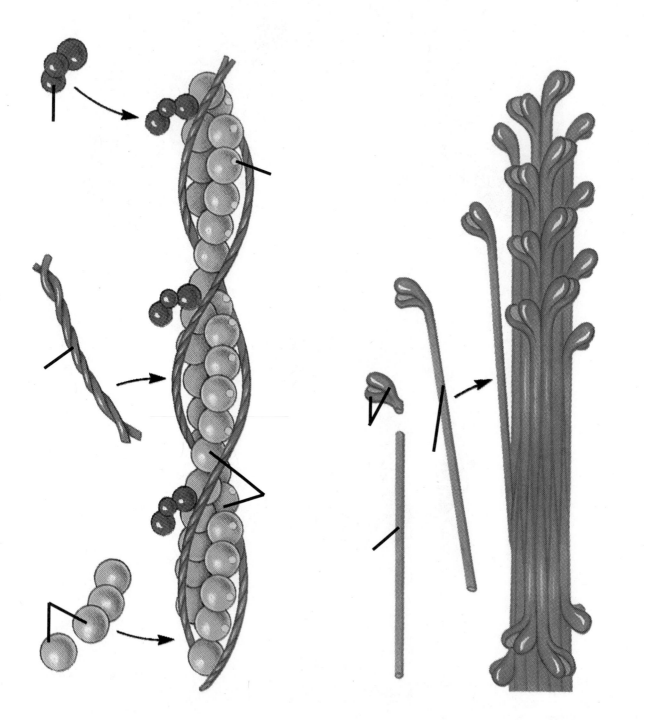

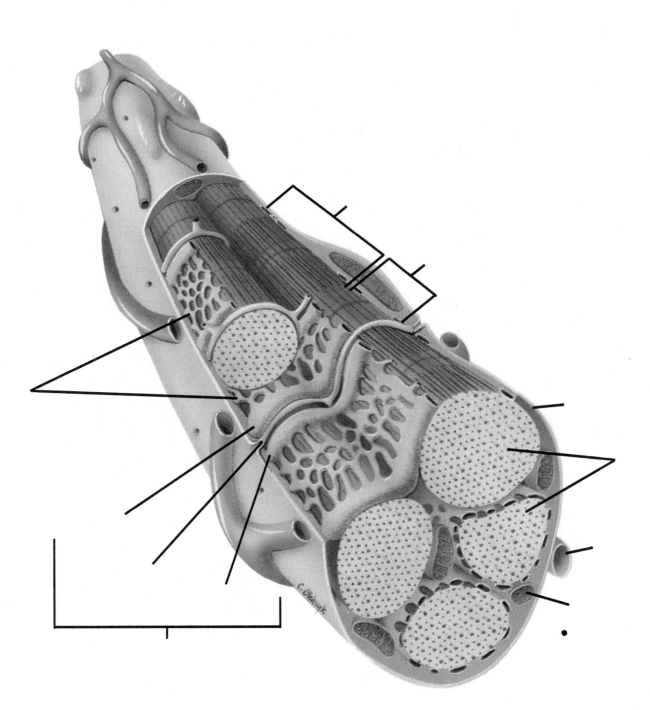

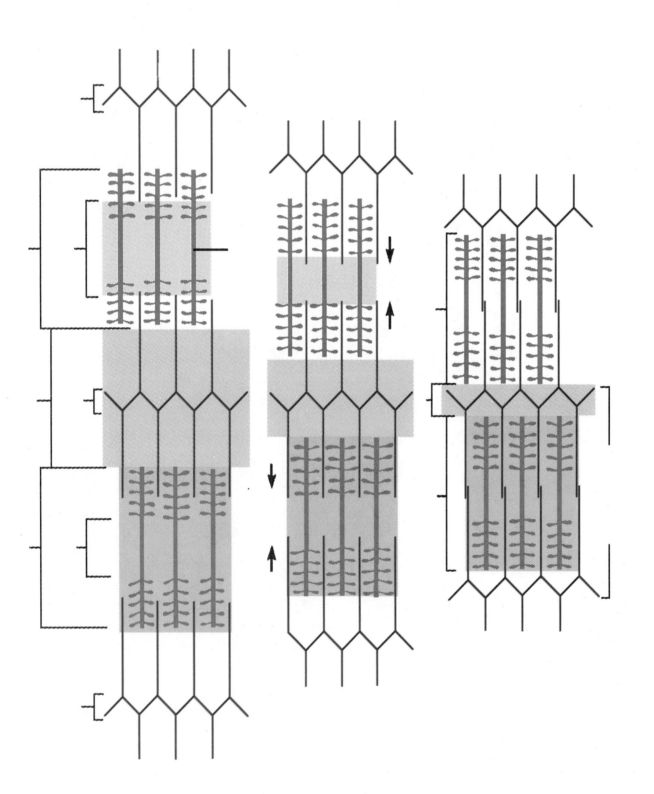

Seeley/Stephens/Tate: Anatomy & Physiology, third edition
© 1995 Mosby–Year Book, Inc.

Innervation and Blood Supply of a Muscle (Fig. 10-9, p. 288)

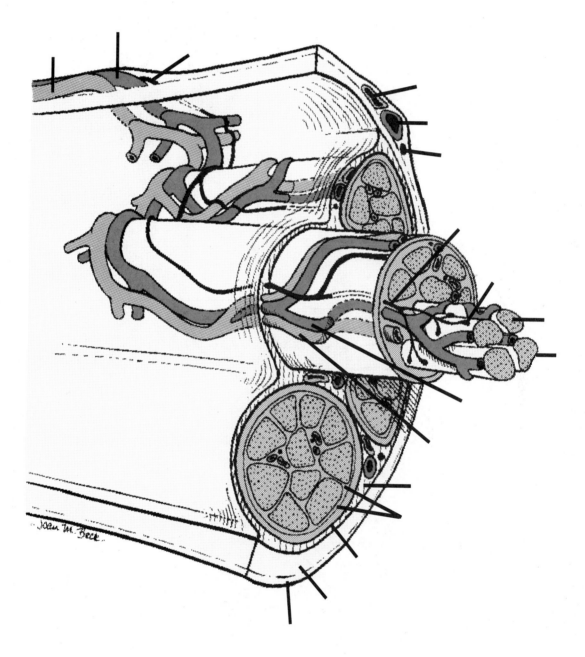

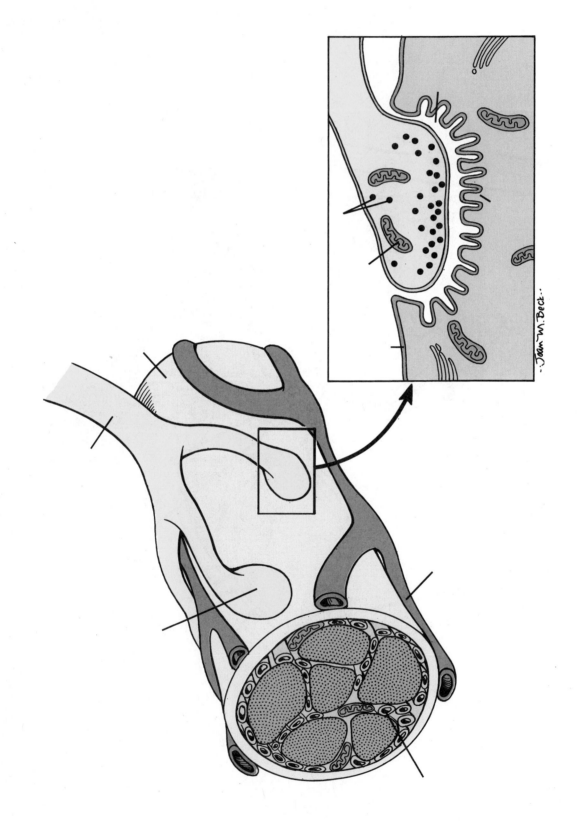

Seeley/Stephens/Tate: Anatomy & Physiology, third edition
© 1995 Mosby–Year Book, Inc.

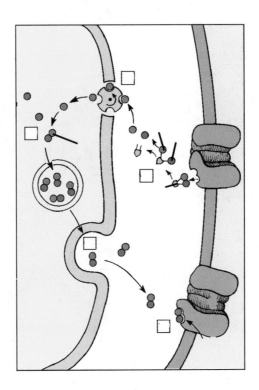

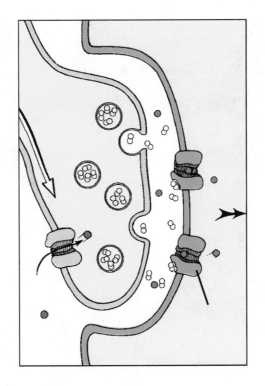

TA 120
Action Potentials and Muscle Contraction
(Fig. 10-12 A-C, p. 291)

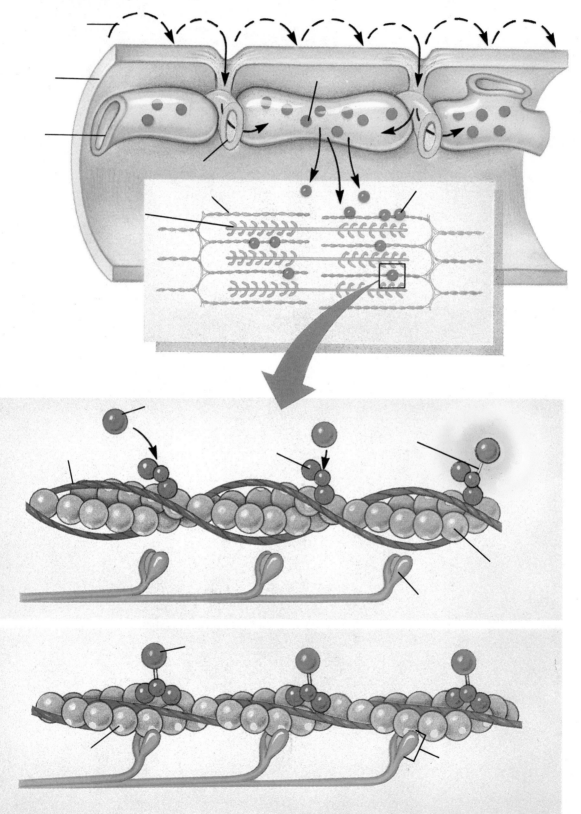

Seeley/Stephens/Tate: Anatomy & Physiology, third edition
© 1995 Mosby–Year Book, Inc.

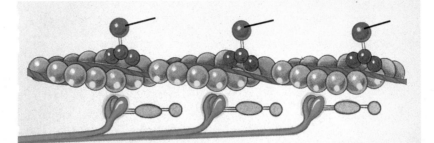

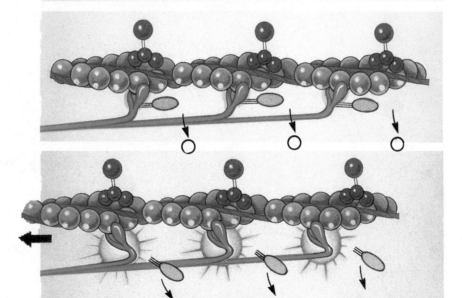

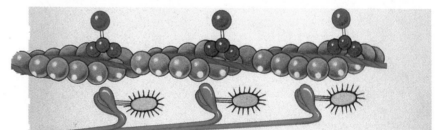

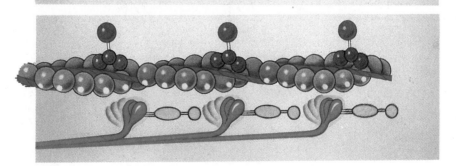

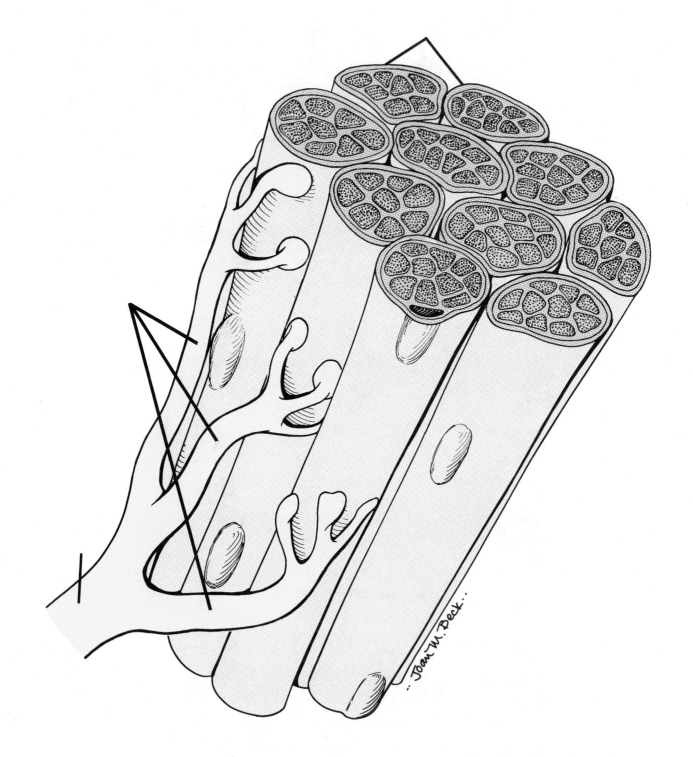

Seeley/Stephens/Tate: Anatomy & Physiology, third edition
© 1995 Mosby–Year Book, Inc.

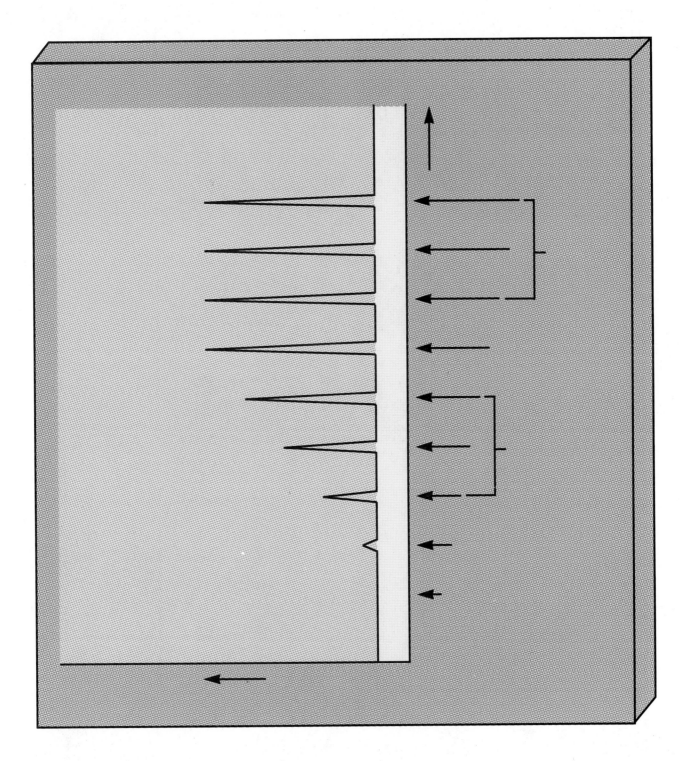

TA 124

Multiple Wave Summation (Fig. 10-17, p. 295)

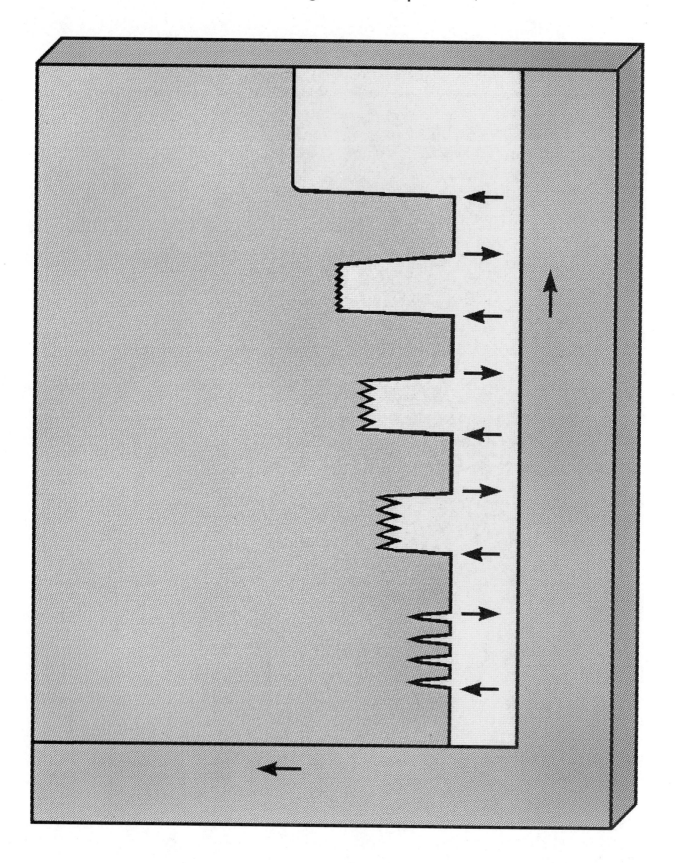

Seeley/Stephens/Tate: Anatomy & Physiology, third edition
© 1995 Mosby–Year Book, Inc.

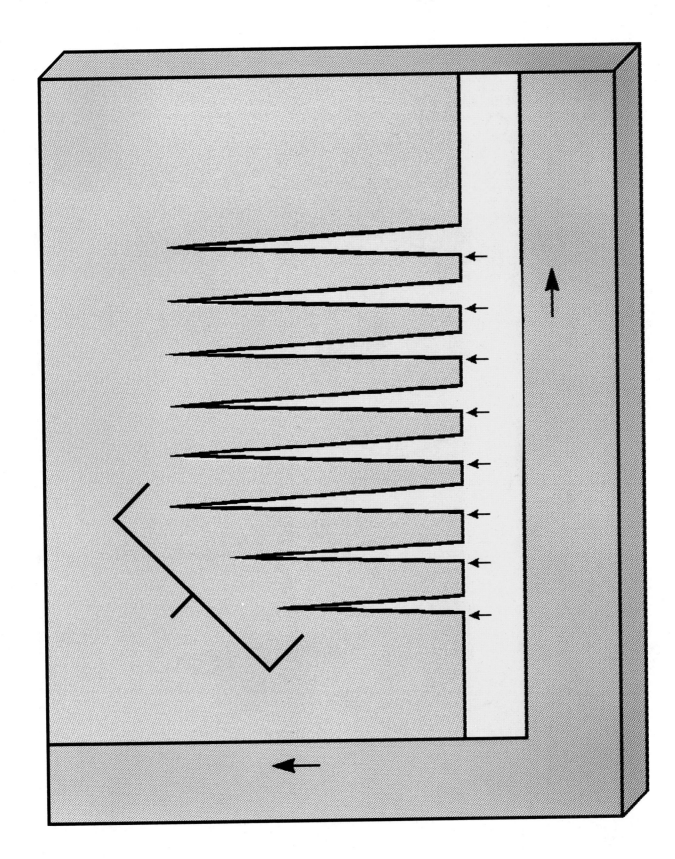

Ca2+ Ions in Smooth Muscle (Fig. 10-21, p. 304)

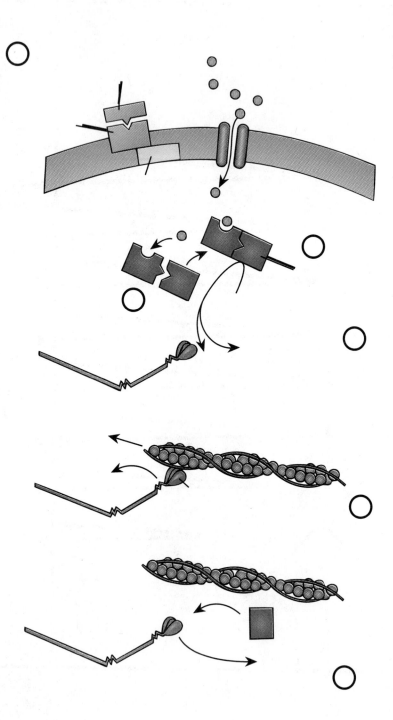

Seeley/Stephens/Tate: Anatomy & Physiology, third edition
© 1995 Mosby–Year Book, Inc.

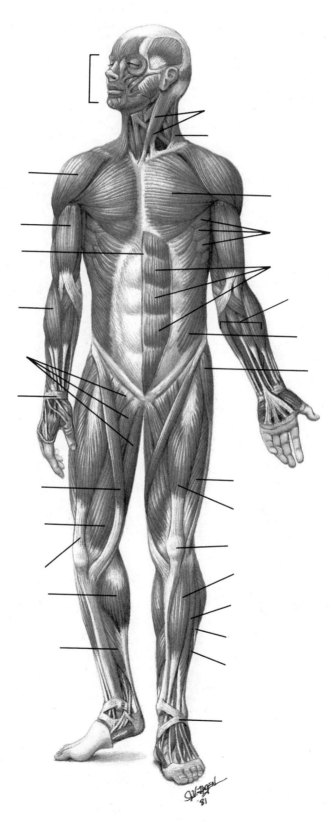

General Overview of Body Musculature (Posterior)
(Fig. 11-3 B, p. 317)

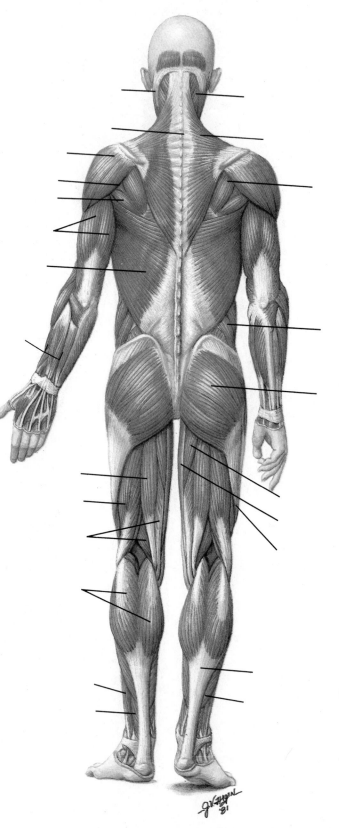

Seeley/Stephens/Tate: Anatomy & Physiology, third edition
© 1995 Mosby–Year Book, Inc.

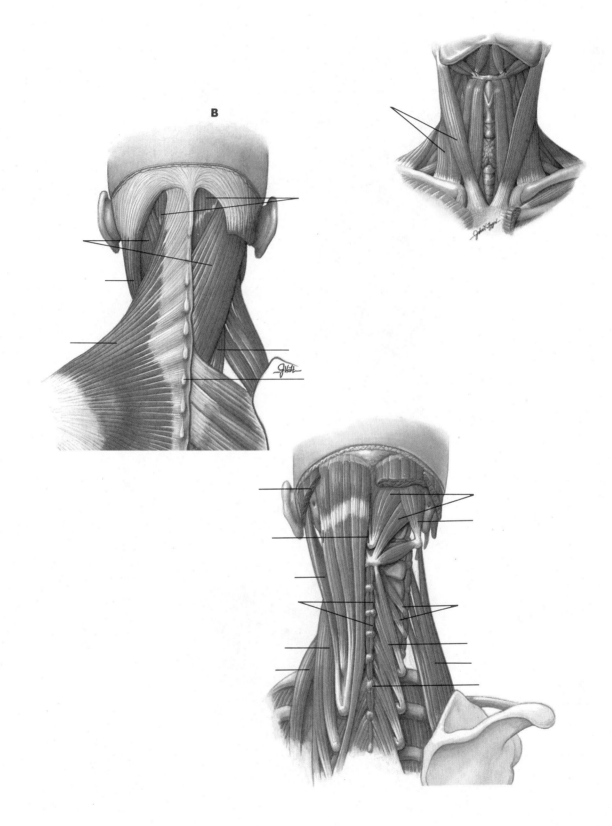

B

Muscles of Facial Expression (Fig. 11-6 A & B, p. 320)

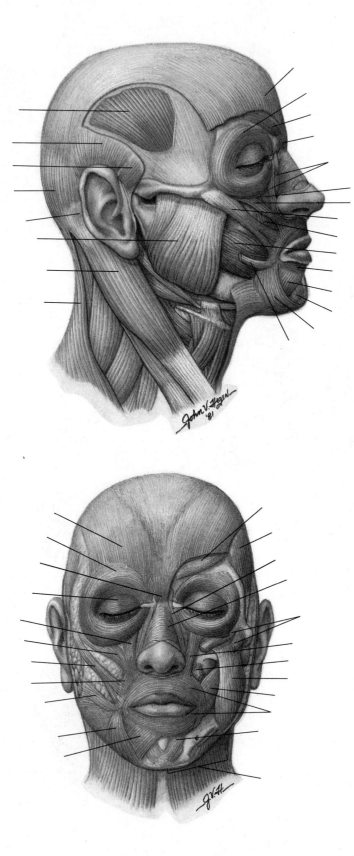

Seeley/Stephens/Tate: Anatomy & Physiology, third edition
© 1995 Mosby–Year Book, Inc.

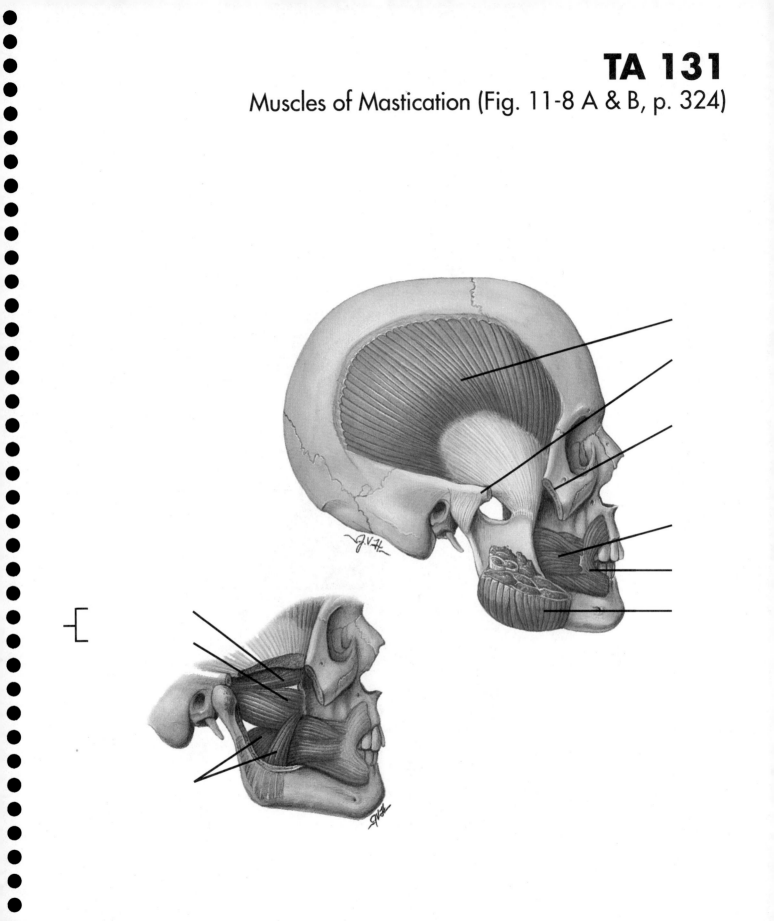

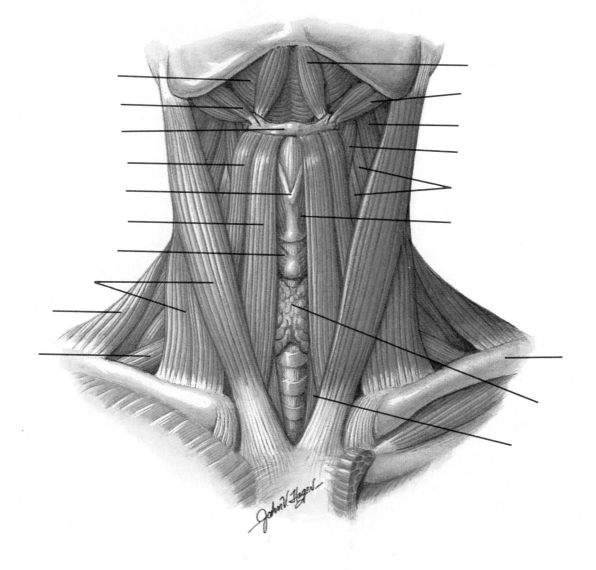

Seeley/Stephens/Tate: Anatomy & Physiology, third edition
© 1995 Mosby–Year Book, Inc.

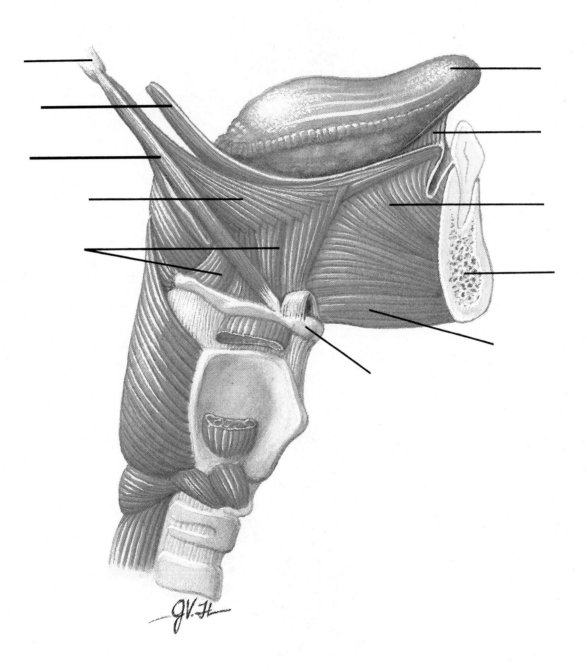

TA 134
Muscles of the Palate, Pharynx, and Larynx
(Fig. 11-11 A & B, p. 329)

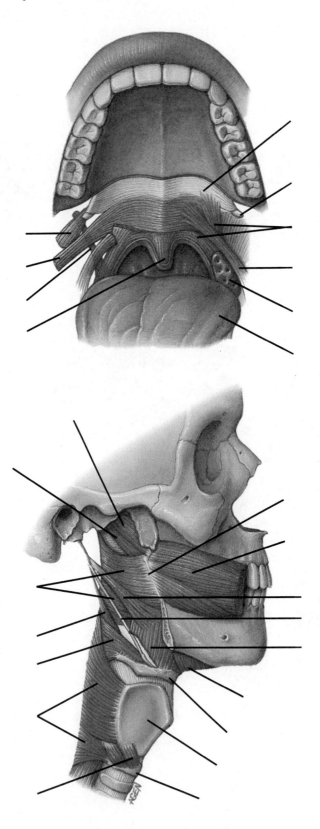

Seeley/Stephens/Tate: Anatomy & Physiology, third edition
© 1995 Mosby–Year Book, Inc.

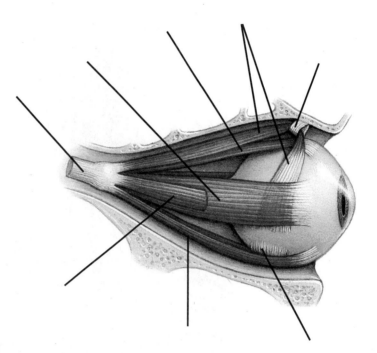

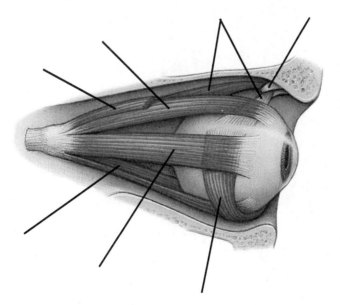

Deep Back Muscles (Fig. 11-13, p. 333)

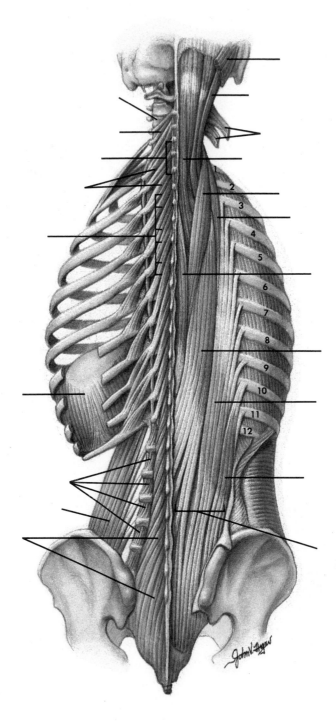

Seeley/Stephens/Tate: Anatomy & Physiology, third edition
© 1995 Mosby–Year Book, Inc.

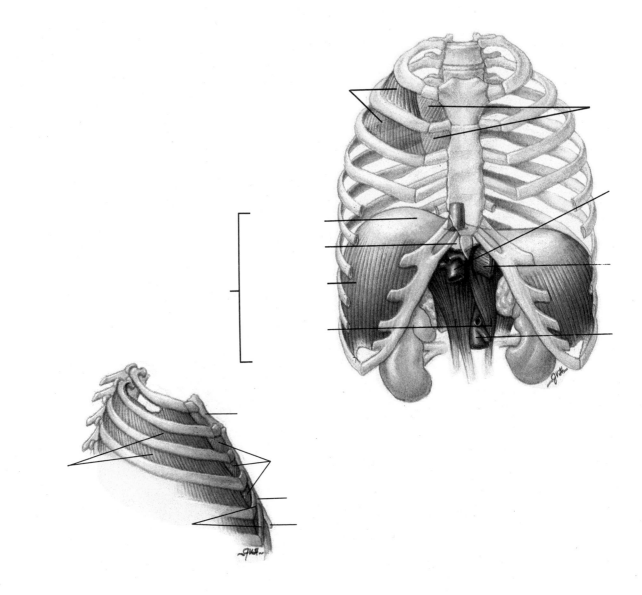

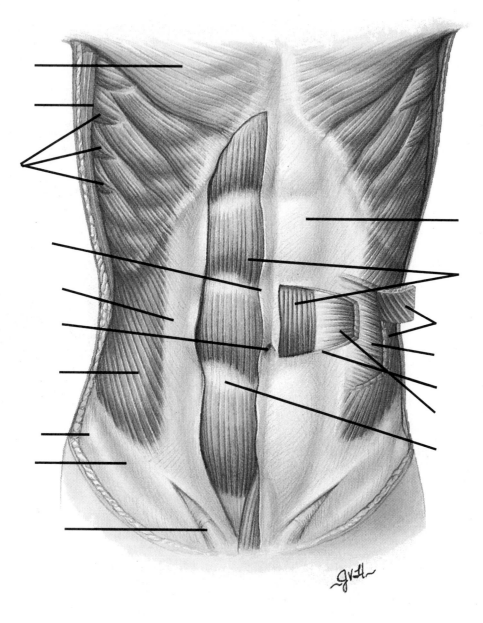

Seeley/Stephens/Tate: Anatomy & Physiology, third edition
© 1995 Mosby–Year Book, Inc.

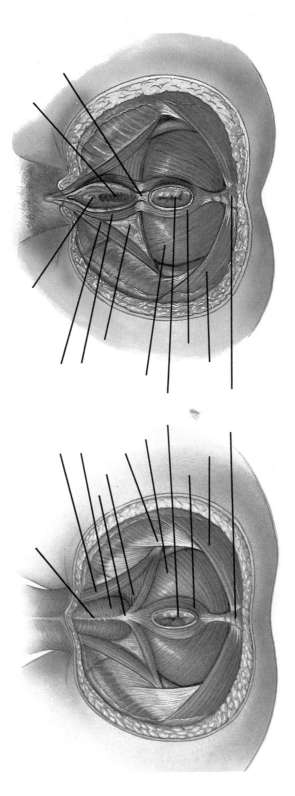

Seeley/Stephens/Tate: Anatomy & Physiology, third edition
© 1995 Mosby–Year Book, Inc.

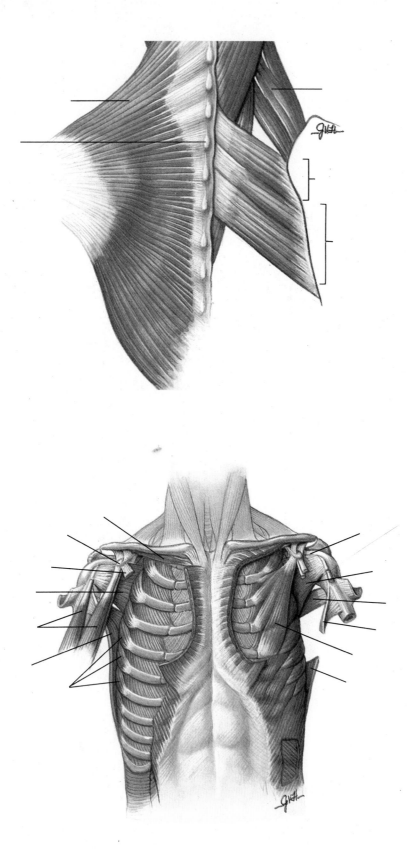

Seeley/Stephens/Tate: Anatomy & Physiology, third edition
© 1995 Mosby–Year Book, Inc.

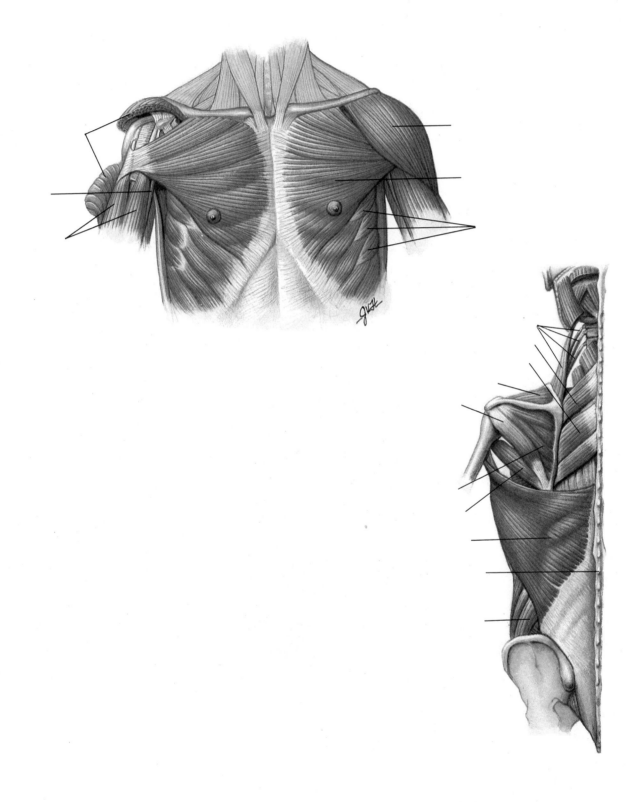

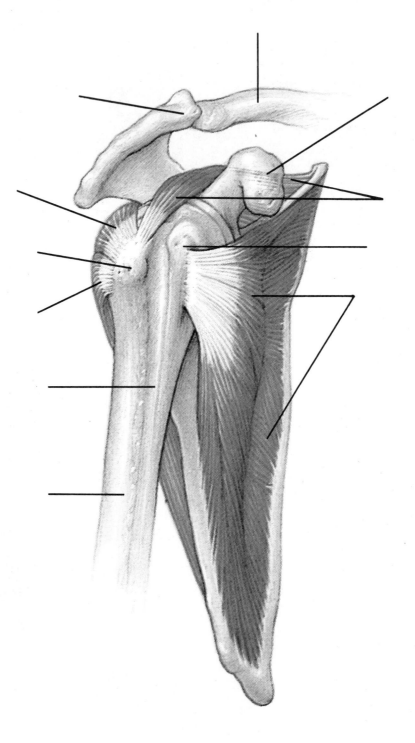

Seeley/Stephens/Tate: Anatomy & Physiology, third edition
© 1995 Mosby–Year Book, Inc.

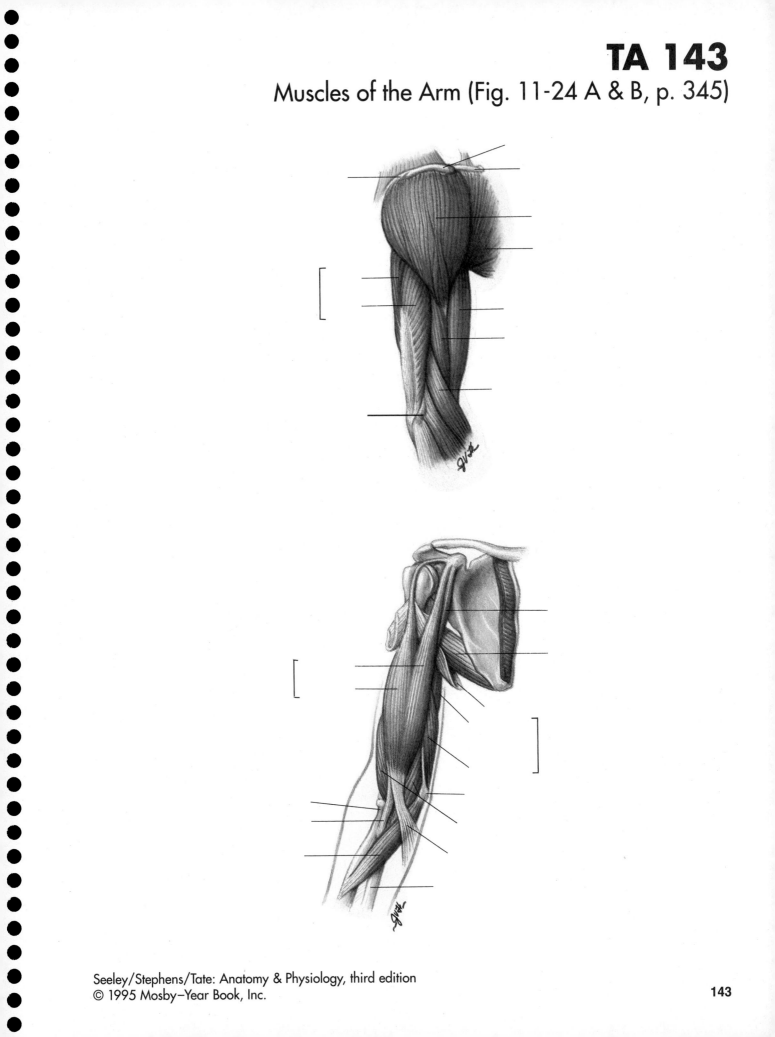

Muscles of the Forearm (Fig. 11-25 A-D, p. 346)

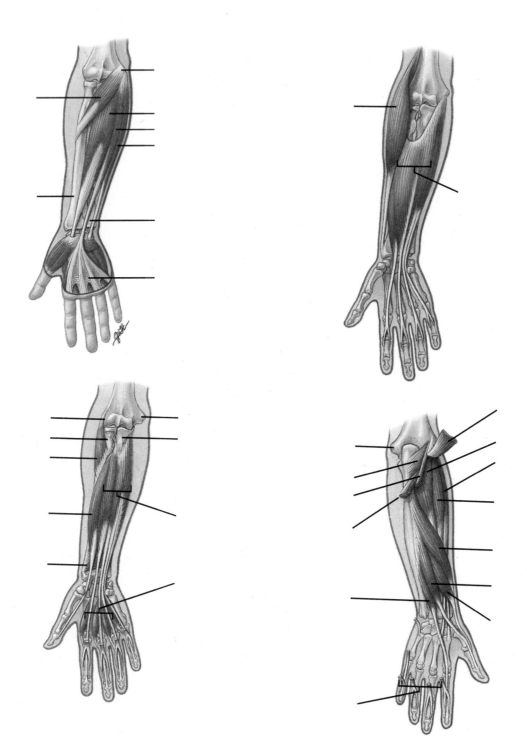

Seeley/Stephens/Tate: Anatomy & Physiology, third edition
© 1995 Mosby–Year Book, Inc.

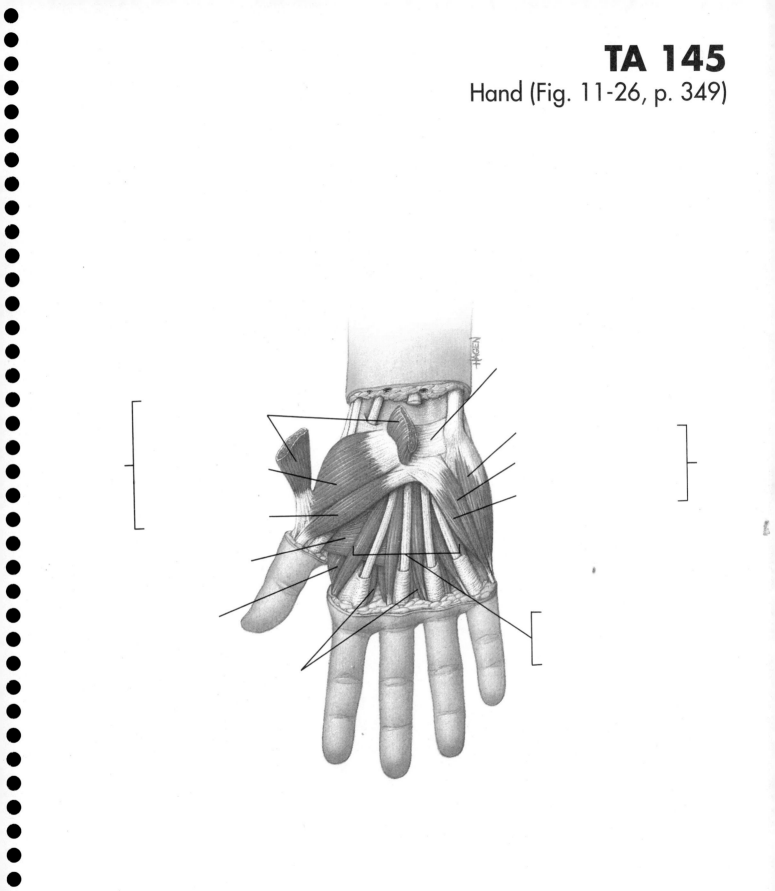

Muscles of the Posterior Hip (Fig. 11-28 A & B, p. 352)

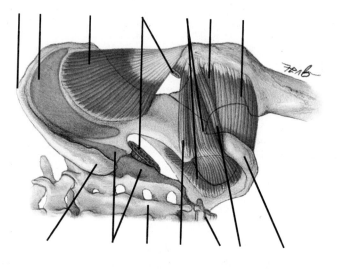

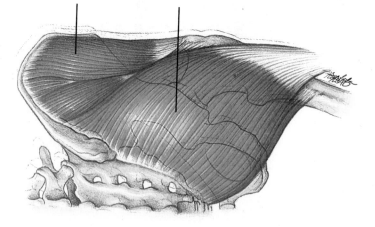

Muscles of the Anterior Thigh (Fig. 11-29 A & B, p. 353)

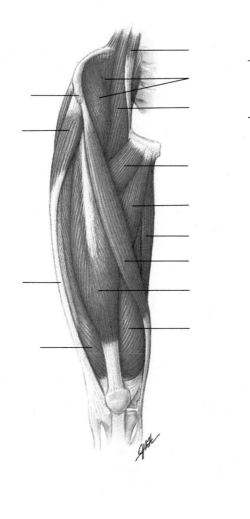

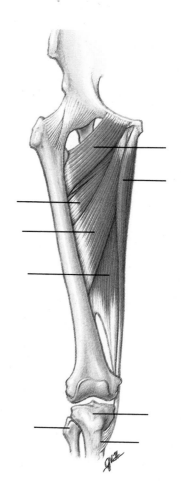

Posterior Muscles of the Right Thigh (Fig. 11-30, p. 355)

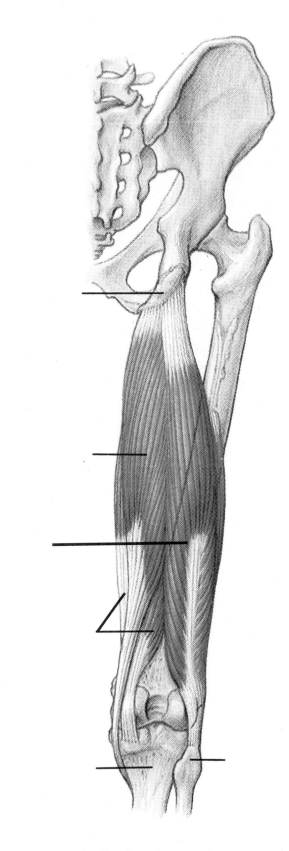

Seeley/Stephens/Tate: Anatomy & Physiology, *third edition*
© 1995 Mosby–Year Book, Inc.

Muscles of the Leg (Fig. 11-31 A-D, p. 356)

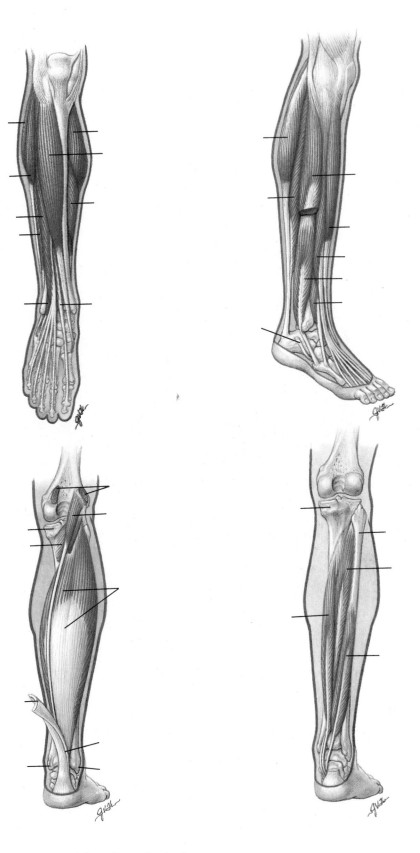

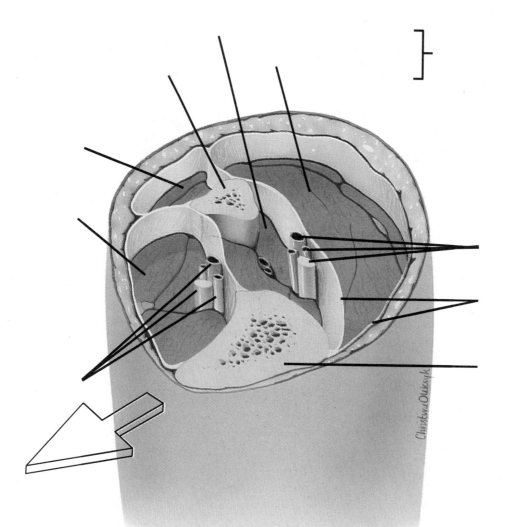

Seeley/Stephens/Tate: Anatomy & Physiology, third edition
© 1995 Mosby—Year Book, Inc.

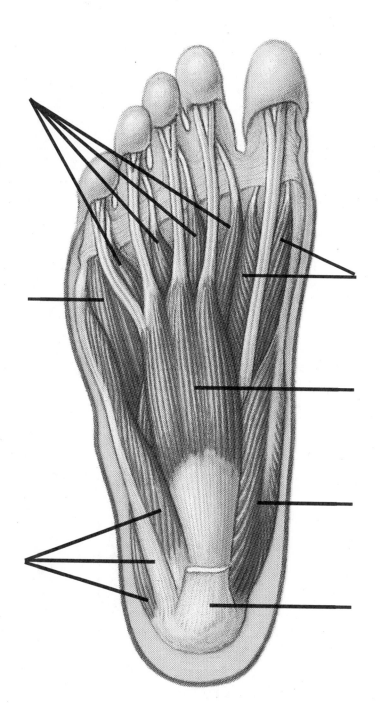

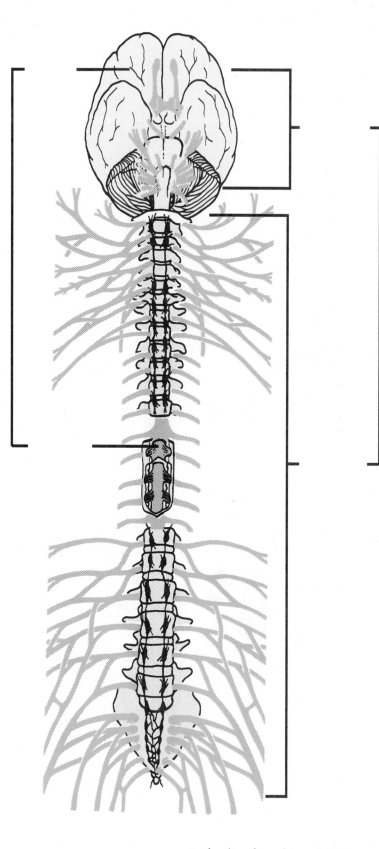

TA 153

Divisions of the Peripheral Nervous System
(Fig. 12-3 A-C, p. 371)

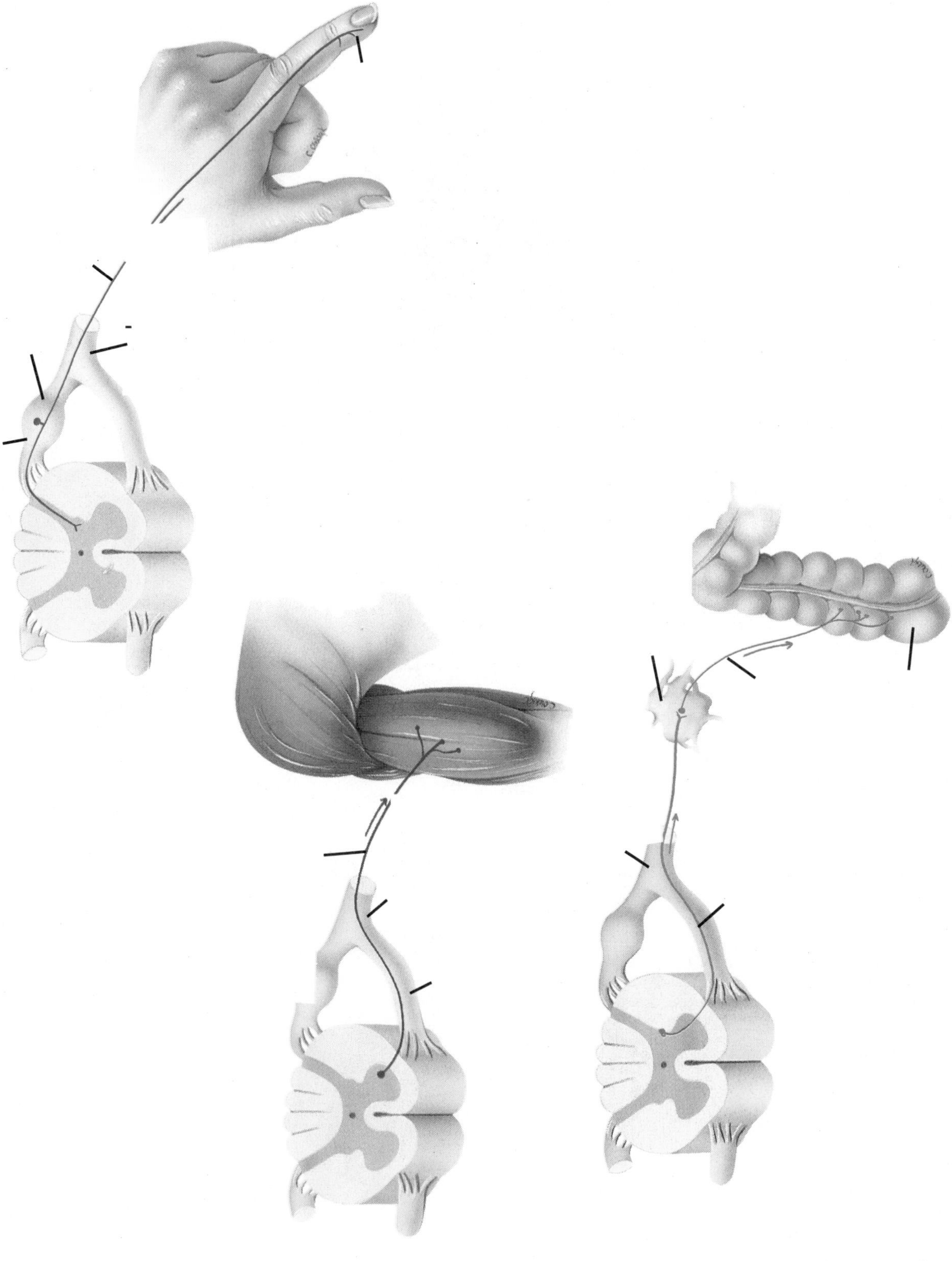

Seeley/Stephens/Tate: Anatomy & Physiology, third edition

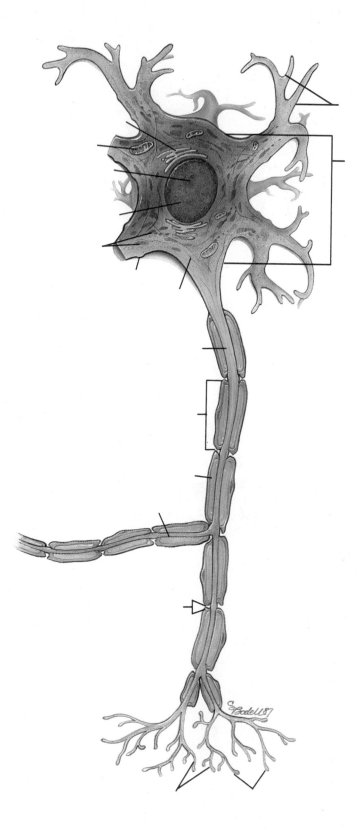

Seeley/Stephens/Tate: Anatomy & Physiology, third edition
© 1995 Mosby−Year Book, Inc.

Types of Neurons (Fig. 12-5 A-C, p. 373)

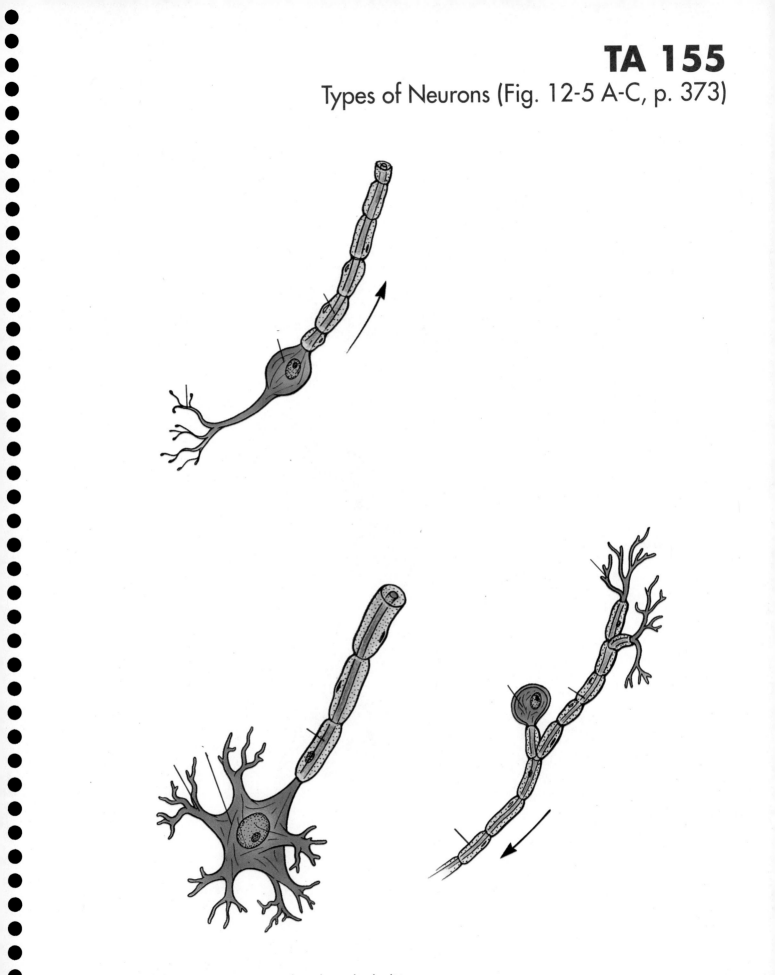

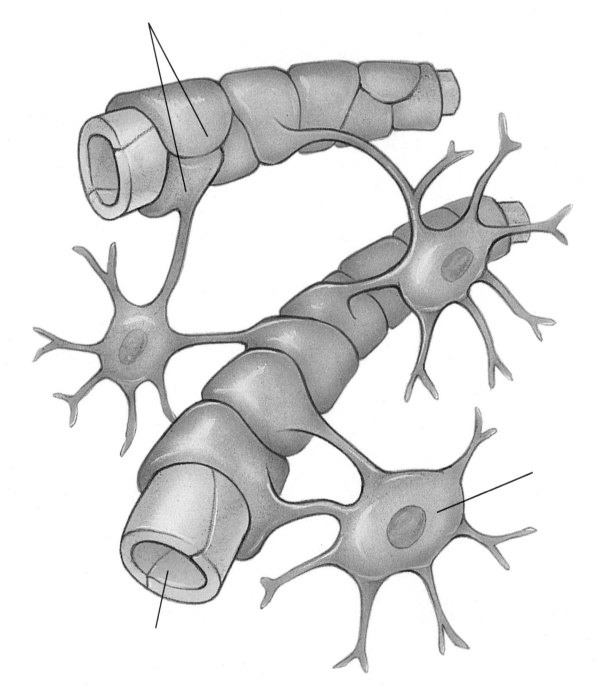

Seeley/Stephens/Tate: Anatomy & Physiology, third edition
© 1995 Mosby–Year Book, Inc.

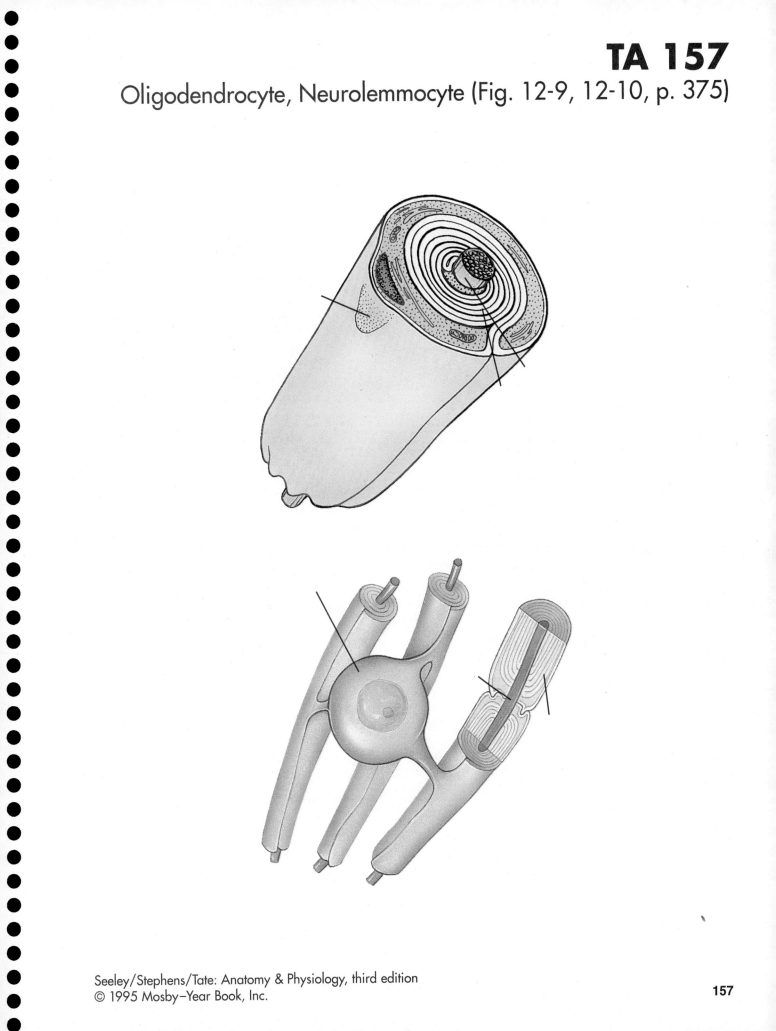

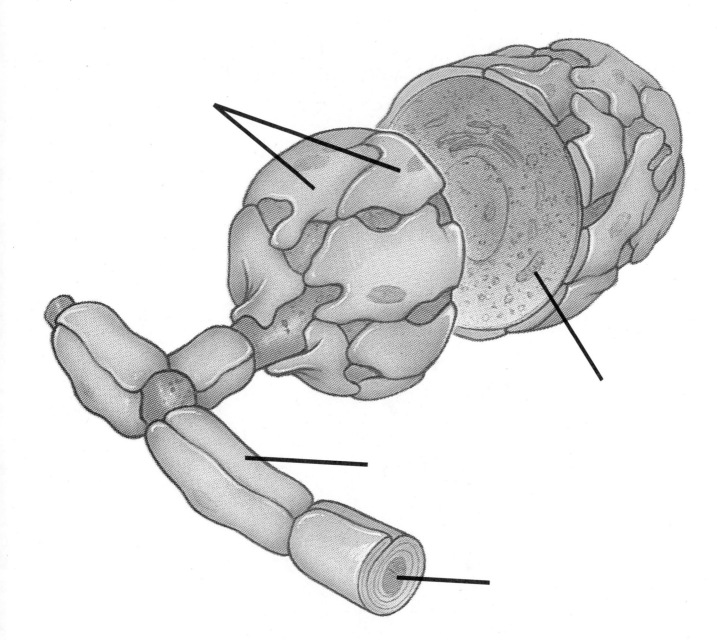

Seeley/Stephens/Tate: Anatomy & Physiology, third edition
© 1995 Mosby–Year Book, Inc.

Comparison of Myelinated and Unmyelinated Axons
(Fig. 12-12 A & B, p. 376)

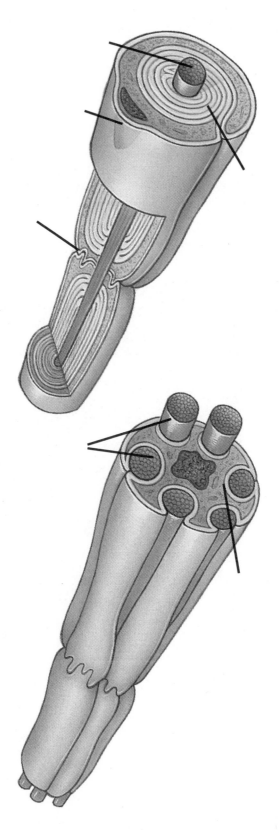

Seeley/Stephens/Tate: Anatomy & Physiology, third edition
© 1995 Mosby–Year Book, Inc.

Seeley/Stephens/Tate: Anatomy & Physiology, third edition
© 1995 Mosby–Year Book, Inc.

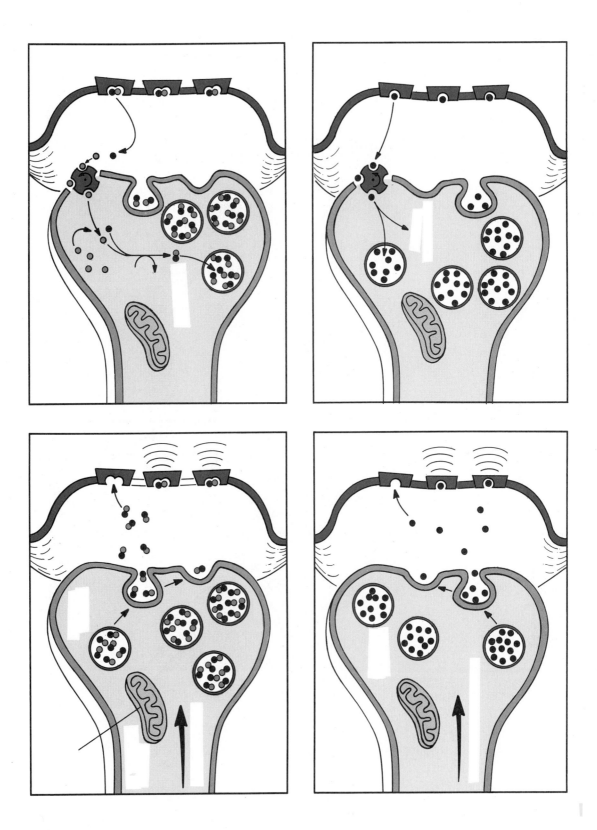

TA 162

Presynaptic Inhibition at an Axo-Axonic Synapse
(Fig. 12-18 A & B, p. 384)

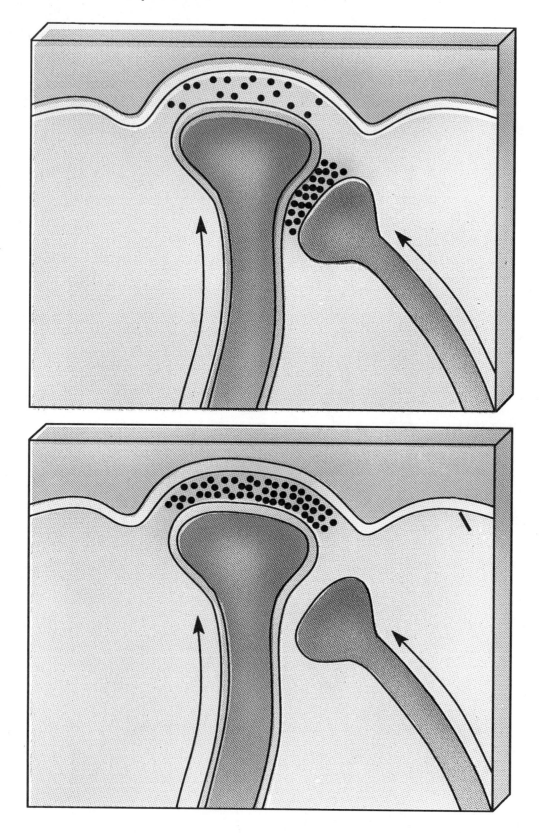

Seeley/Stephens/Tate: Anatomy & Physiology, third edition
© 1995 Mosby–Year Book, Inc.

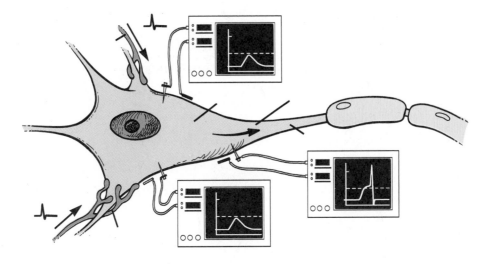

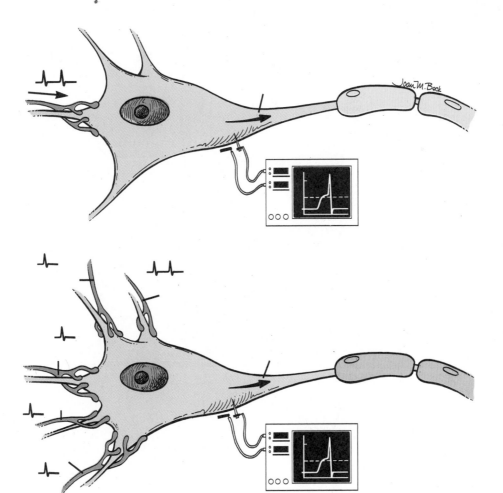

Seeley/Stephens/Tate: Anatomy & Physiology, third edition
© 1995 Mosby–Year Book, Inc.

Reflex Arc (Fig. 12-20, p. 386)

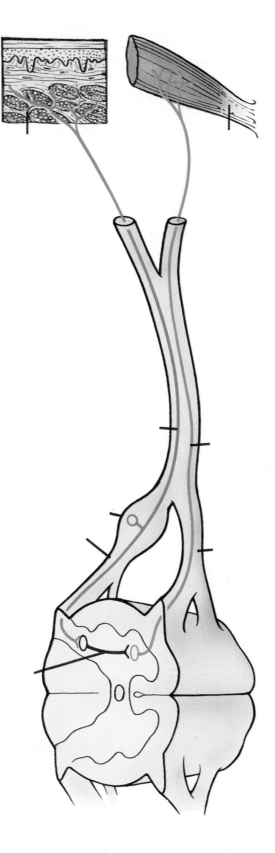

Seeley/Stephens/Tate: Anatomy & Physiology, third edition
© 1995 Mosby–Year Book, Inc.

TA 165

Convergent and Divergent Pathways
(Fig. 12-21 A & B, 12-22 A & B, p. 389)

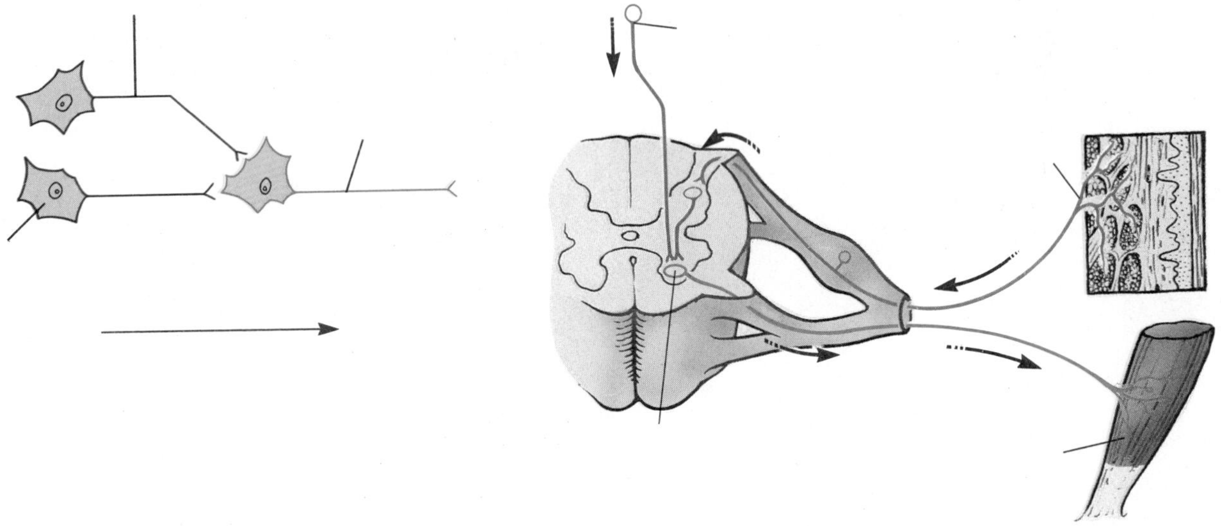

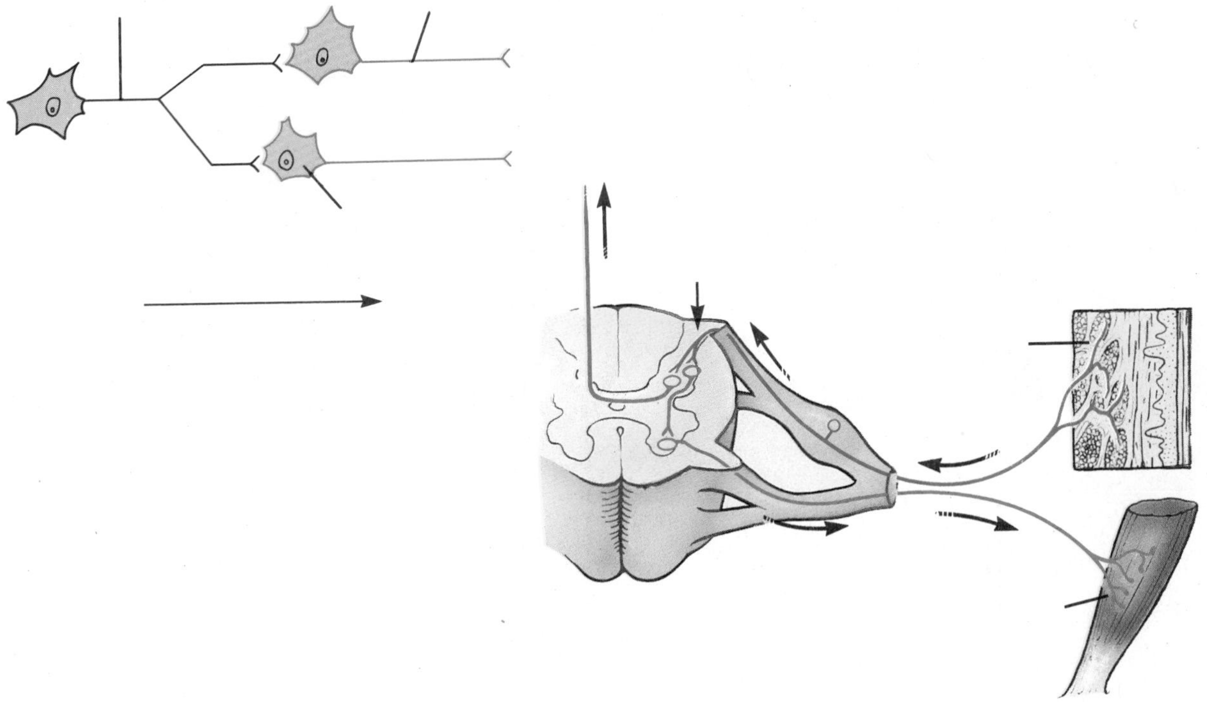

TA 166
Oscillating Circuits (Fig. 12-23 A & B, p. 389)

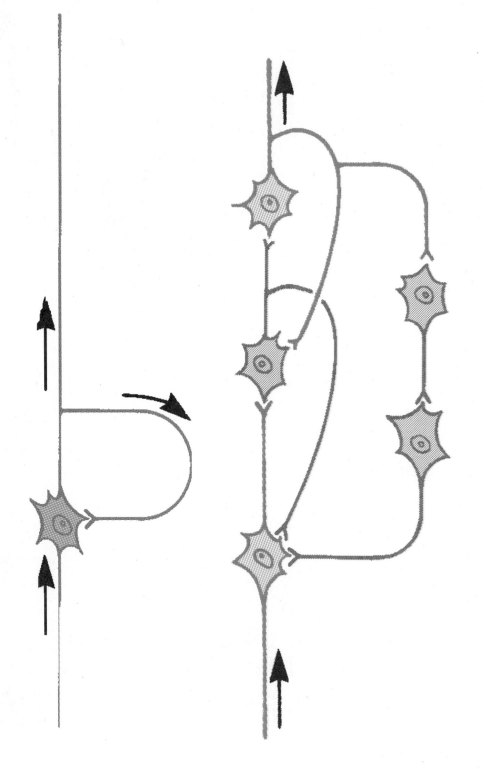

Seeley/Stephens/Tate: Anatomy & Physiology, third edition
© 1995 Mosby–Year Book, Inc.

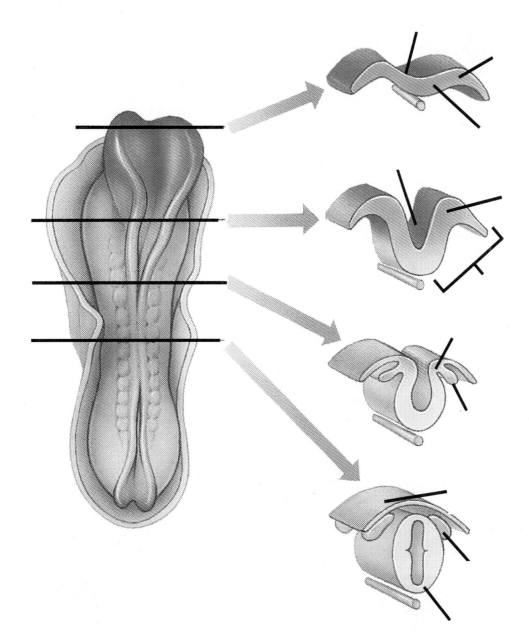

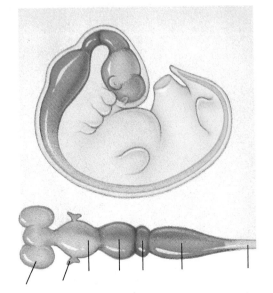

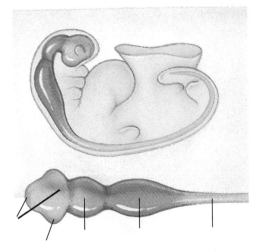

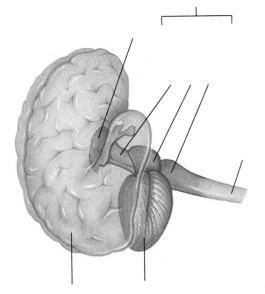

Seeley/Stephens/Tate: Anatomy & Physiology, third edition
© 1995 Mosby–Year Book, Inc.

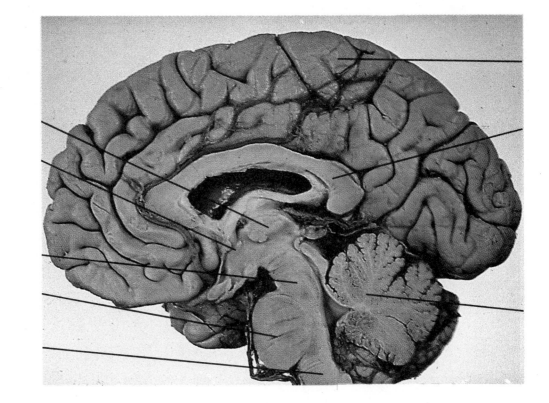

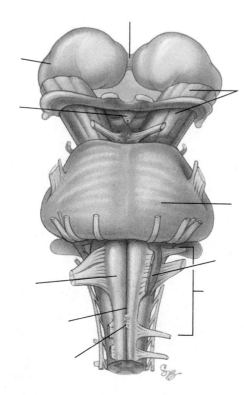

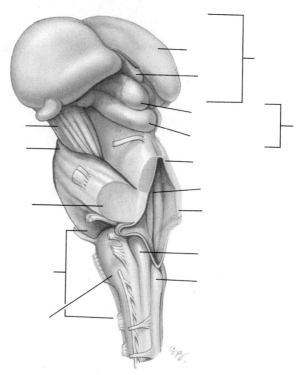

Seeley/Stephens/Tate: Anatomy & Physiology, third edition
© 1995 Mosby–Year Book, Inc.

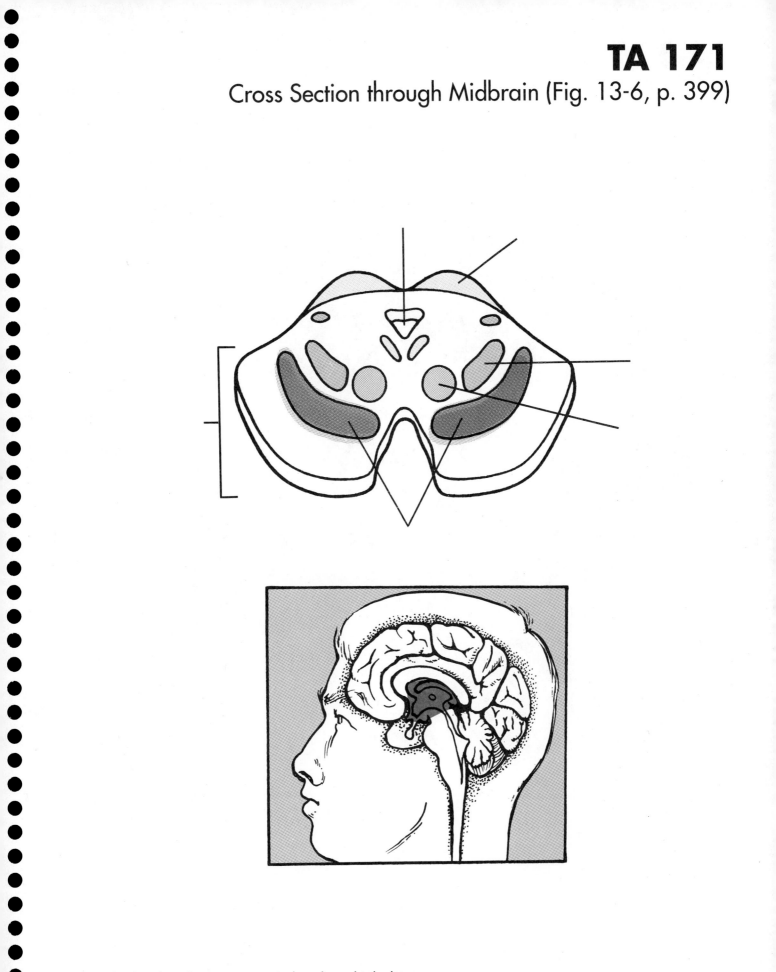

Seeley/Stephens/Tate: Anatomy & Physiology, third edition
© 1995 Mosby–Year Book, Inc.

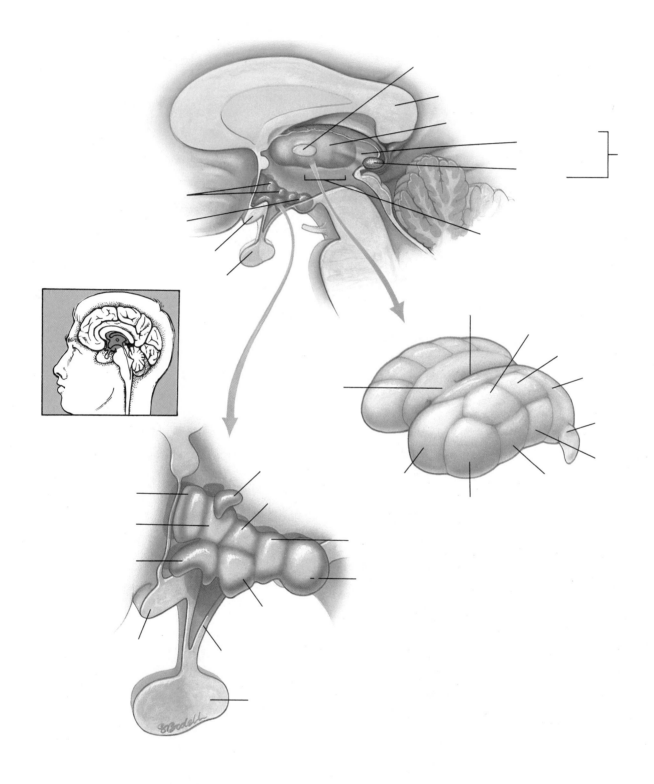

Seeley/Stephens/Tate: Anatomy & Physiology, third edition
© 1995 Mosby–Year Book, Inc.

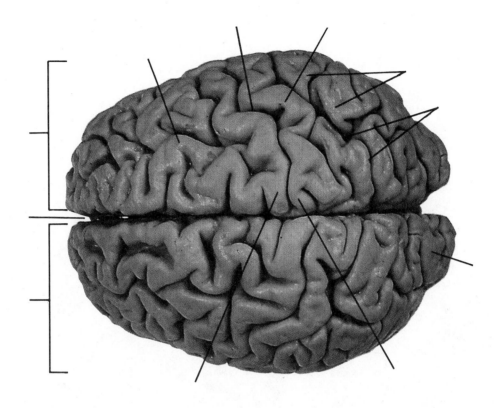

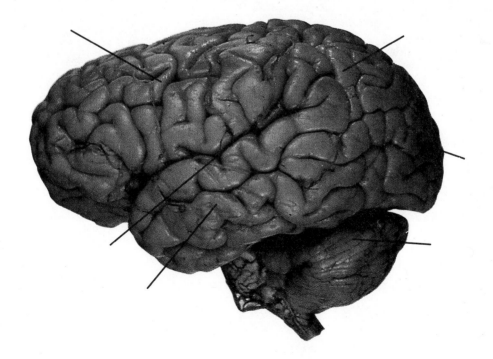

TA 174

Some Functional Areas of the Lateral Side of the Right
Cerebral Cortex (Fig. 13-10, p. 404)

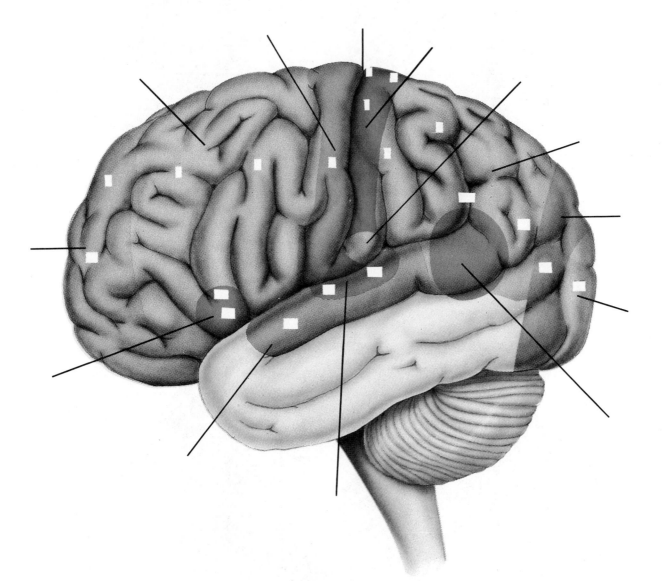

Seeley/Stephens/Tate: Anatomy & Physiology, third edition
© 1995 Mosby–Year Book, Inc.

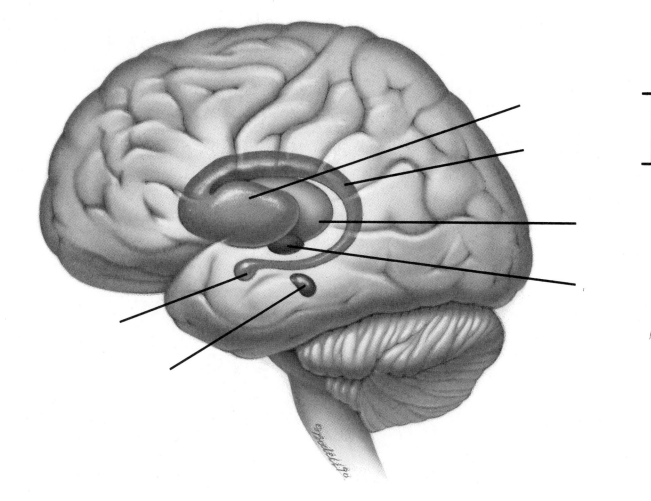

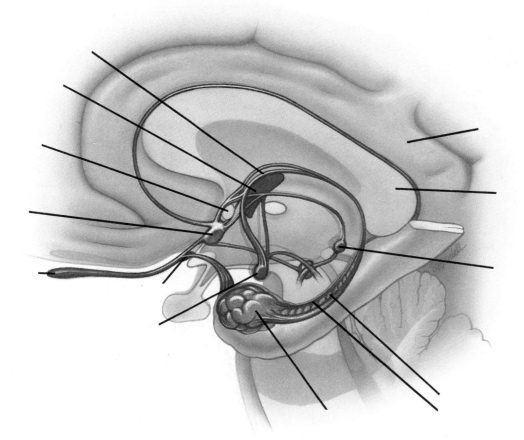

Seeley/Stephens/Tate: Anatomy & Physiology, third edition
© 1995 Mosby–Year Book, Inc.

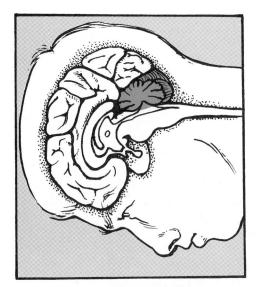

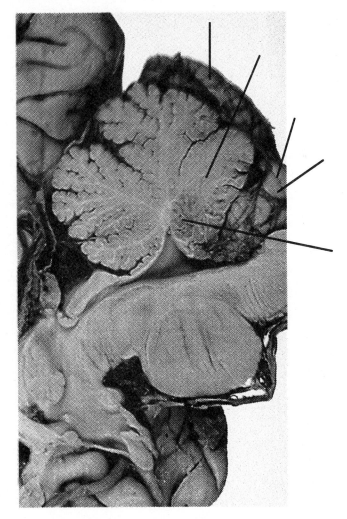

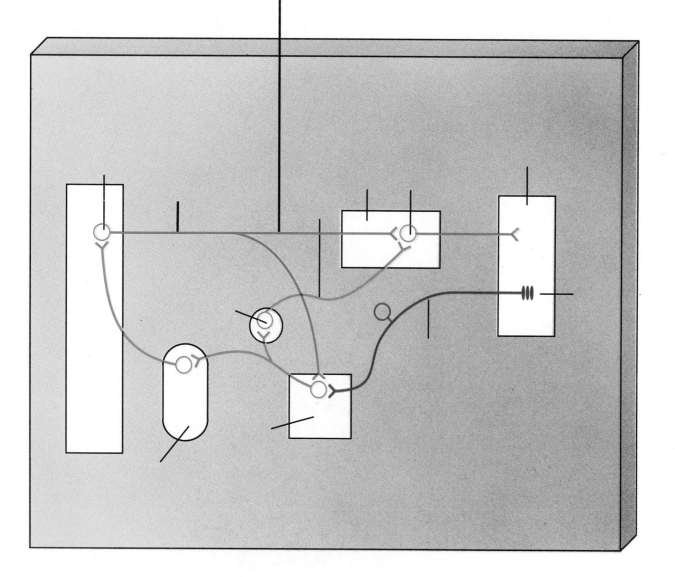

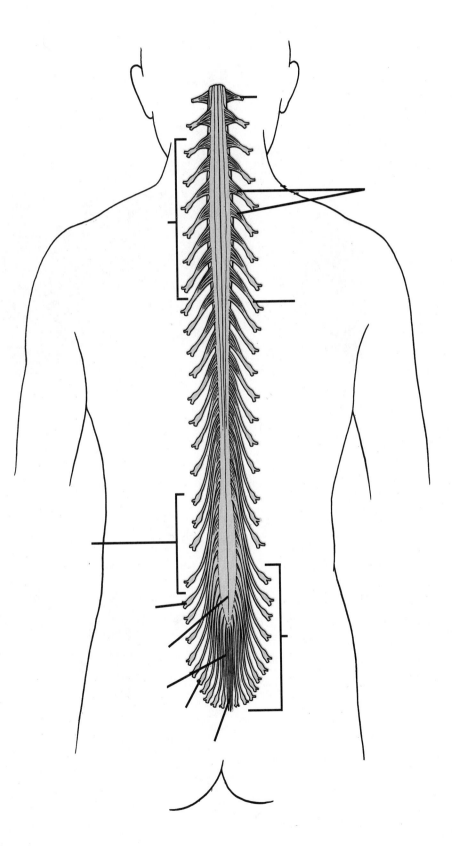

TA 180
Cross Section of the Spinal Cord (Fig. 13-19 A & B, p. 414)

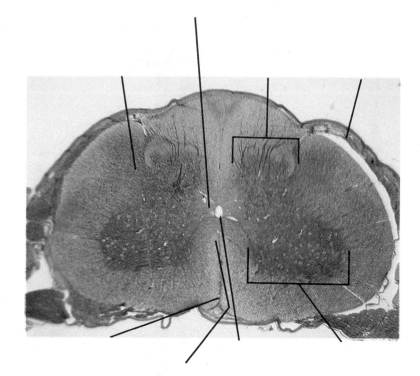

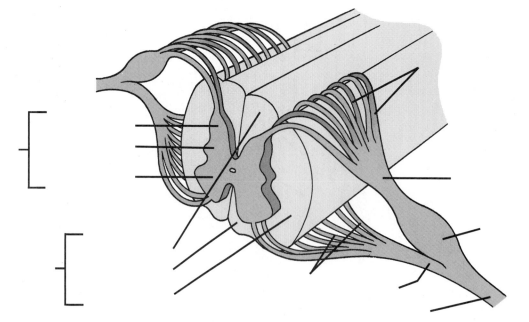

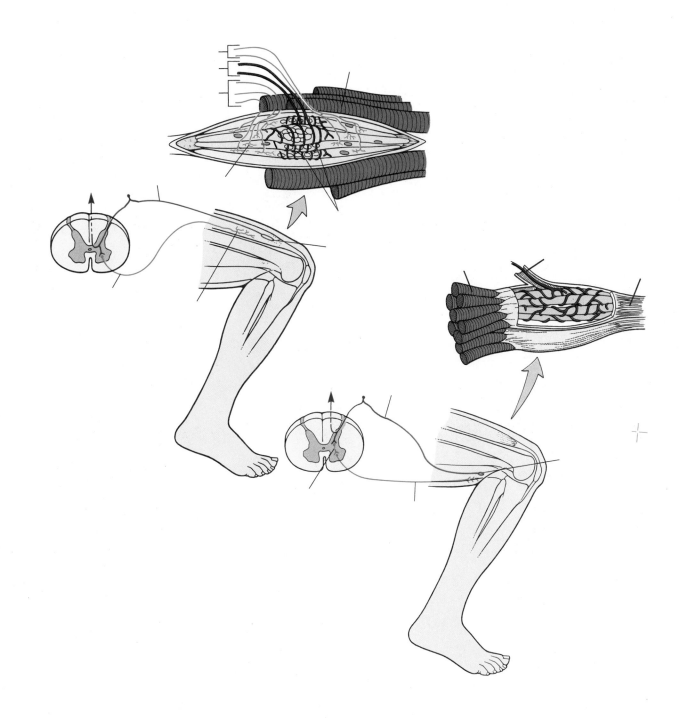

Spinal Cord Reflexes—cont'd (Fig. 13-20 C-E, p. 417)

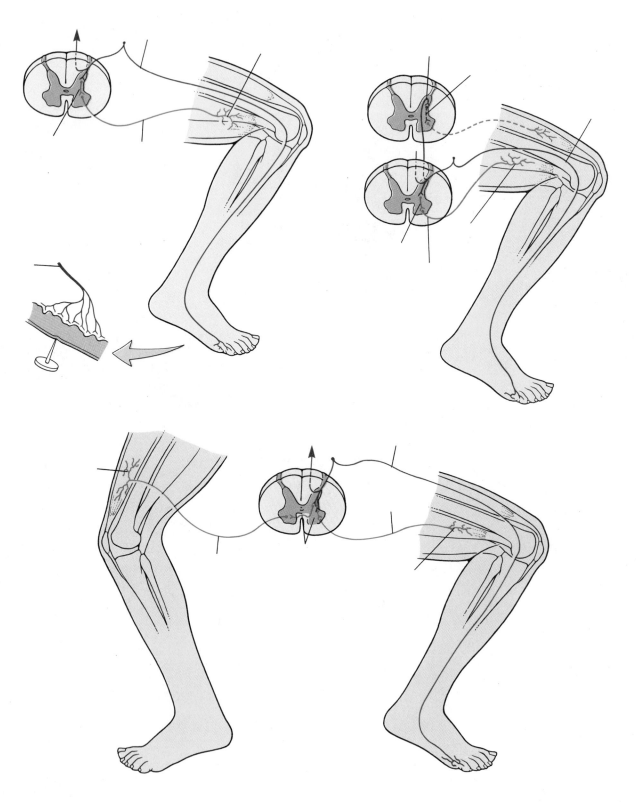

Seeley/Stephens/Tate: Anatomy & Physiology, third edition
© 1995 Mosby–Year Book, Inc.

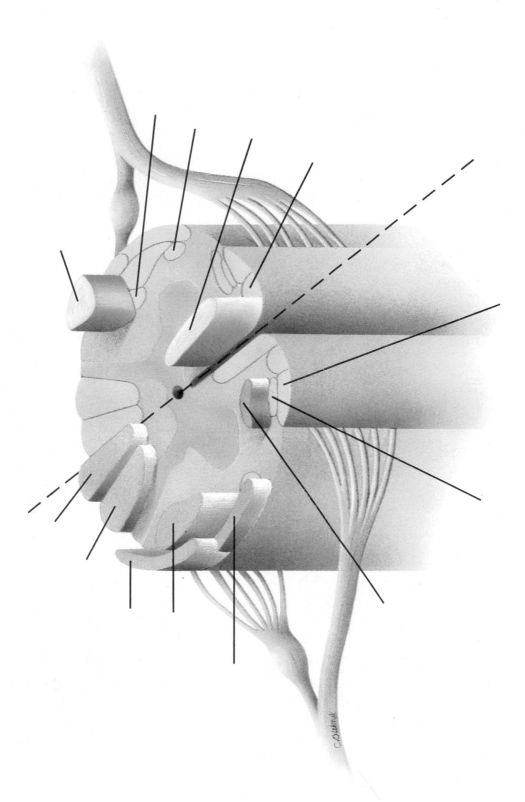

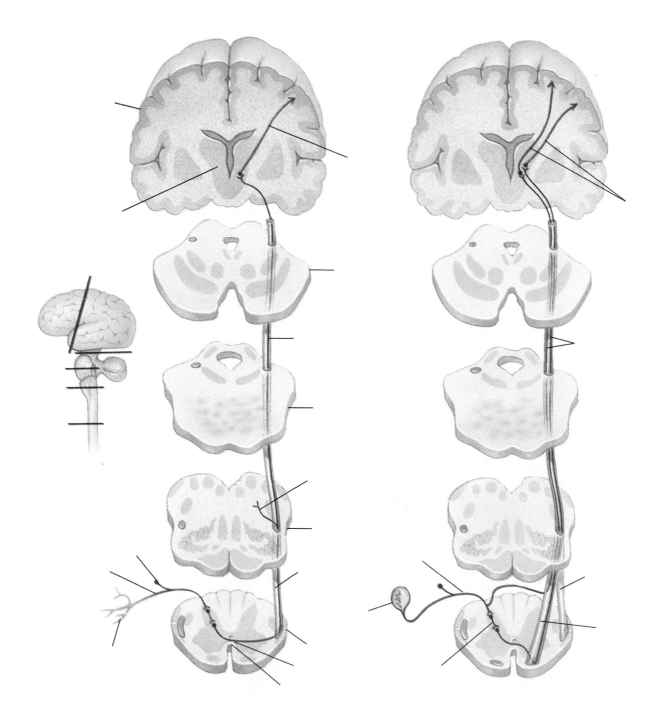

Seeley/Stephens/Tate: Anatomy & Physiology, third edition
© 1995 Mosby–Year Book, Inc.

Dorsal Column-Medial Lemniscal System (Fig. 13-23, p. 423)

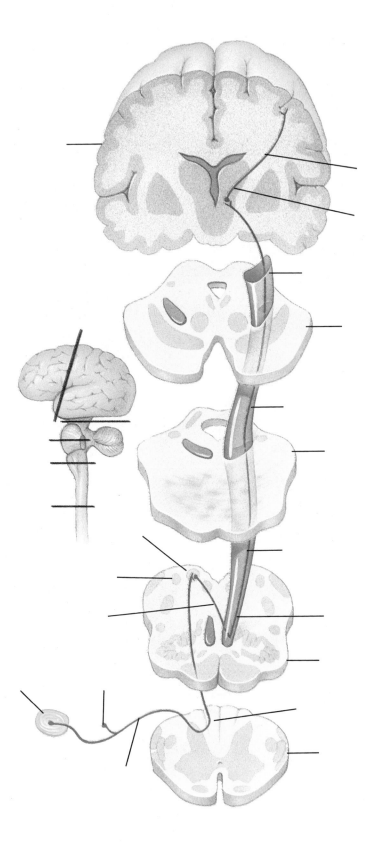

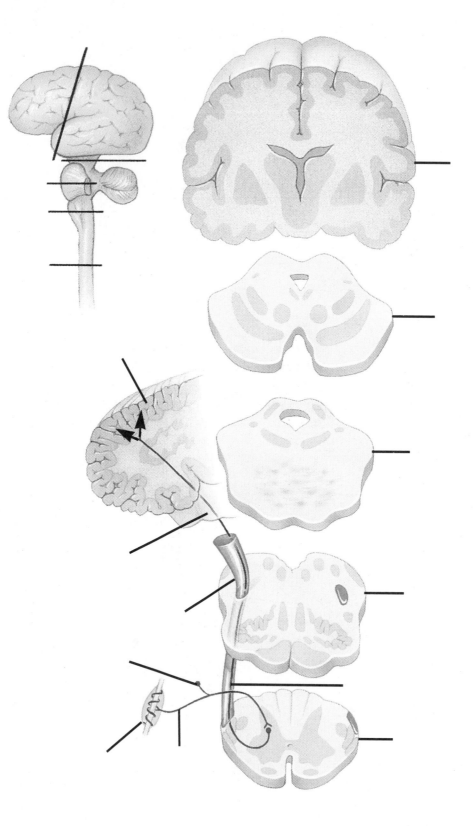

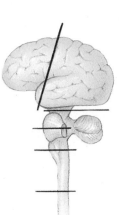

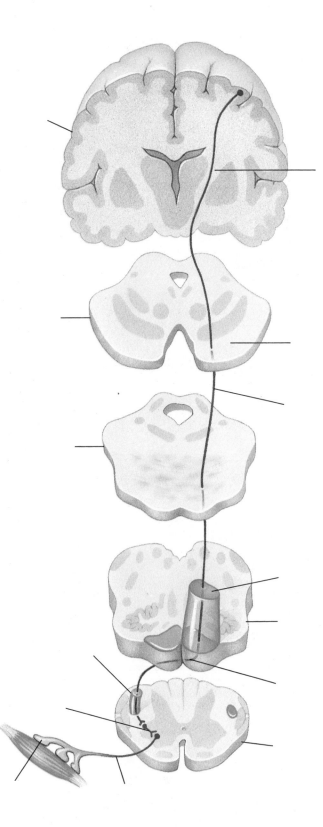

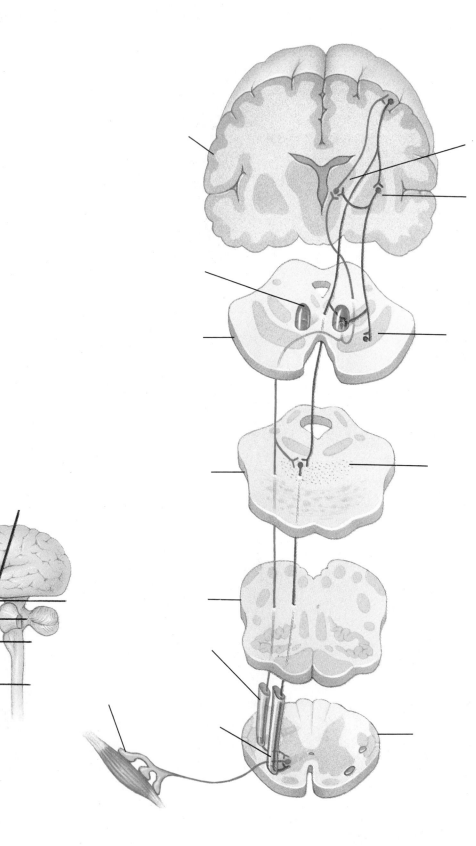

Seeley/Stephens/Tate: Anatomy & Physiology, third edition
© 1995 Mosby–Year Book, Inc.

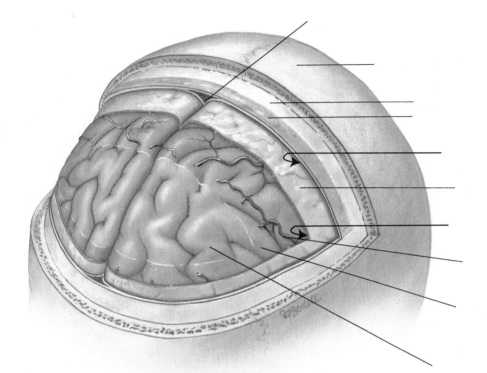

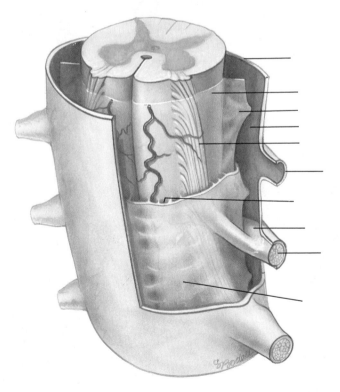

Seeley/Stephens/Tate: Anatomy & Physiology, third edition
© 1995 Mosby–Year Book, Inc.

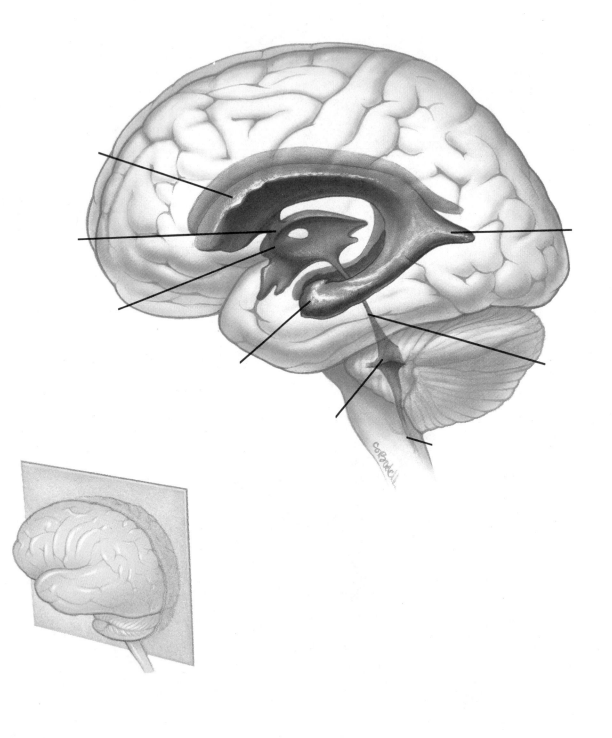

Seeley/Stephens/Tate: Anatomy & Physiology, third edition
© 1995 Mosby–Year Book, Inc.

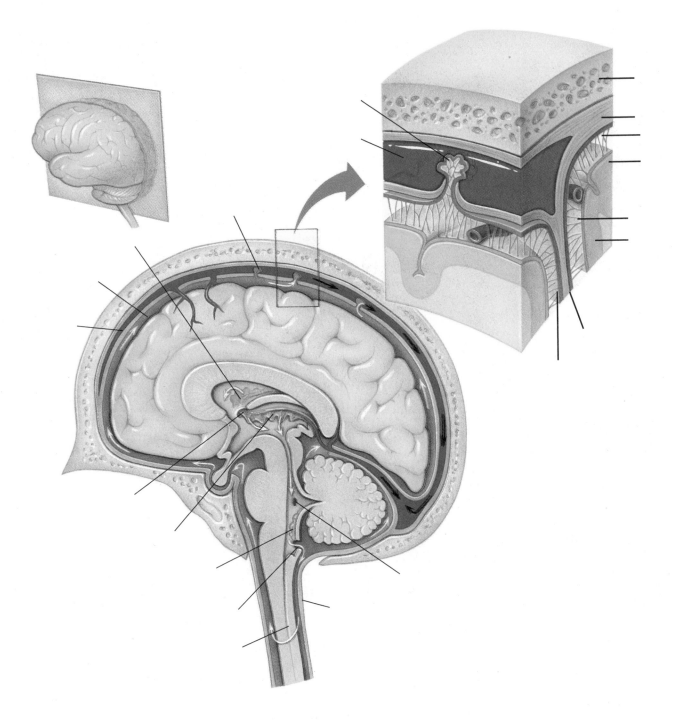

Inferior Surface of the Brain Showing the Origin of the
Cranial Nerves (Fig. 14-1, p. 444)

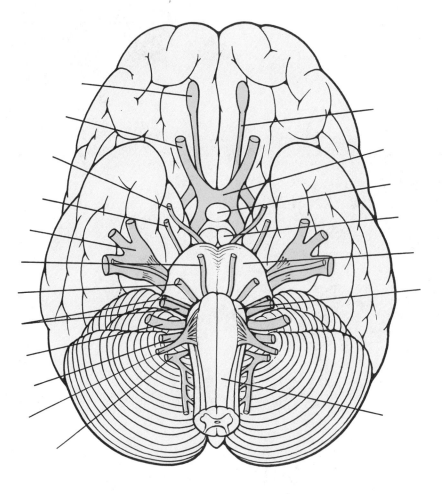

Seeley/Stephens/Tate: Anatomy & Physiology, third edition
© 1995 Mosby–Year Book, Inc.

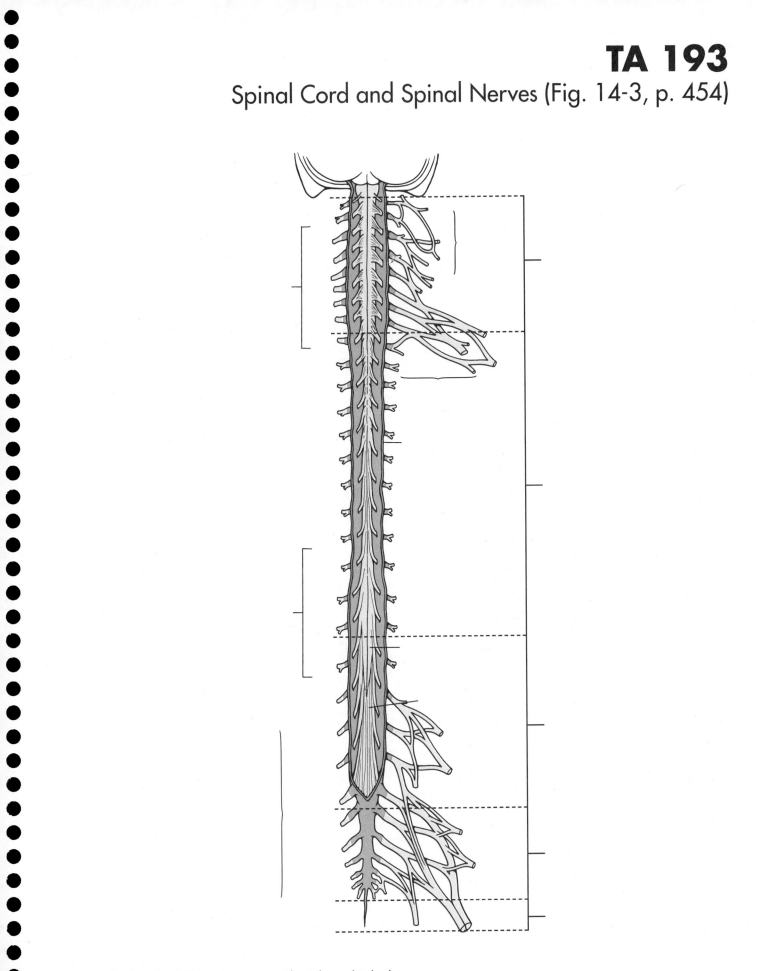

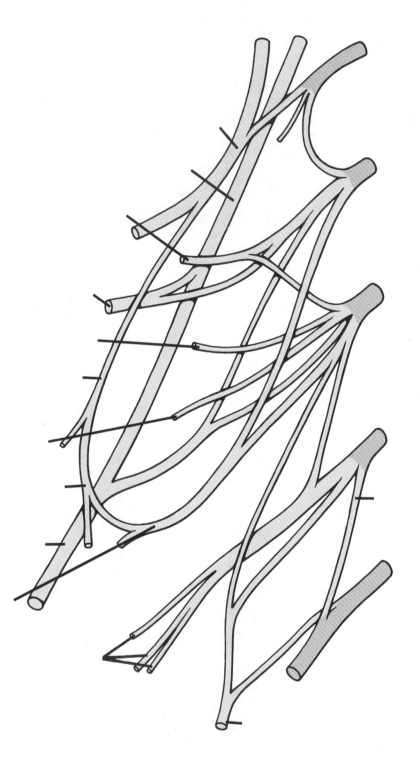

Seeley/Stephens/Tate: Anatomy & Physiology, third edition
© 1995 Mosby–Year Book, Inc.

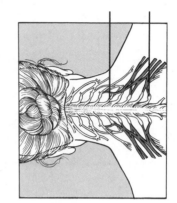

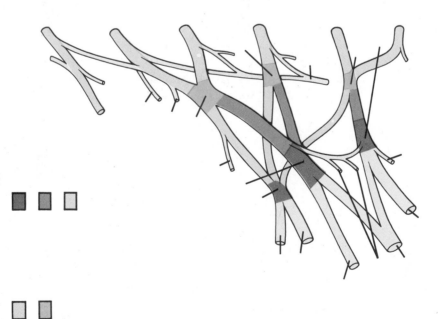

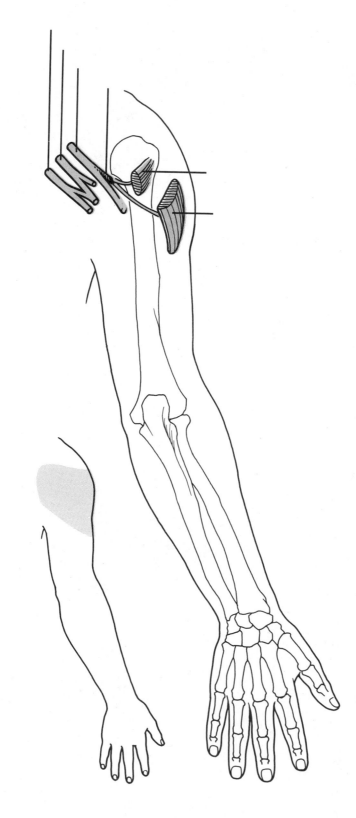

Seeley/Stephens/Tate: Anatomy & Physiology, third edition
© 1995 Mosby–Year Book, Inc.

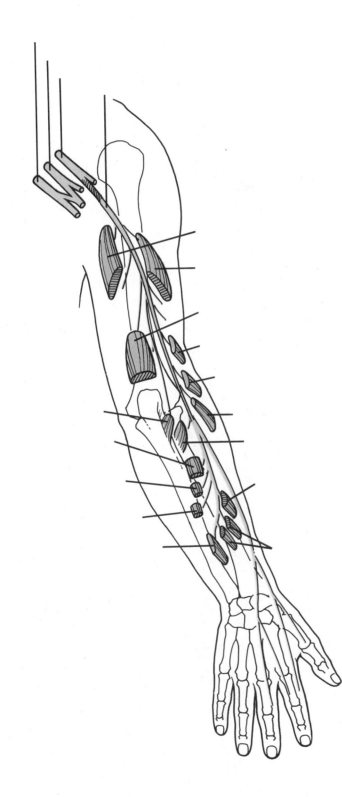

TA 198
Musculocutaneous Nerve (Fig. 14-9, p. 459)

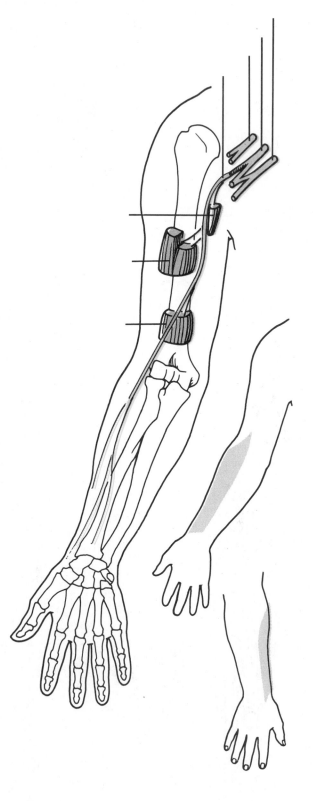

Seeley/Stephens/Tate: Anatomy & Physiology, third edition
© 1995 Mosby–Year Book, Inc.

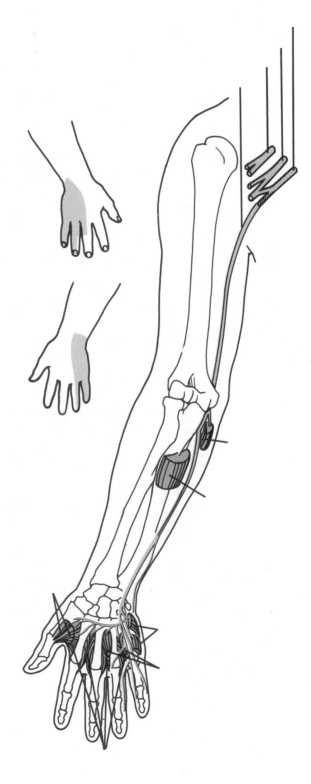

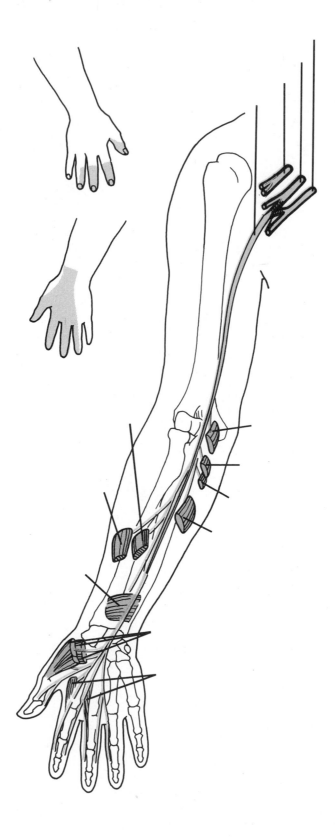

Seeley/Stephens/Tate: Anatomy & Physiology, *third edition*
© 1995 Mosby–Year Book, Inc.

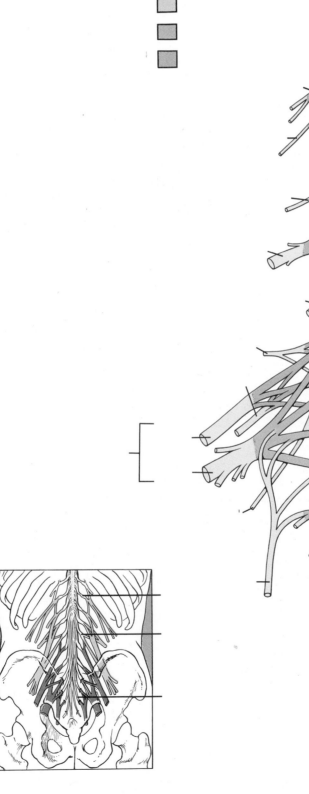

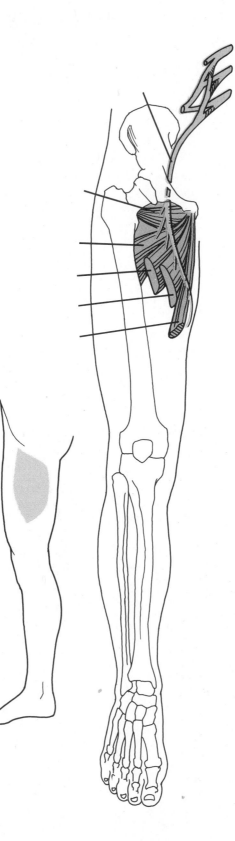

Seeley/Stephens/Tate: Anatomy & Physiology, third edition
© 1995 Mosby–Year Book, Inc.

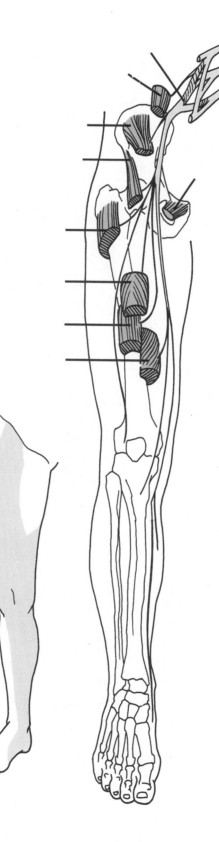

TA 204
Tibial Nerve (Fig. 14-15, p. 465)

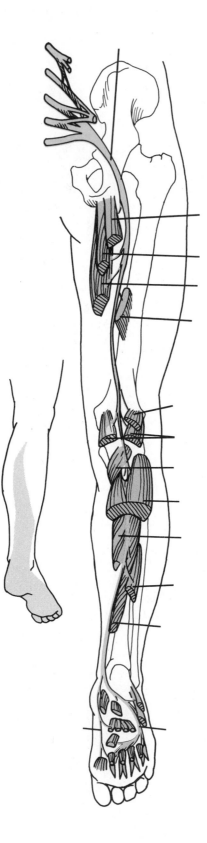

Seeley/Stephens/Tate: Anatomy & Physiology, third edition
© 1995 Mosby–Year Book, Inc.

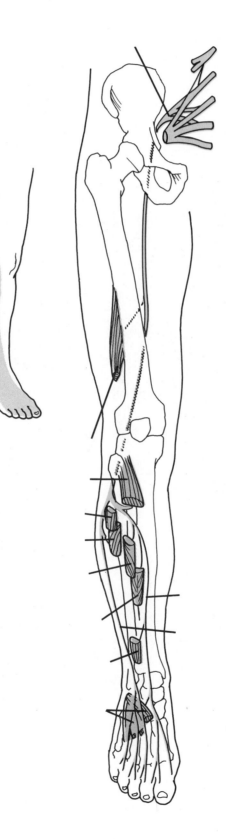

TA 206
Sensory Cutaneous Nerve Endings (Fig. 15-1, p. 474)

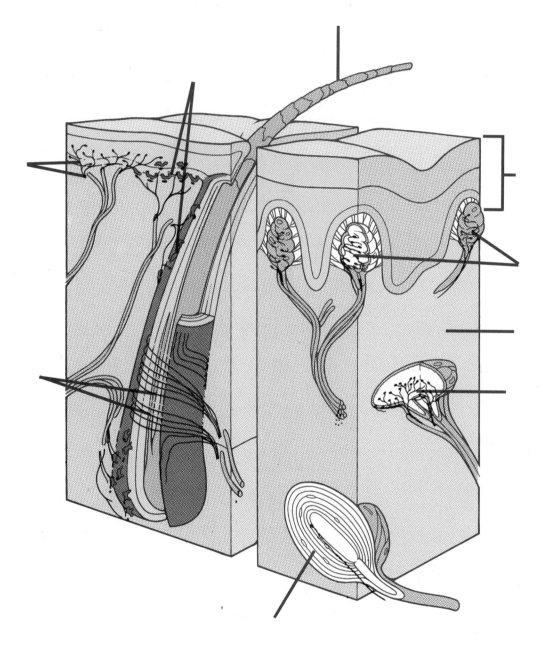

Seeley/Stephens/Tate: Anatomy & Physiology, third edition
© 1995 Mosby–Year Book, Inc.

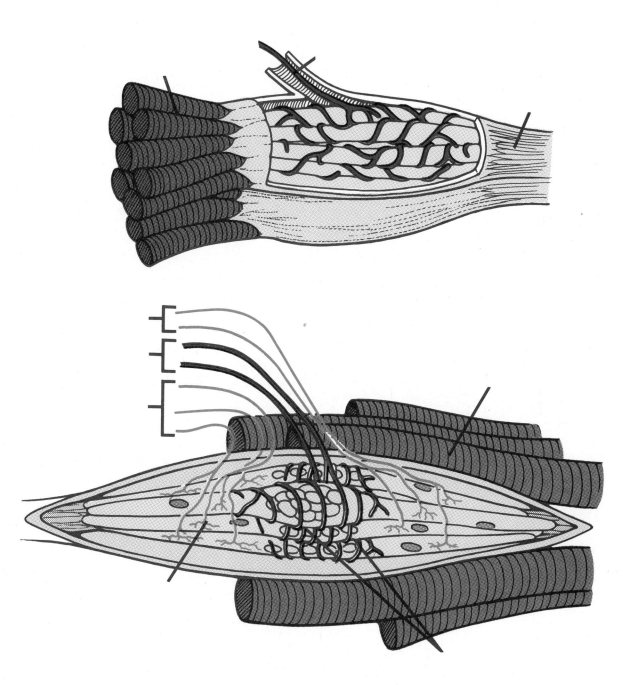

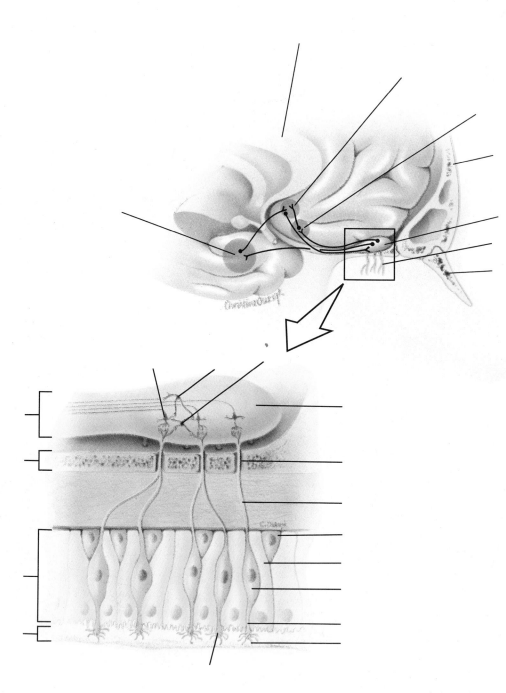

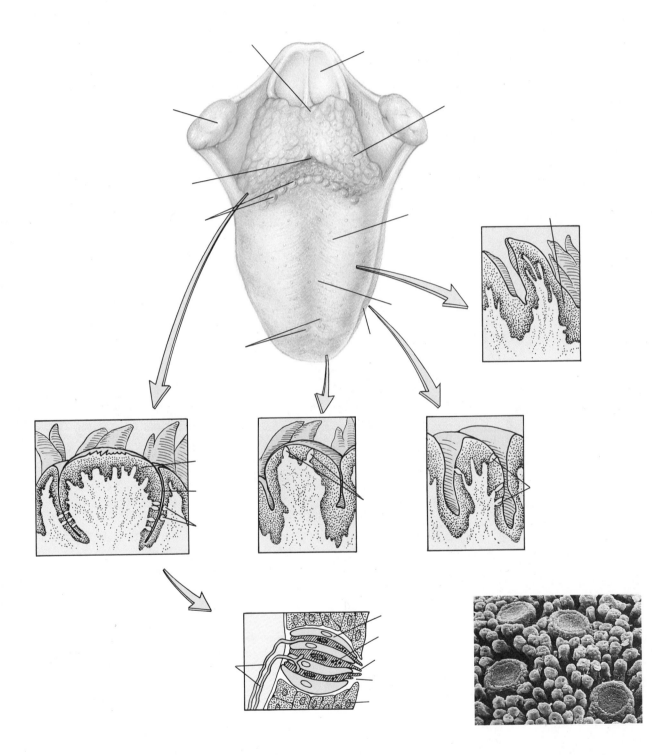

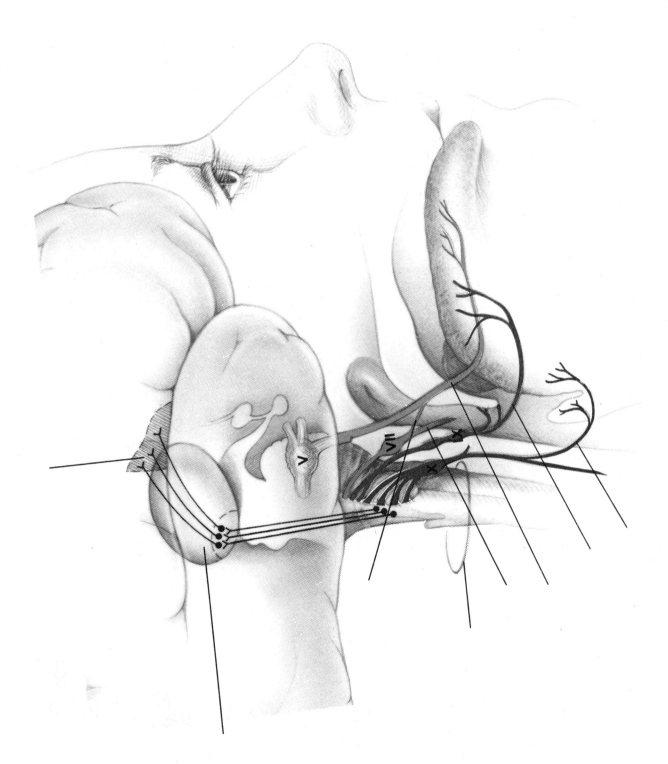

Sagittal Section through the Eye Showing Its Accessory Structures
(Fig. 15-9, p. 481)

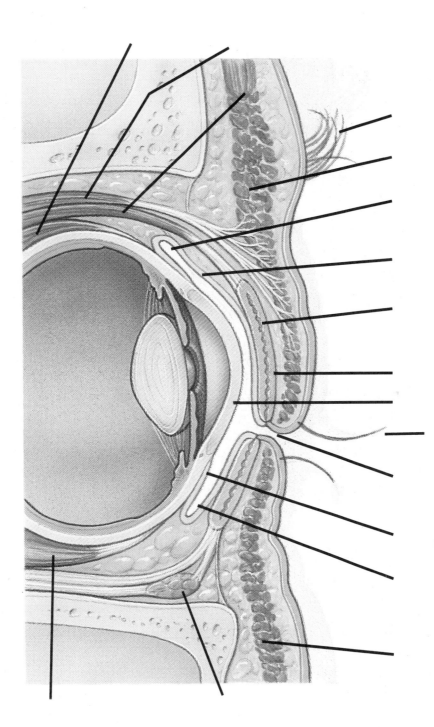

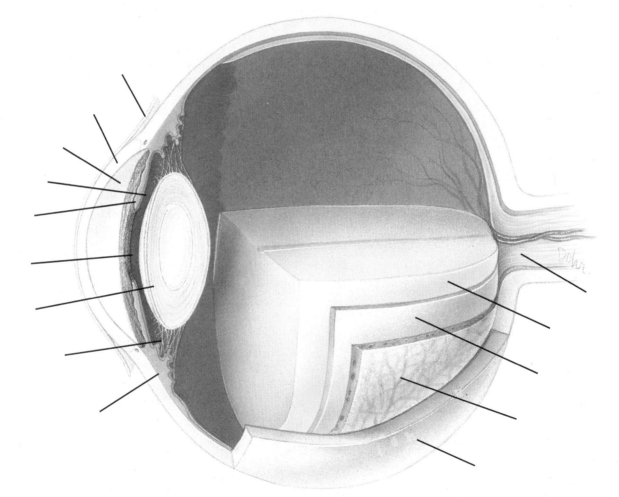

Seeley/Stephens/Tate: Anatomy & Physiology, third edition
© 1995 Mosby–Year Book, Inc.

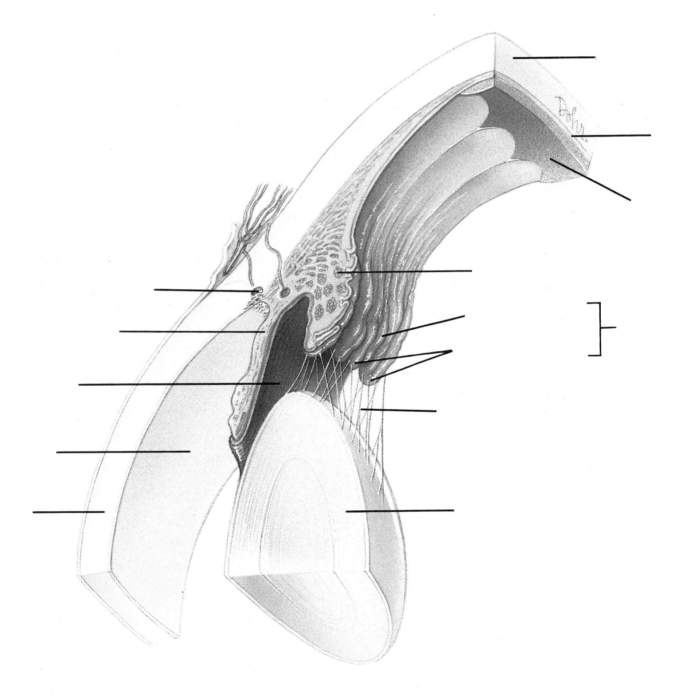

Section through the Retina with its Major Layers Labeled
(Fig. 15-18, p. 493)

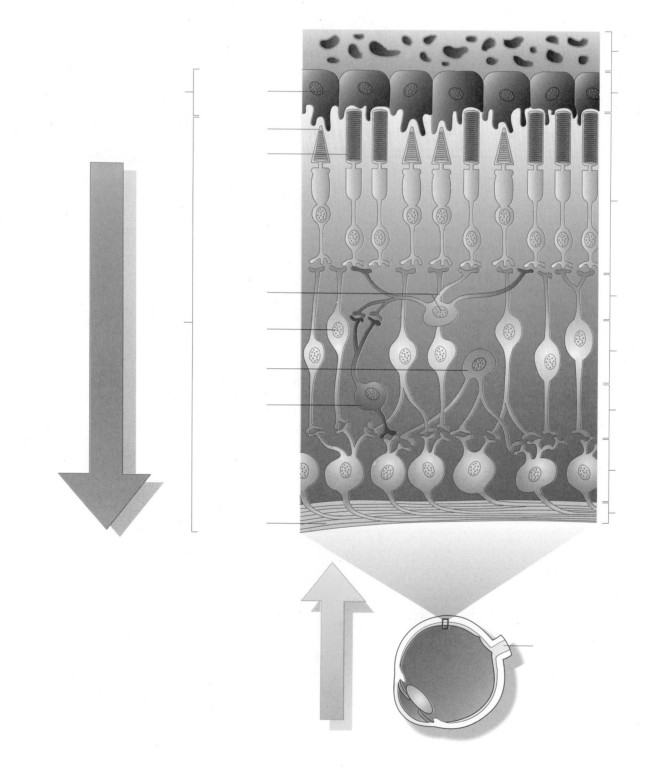

Seeley/Stephens/Tate: Anatomy & Physiology, third edition
© 1995 Mosby–Year Book, Inc.

Rhodopsin Cycle (Fig. 15-20 A-E, p. 495)

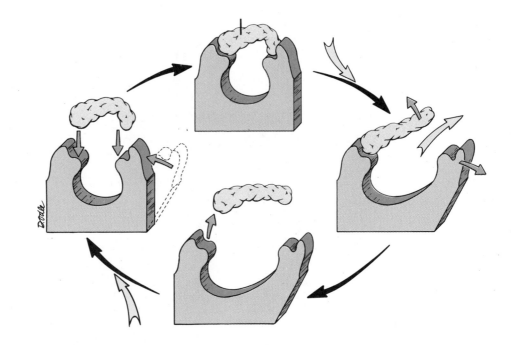

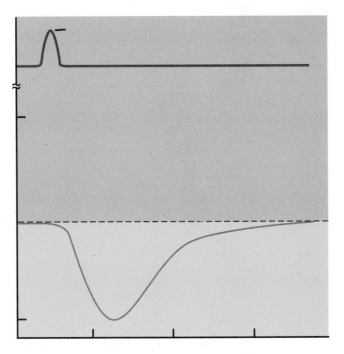

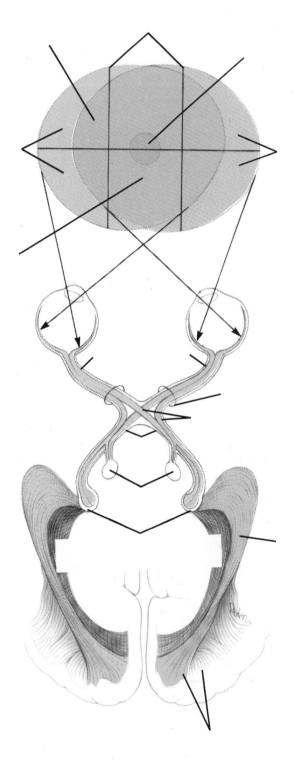

Seeley/Stephens/Tate: Anatomy & Physiology, third edition
© 1995 Mosby–Year Book, Inc.

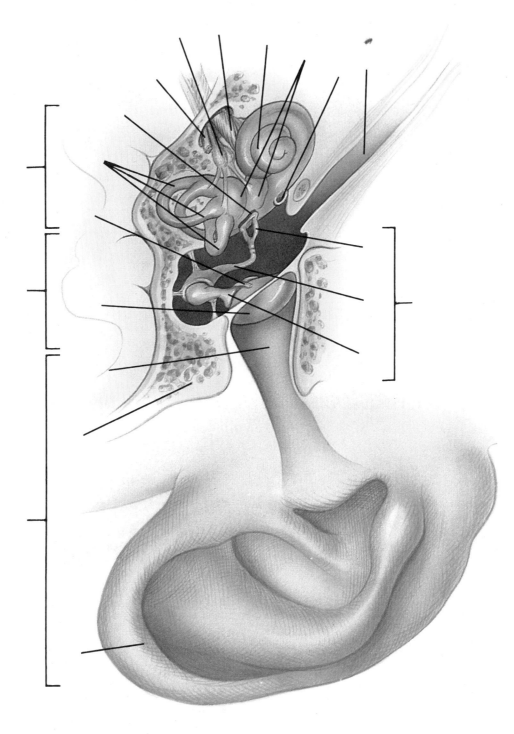

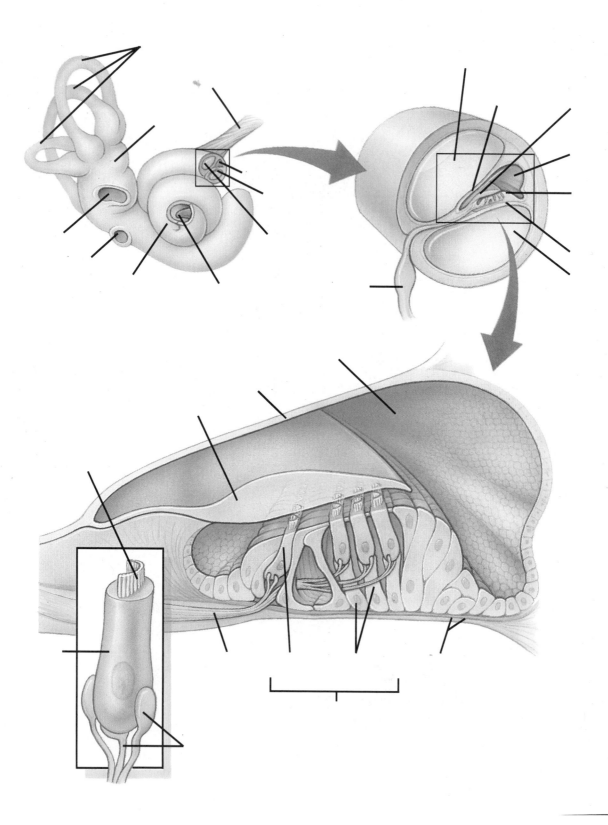

Seeley/Stephens/Tate: Anatomy & Physiology, third edition
© 1995 Mosby–Year Book, Inc.

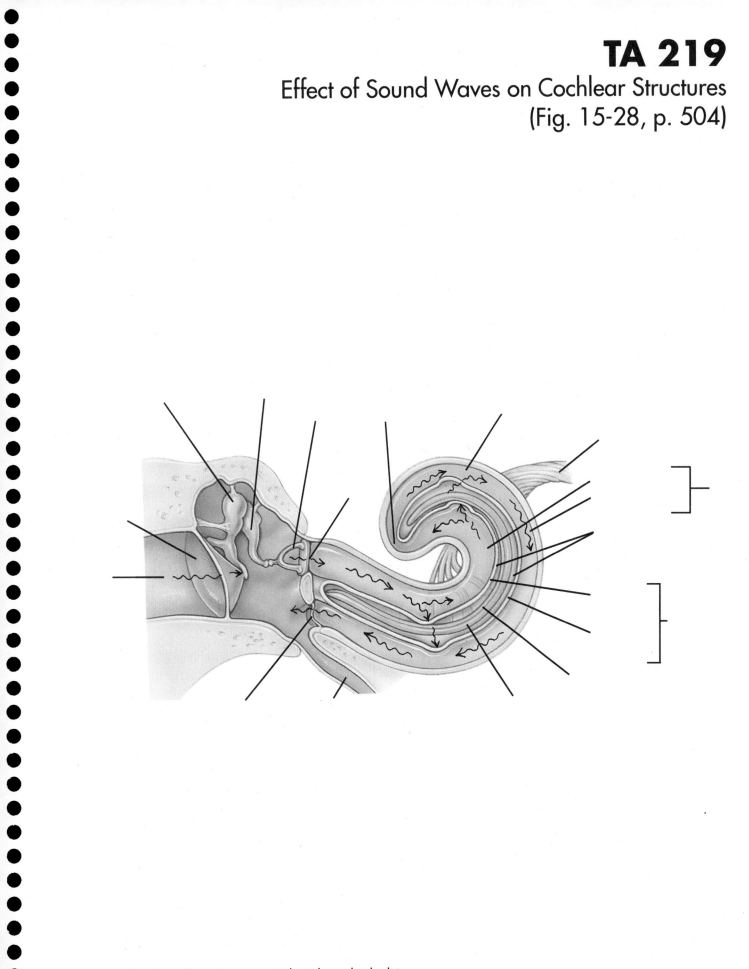

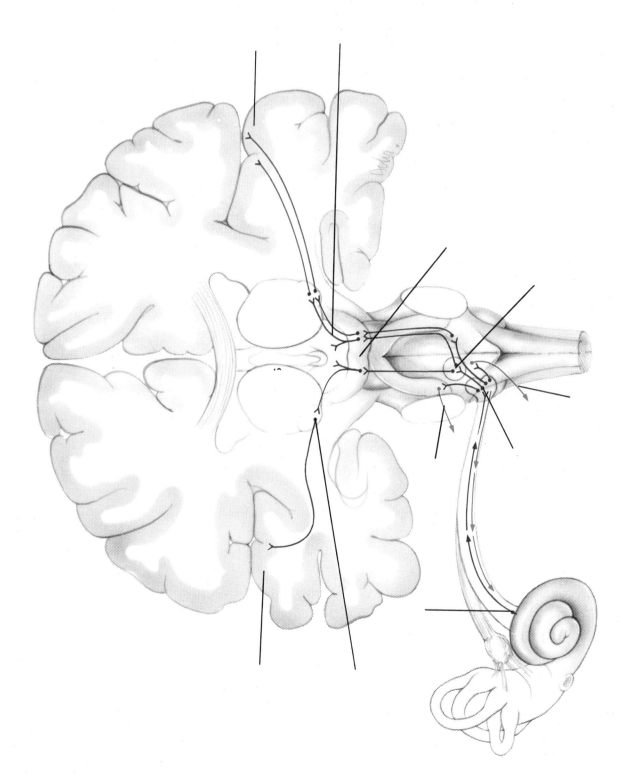

Seeley/Stephens/Tate: Anatomy & Physiology, third edition
© 1995 Mosby–Year Book, Inc.

Structure of the Macula (Fig. 15-32 A-C, p. 509)

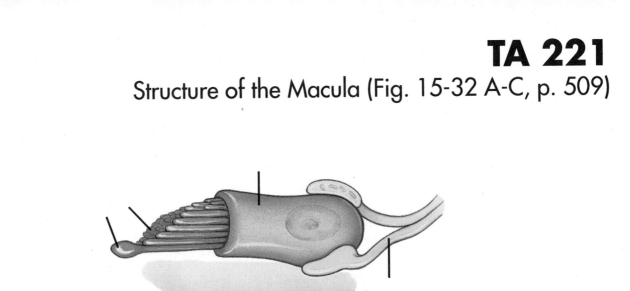

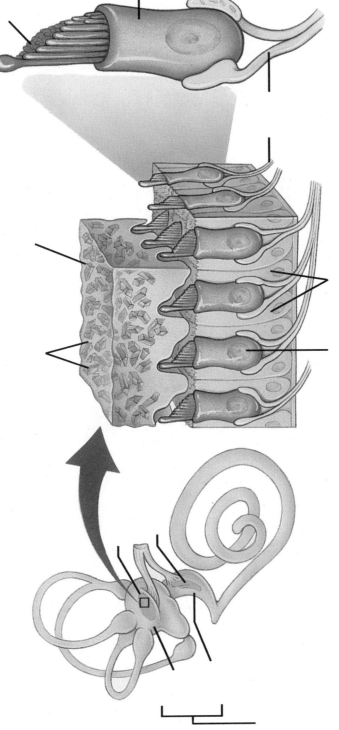

Seeley/Stephens/Tate: Anatomy & Physiology, third edition
© 1995 Mosby–Year Book, Inc.

Semicircular Canals (Fig. 15-34 A-C, p. 510)

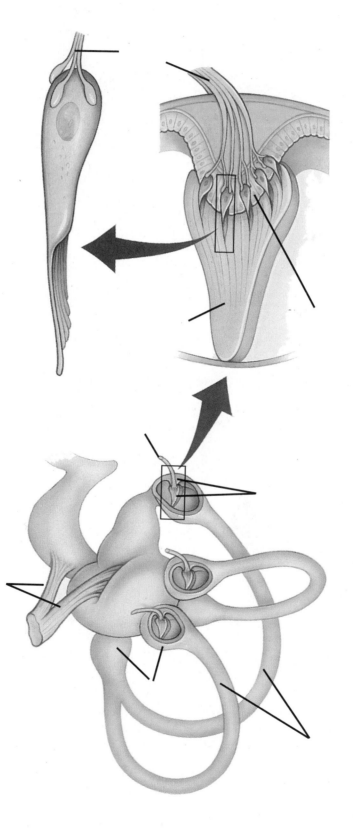

Seeley/Stephens/Tate: Anatomy & Physiology, third edition
© 1995 Mosby–Year Book, Inc.

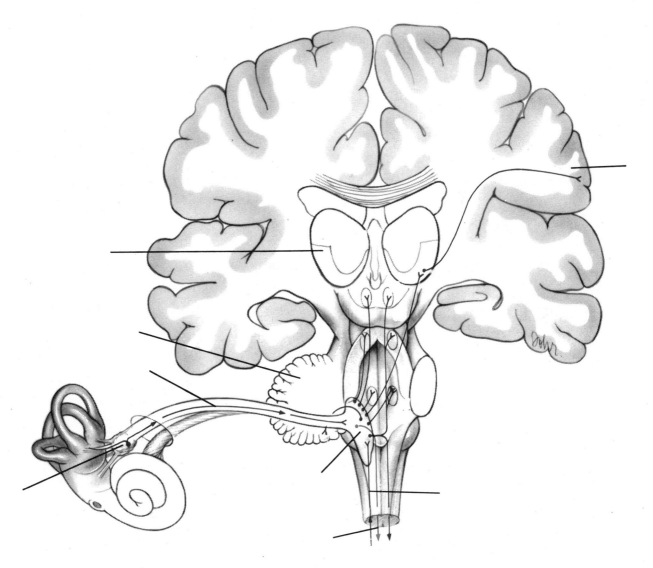

Organization of Autonomic Nervous System Neurons
(Fig. 16-1, p. 521)

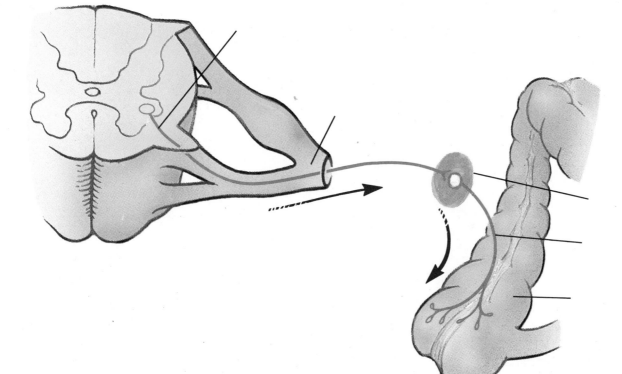

Seeley/Stephens/Tate: Anatomy & Physiology, third edition
© 1995 Mosby–Year Book, Inc.

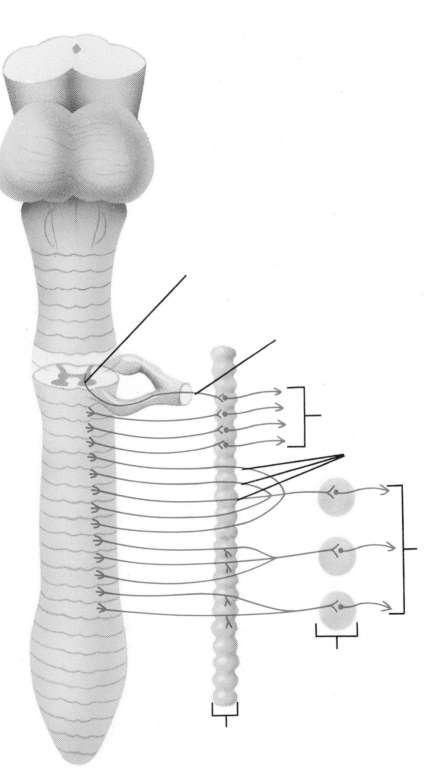

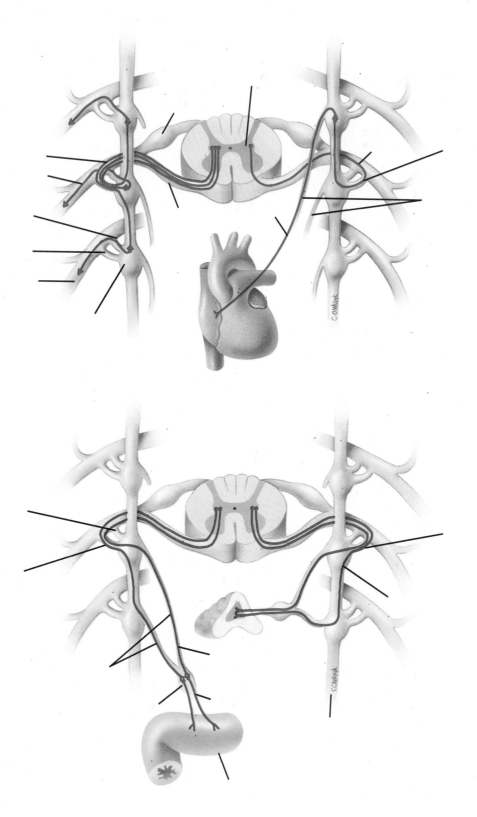

Seeley/Stephens/Tate: Anatomy & Physiology, third edition
© 1995 Mosby–Year Book, Inc.

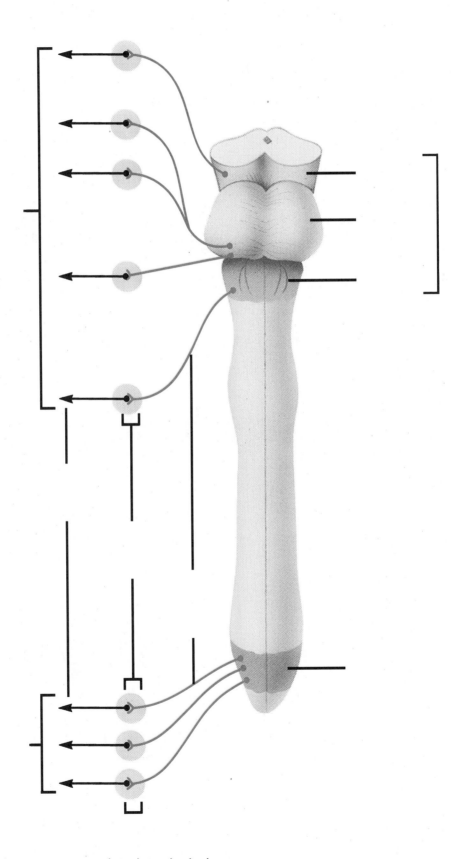

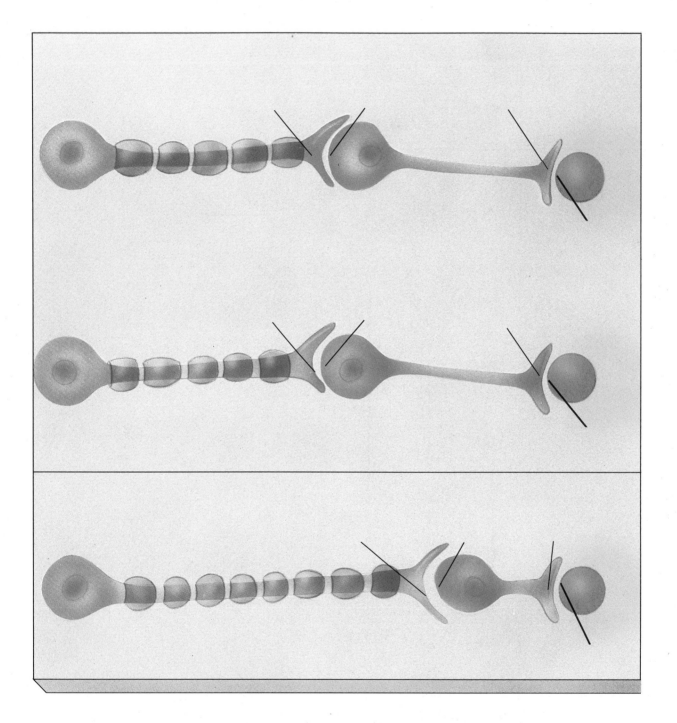

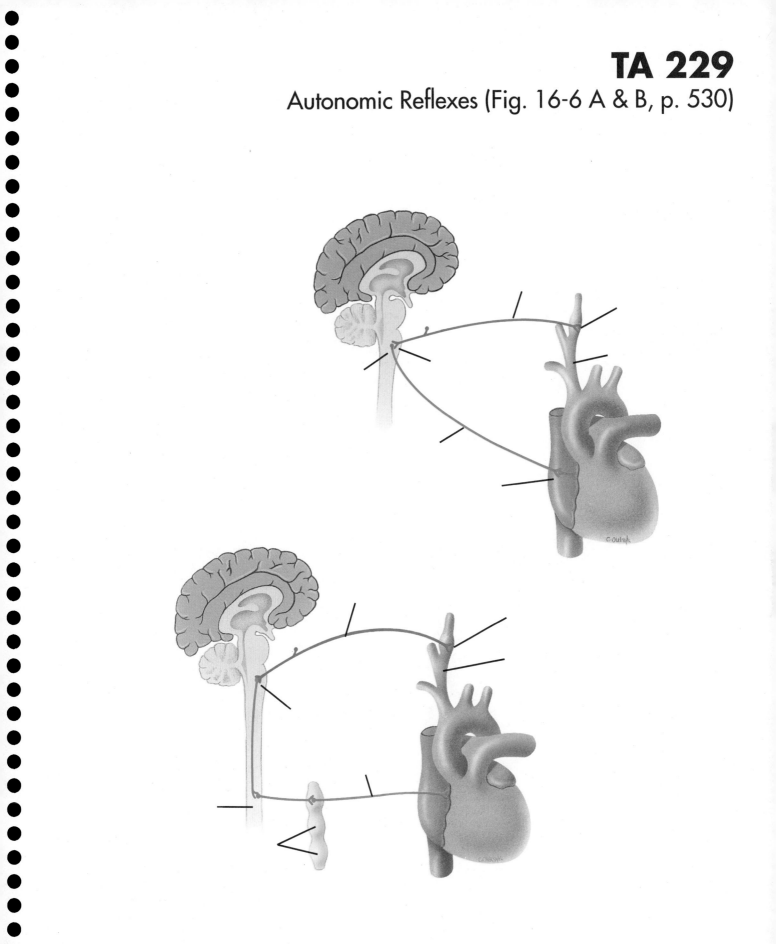

TA 230

Innervation of Organs by the Autonomic Nervous System
(Fig. 16-8, p. 533)

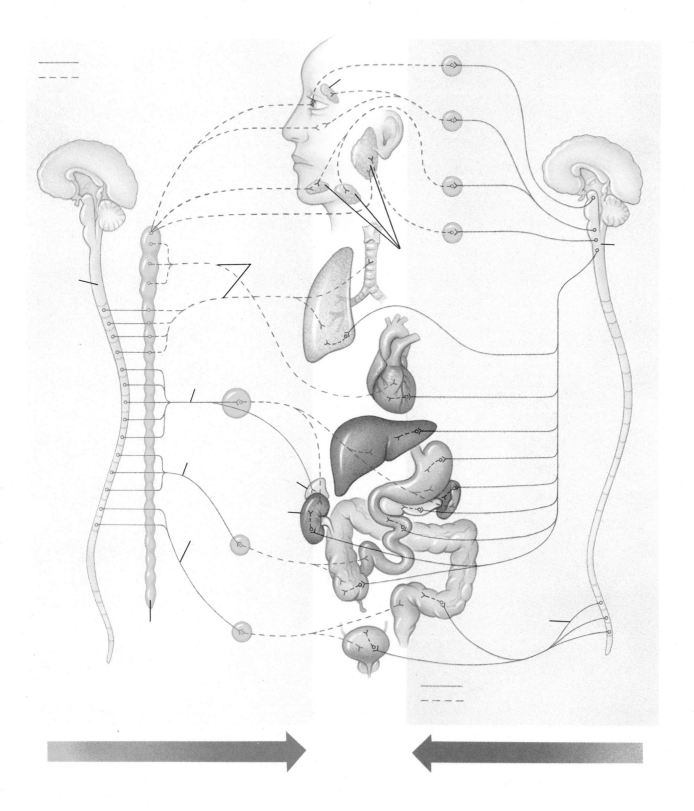

Seeley/Stephens/Tate: Anatomy & Physiology, third edition
© 1995 Mosby–Year Book, Inc.

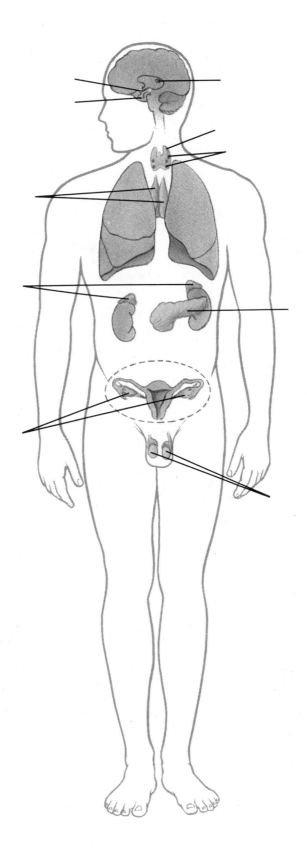

Control of Hormone Secretion (Fig. 17-4 B & C, p. 544)

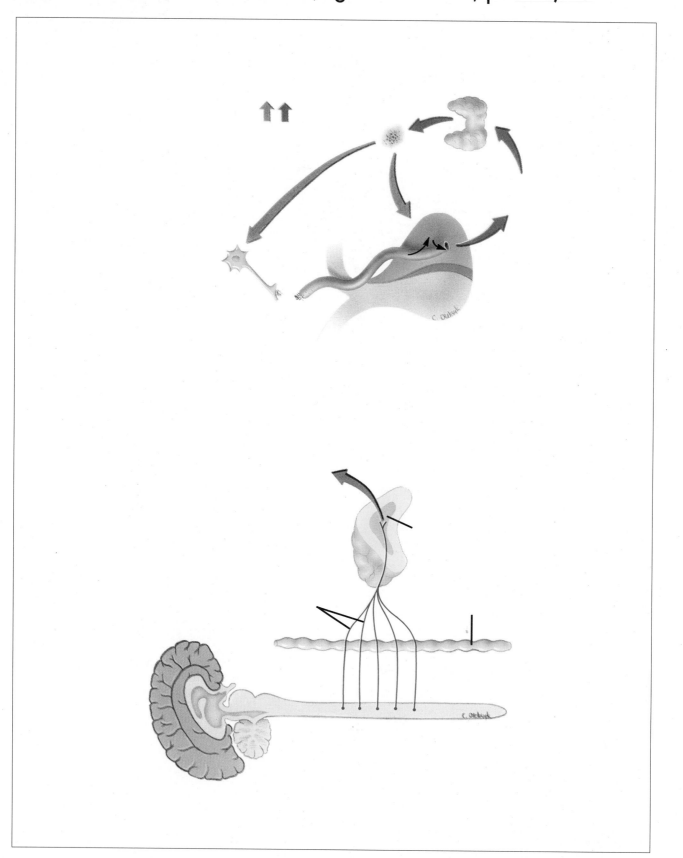

Seeley/Stephens/Tate: Anatomy & Physiology, third edition
© 1995 Mosby–Year Book, Inc.

Positive and Negative Feedback (Fig. 17-5 A & B, p. 546)

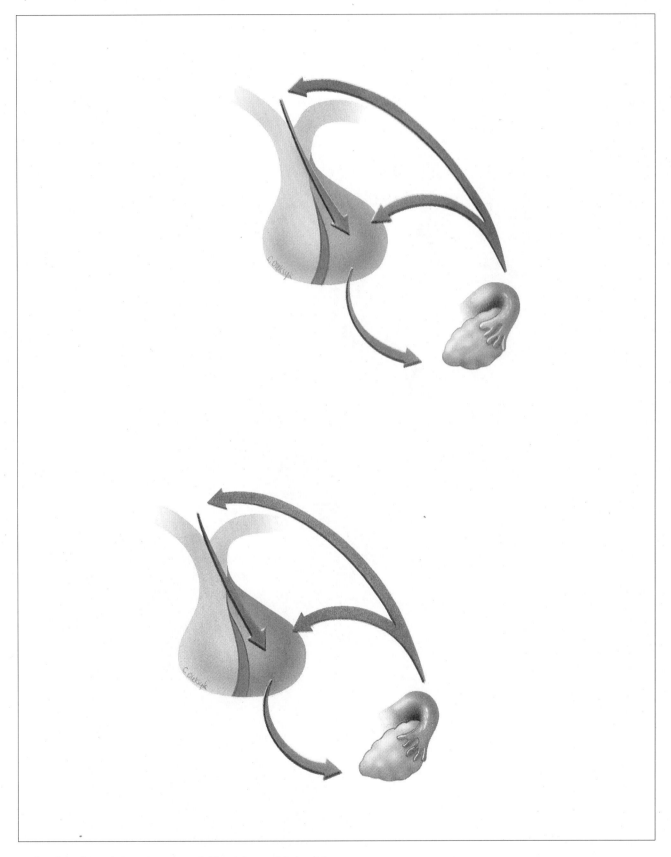

TA 234

Hormone Concentrations at the Target Cell
(Fig. 17-7 A & B, p. 547)

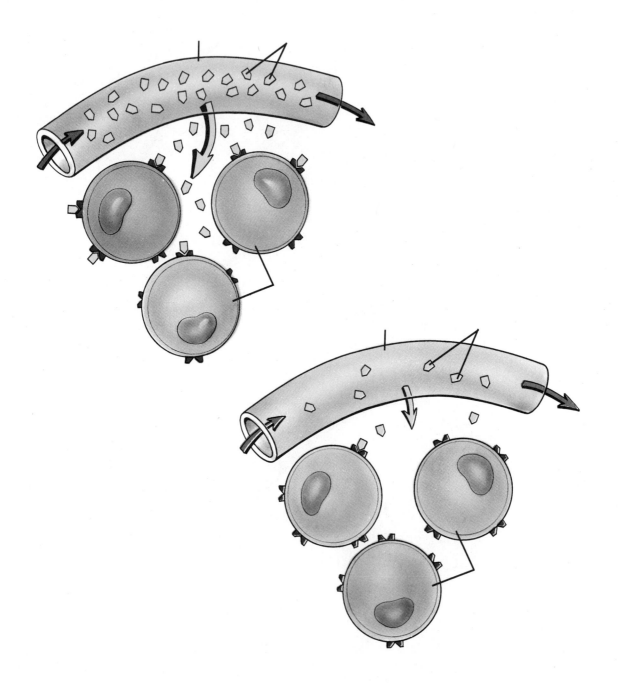

Seeley/Stephens/Tate: Anatomy & Physiology, third edition
© 1995 Mosby—Year Book, Inc.

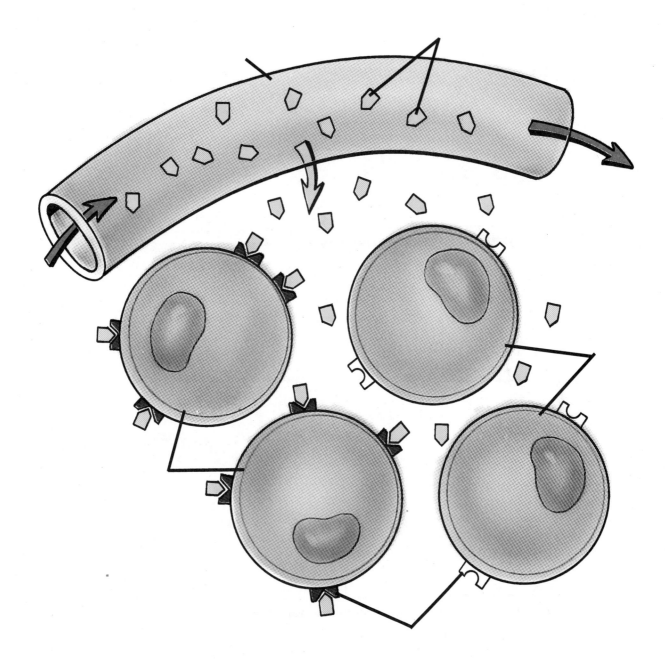

Down Regulation and Up Regulation (Fig. 17-9 A & B, p. 550)

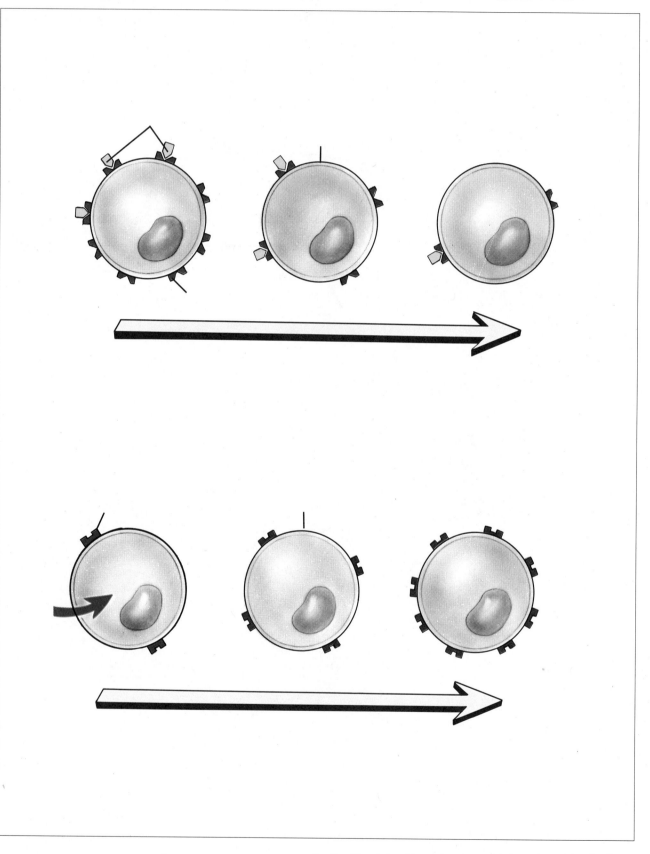

Seeley/Stephens/Tate: Anatomy & Physiology, third edition
© 1995 Mosby—Year Book, Inc.

Membrane-Bound Receptor Model (Fig. 17-10 A & B, p. 552)

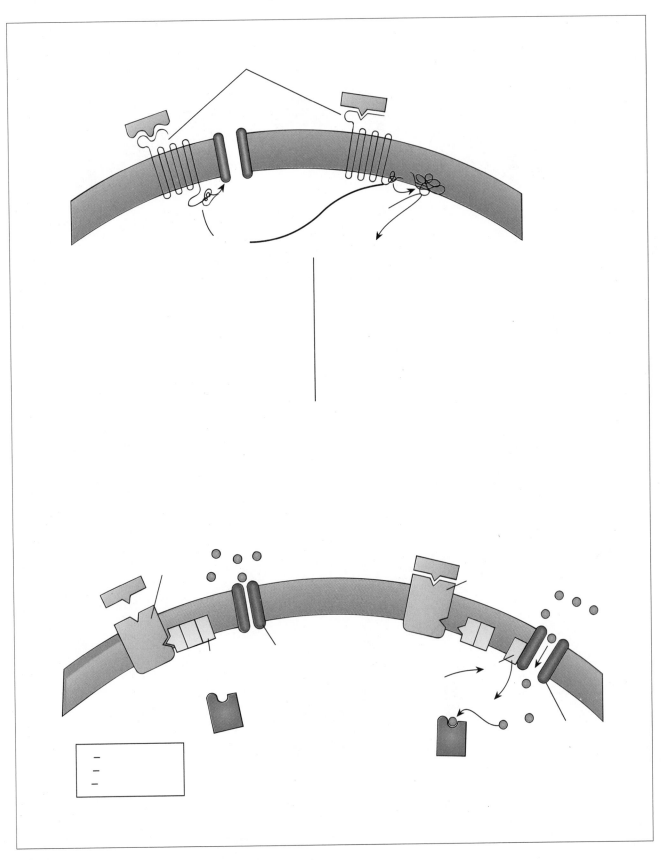

TA 238
Membrane-Bound Receptor Model—cont'd
(Fig. 17-10 C & D, p. 553)

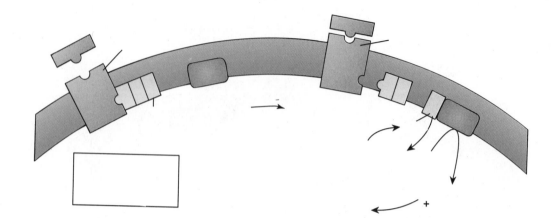

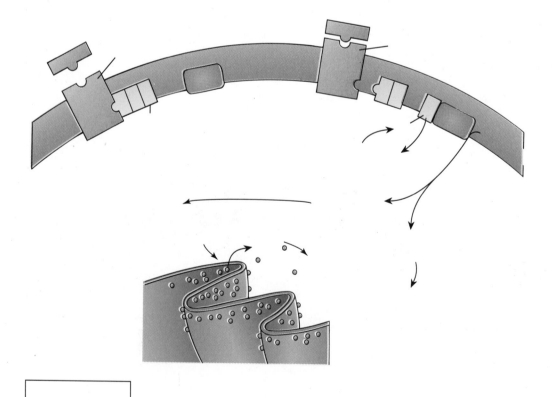

Seeley/Stephens/Tate: Anatomy & Physiology, third edition
© 1995 Mosby–Year Book, Inc.

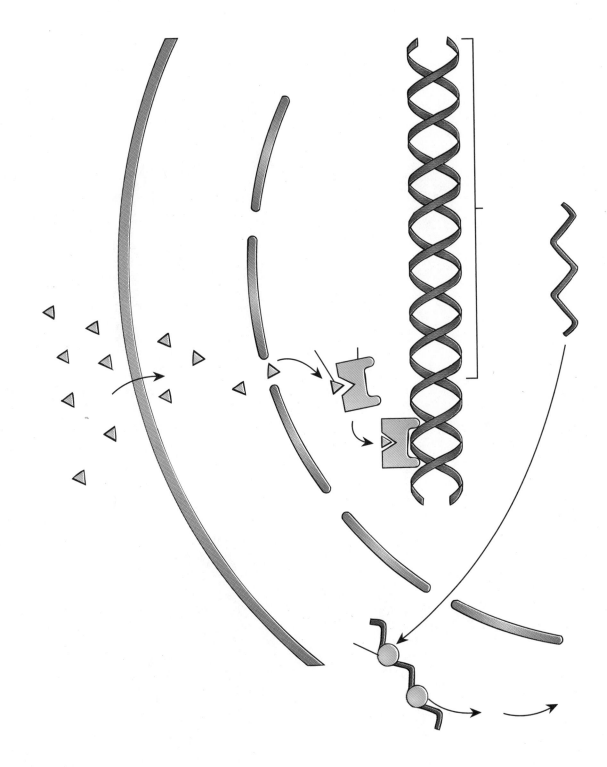

TA 240

The Hypothalamohypophyseal Portal System and the
Hypothalamohypophyseal Tract (Fig. 18-3 A & B, p. 565)

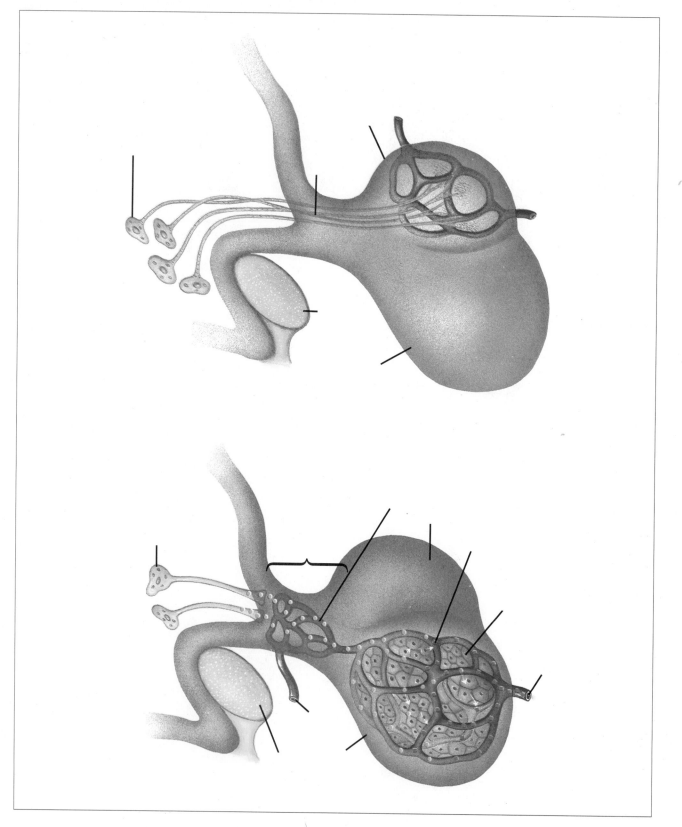

Seeley/Stephens/Tate: Anatomy & Physiology, third edition
© 1995 Mosby–Year Book, Inc.

General Relationship Between the Hypothalamus, the Pituitary, and Target Tissues (Fig. 18-4 A & B, p. 566)

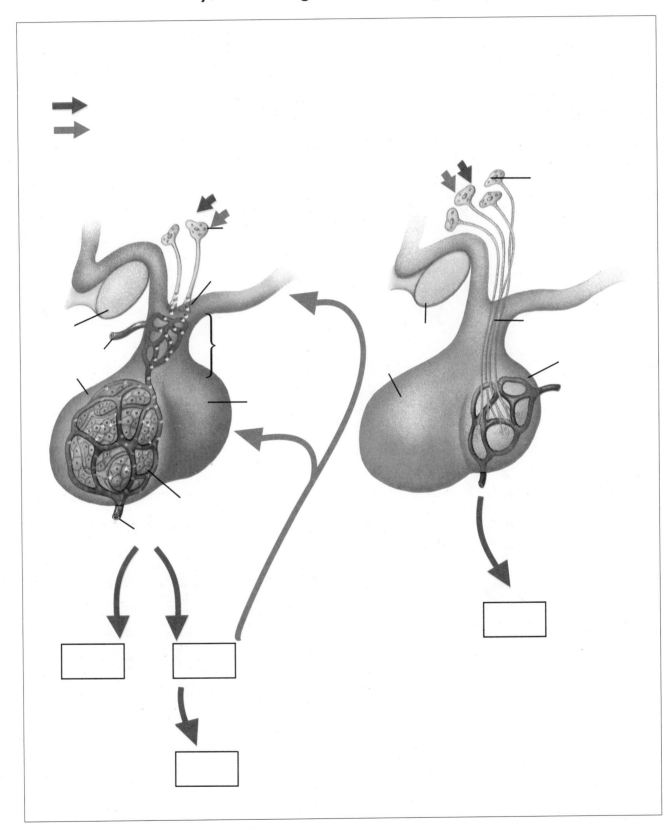

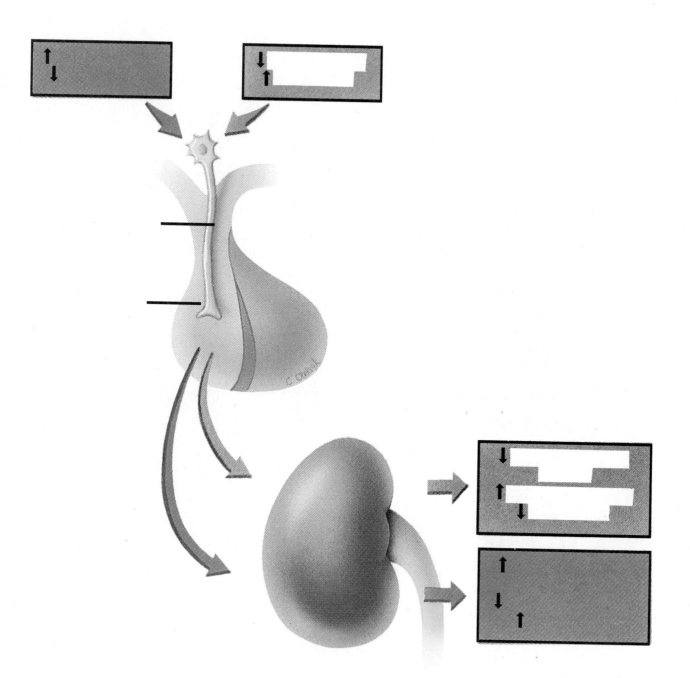

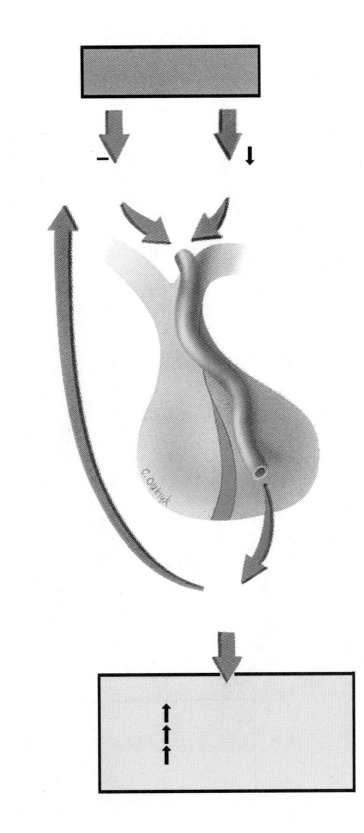

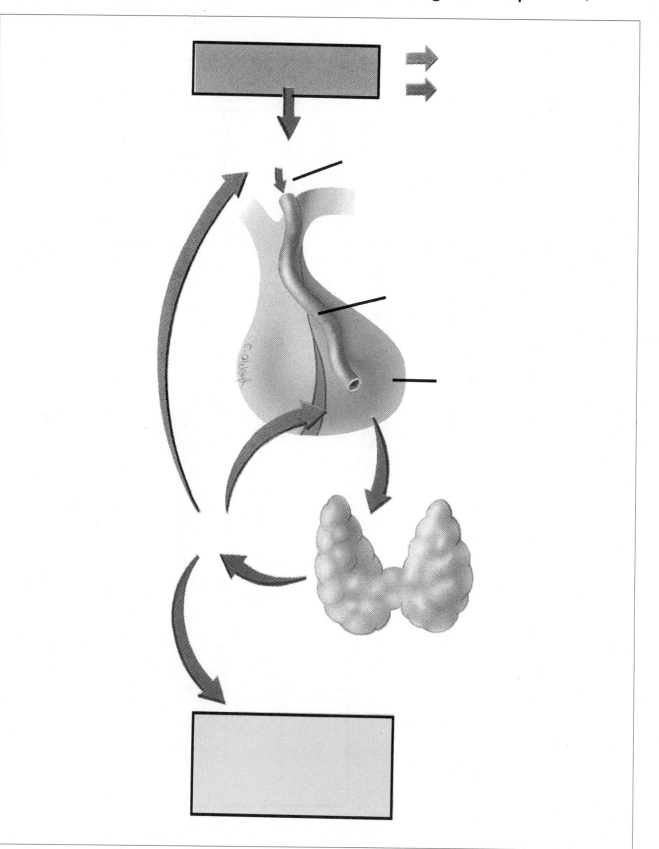

Seeley/Stephens/Tate: Anatomy & Physiology, third edition
© 1995 Mosby–Year Book, Inc.

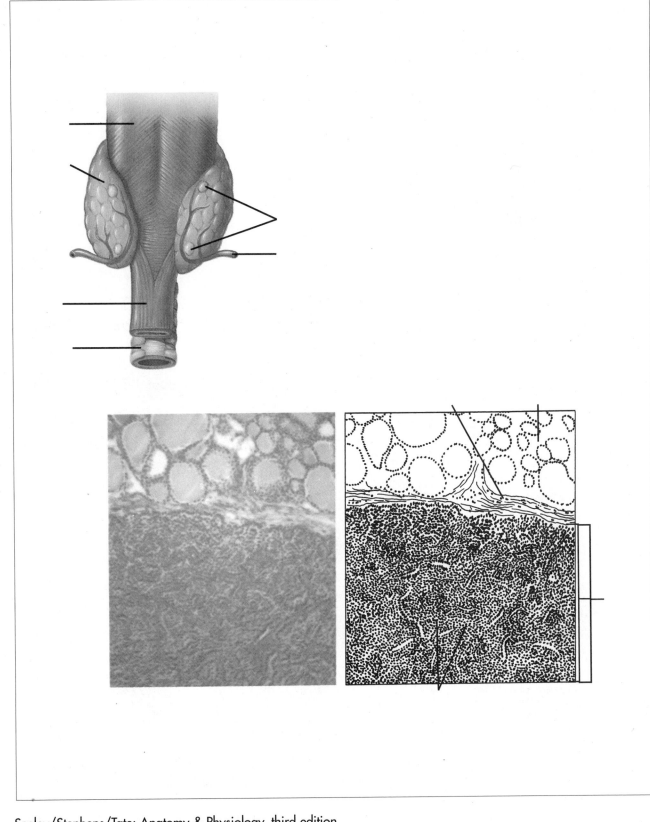

TA 246

Regulation of Parathyroid Hormone (PTH) Secretion
and its Effects on Target Tissues (Fig. 18-11, p. 578)

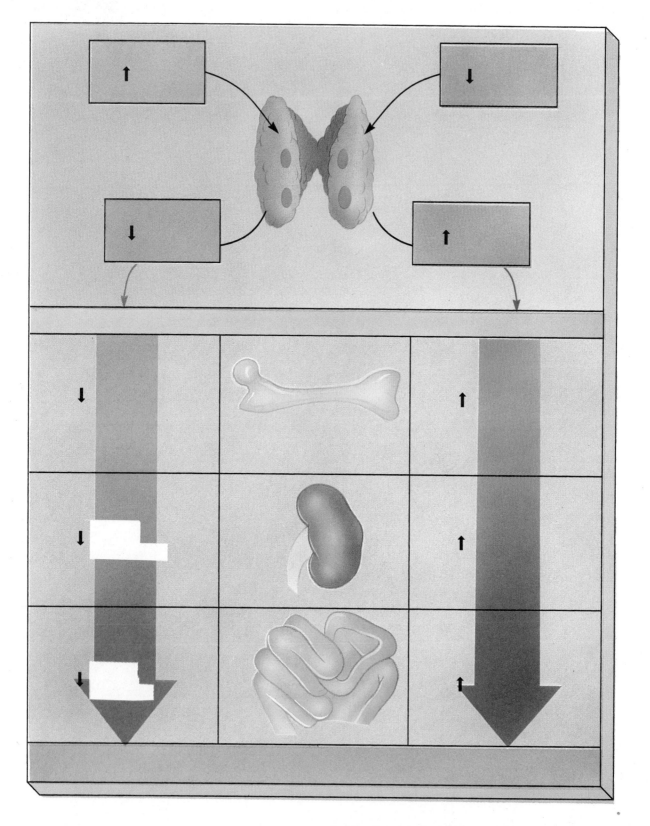

Seeley/Stephens/Tate: Anatomy & Physiology, third edition
© 1995 Mosby–Year Book, Inc.

Regulation of Adrenal Medullary Secretions (Fig. 18-13, p. 582)

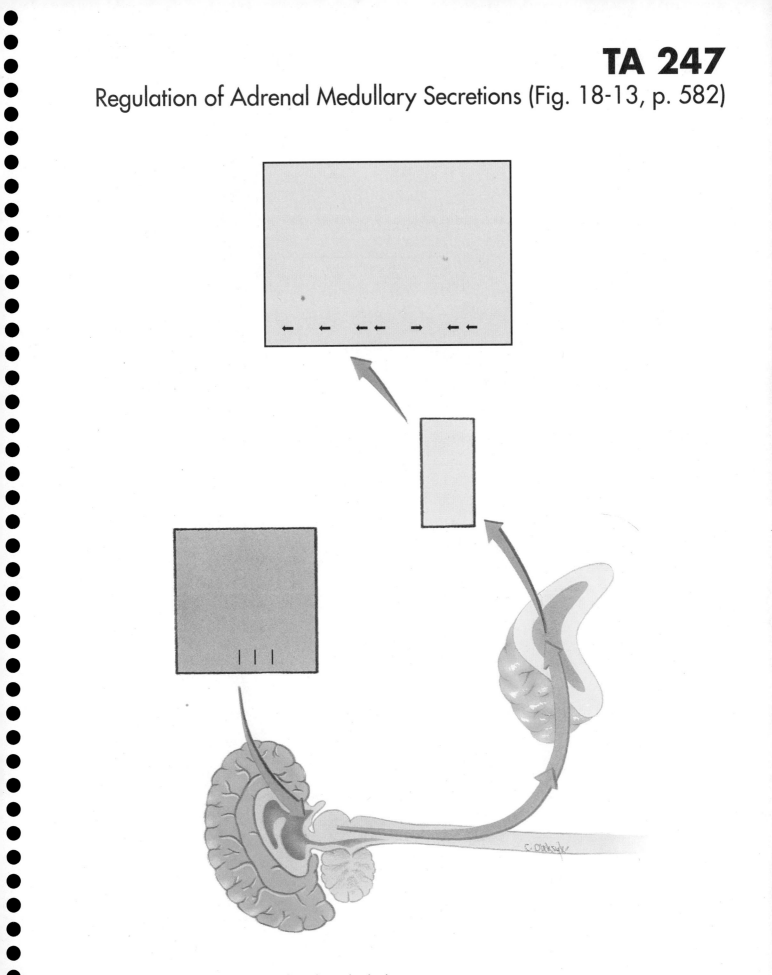

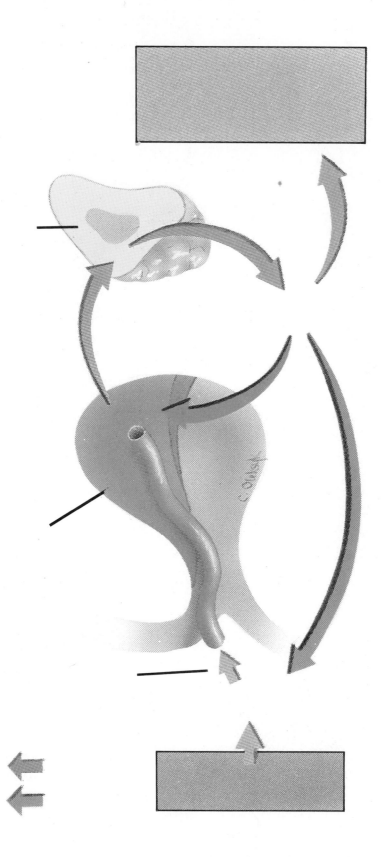

Seeley/Stephens/Tate: Anatomy & Physiology, third edition
© 1995 Mosby–Year Book, Inc.

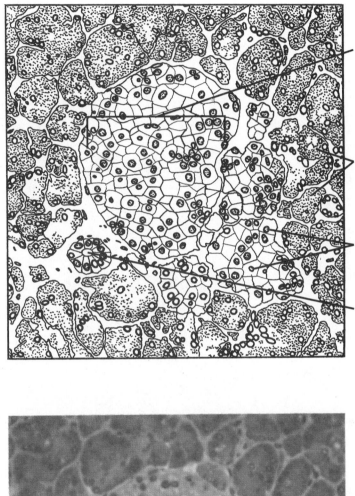

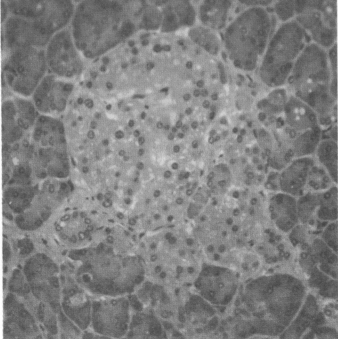

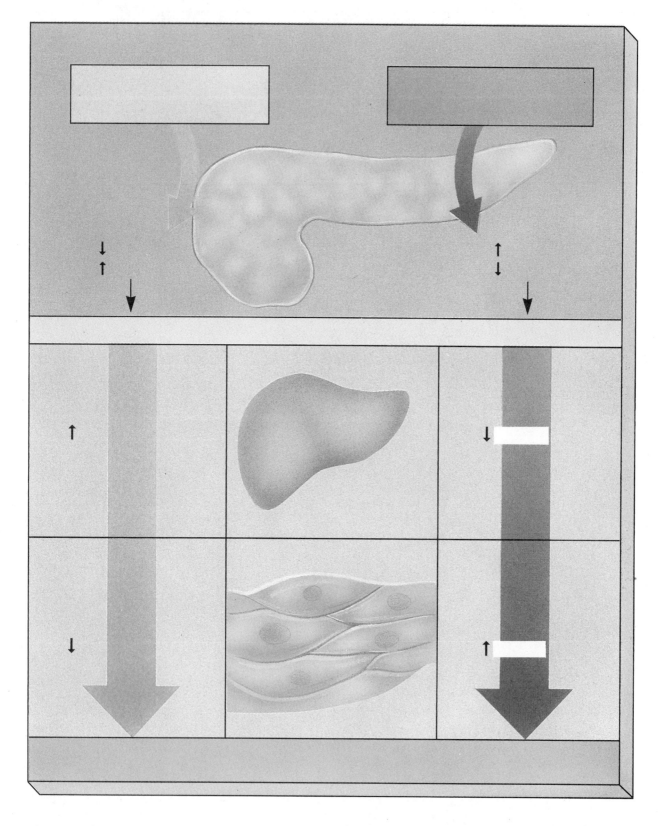

Seeley/Stephens/Tate: Anatomy & Physiology, third edition
© 1995 Mosby–Year Book, Inc.

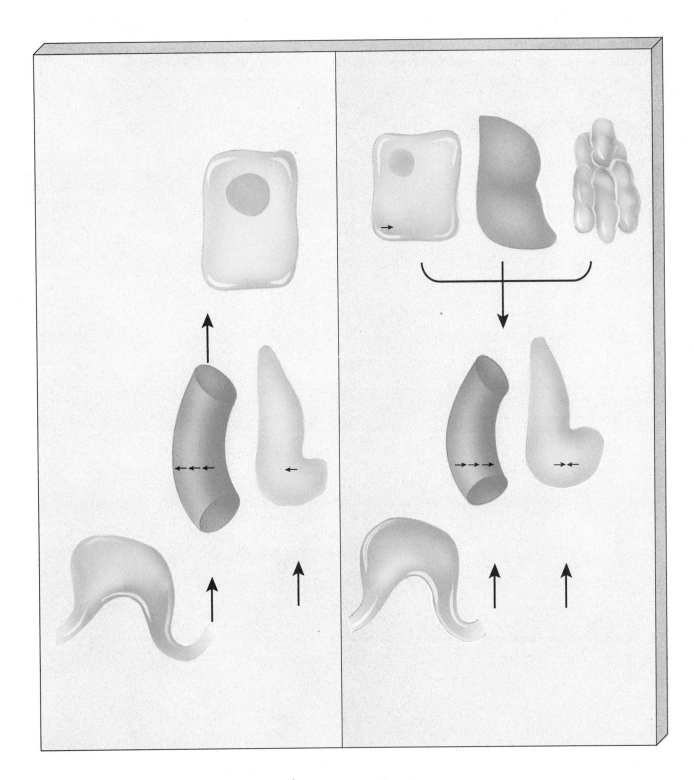

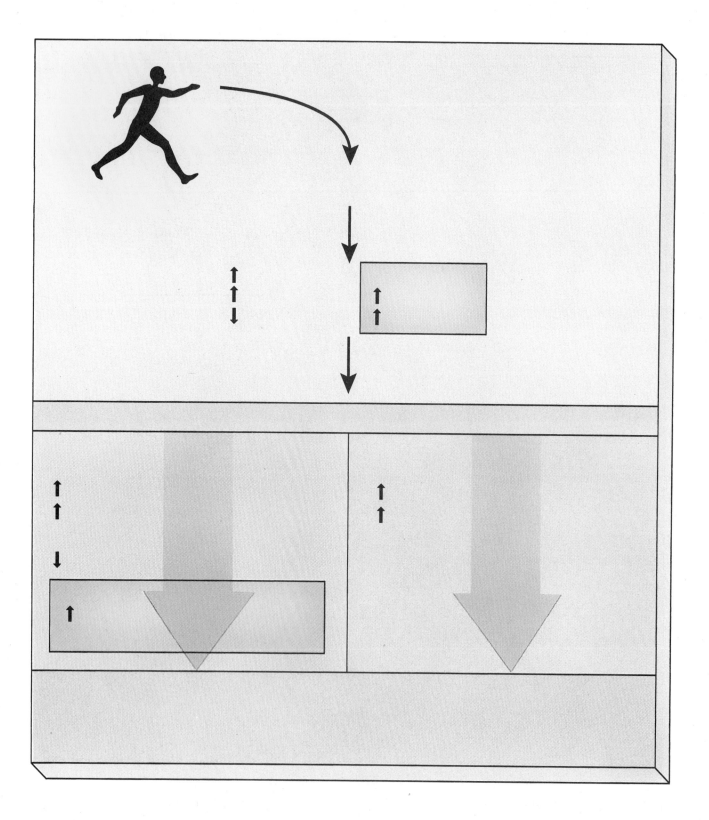

Seeley/Stephens/Tate: Anatomy & Physiology, third edition
© 1995 Mosby–Year Book, Inc.

Regulation of Pineal Secretion (Fig. 18-19, p. 594)

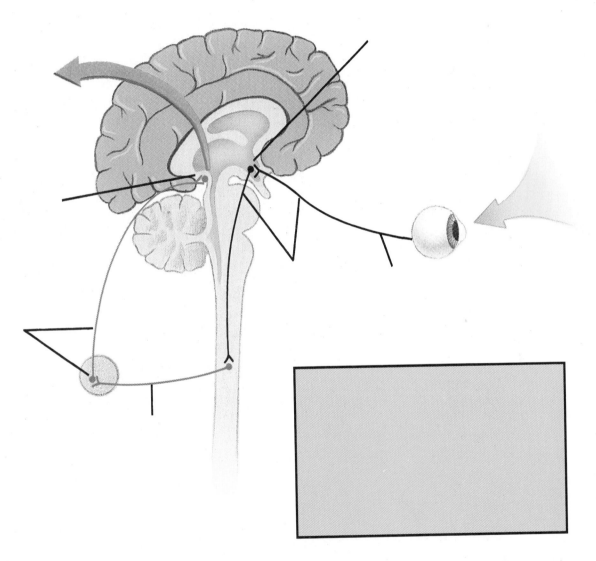

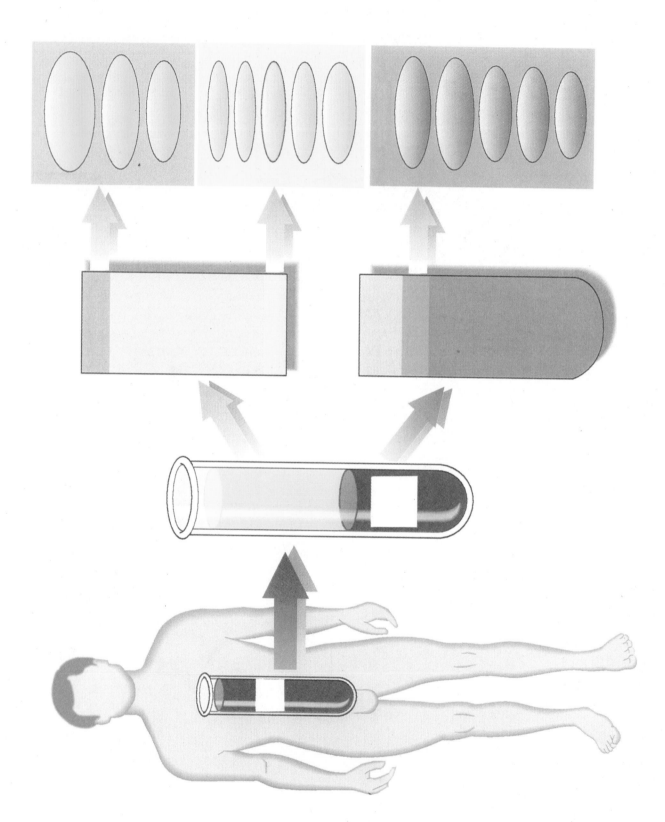

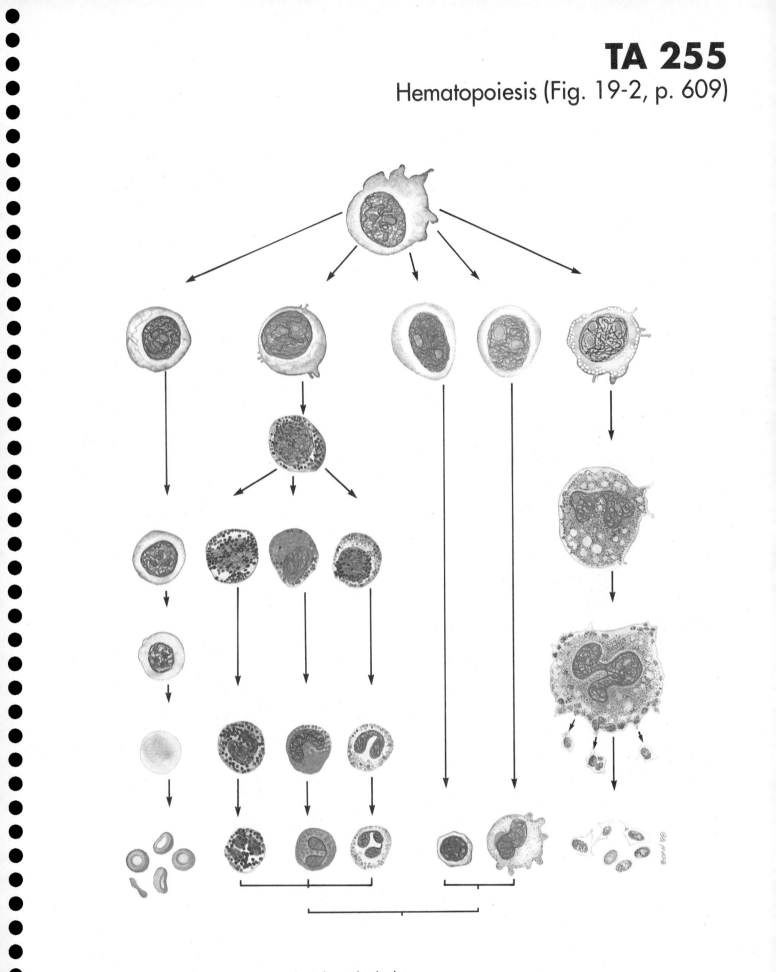

TA 256
Hemoglobin (Fig. 19-4 A & B, p. 611)

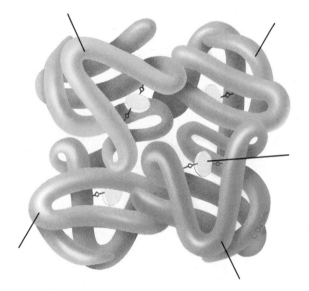

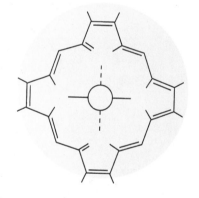

Seeley/Stephens/Tate: Anatomy & Physiology, third edition
© 1995 Mosby–Year Book, Inc.

Erythrocyte Production (Fig. 19-5, p. 614)

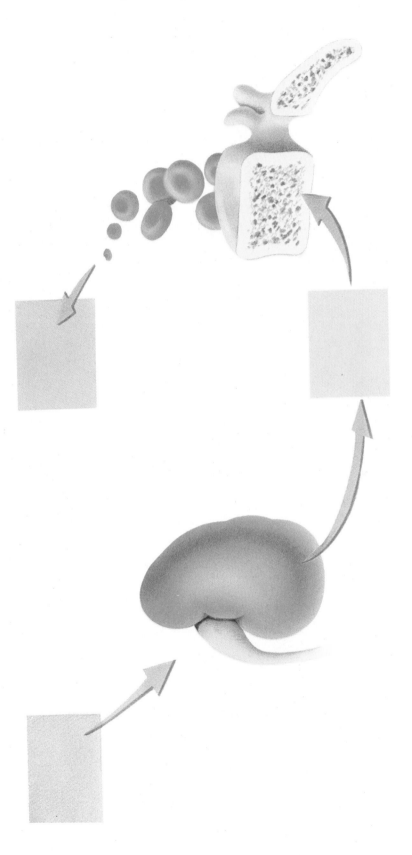

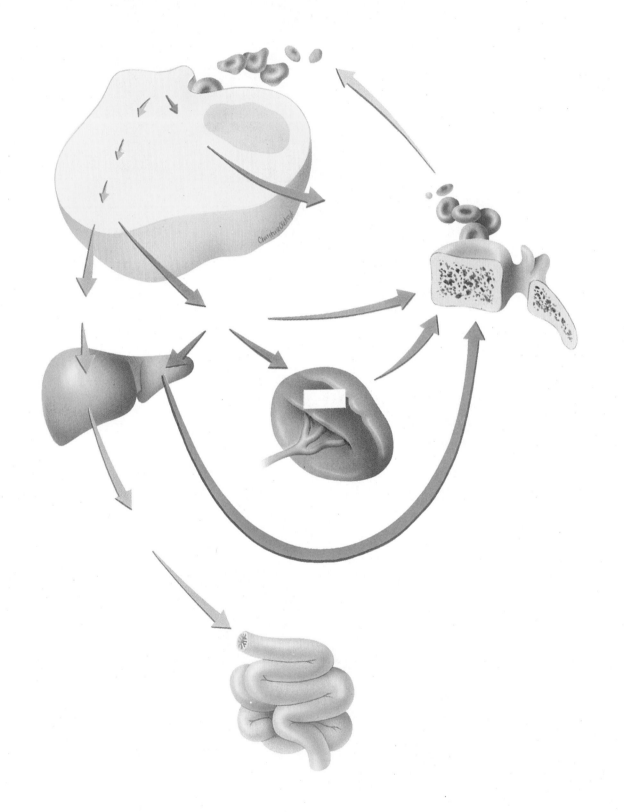

Seeley/Stephens/Tate: Anatomy & Physiology, third edition
© 1995 Mosby–Year Book, Inc.

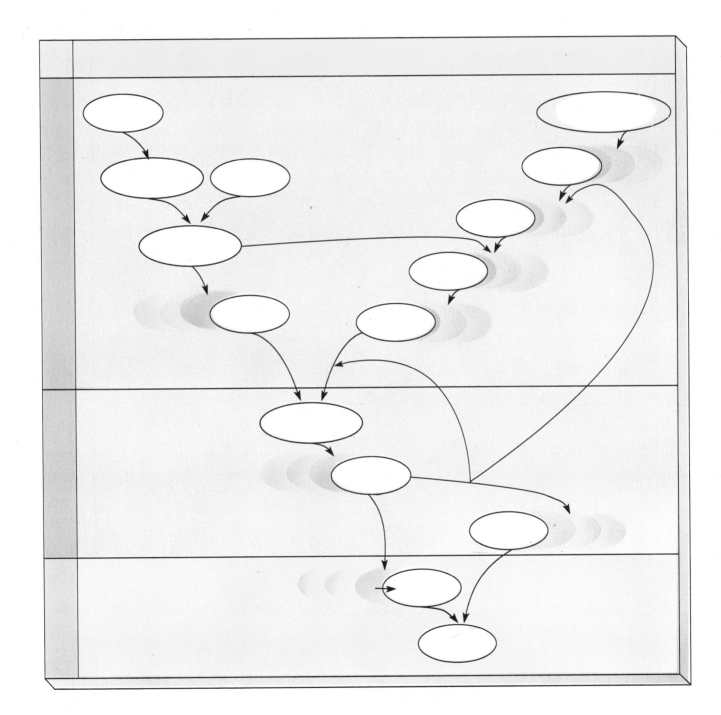

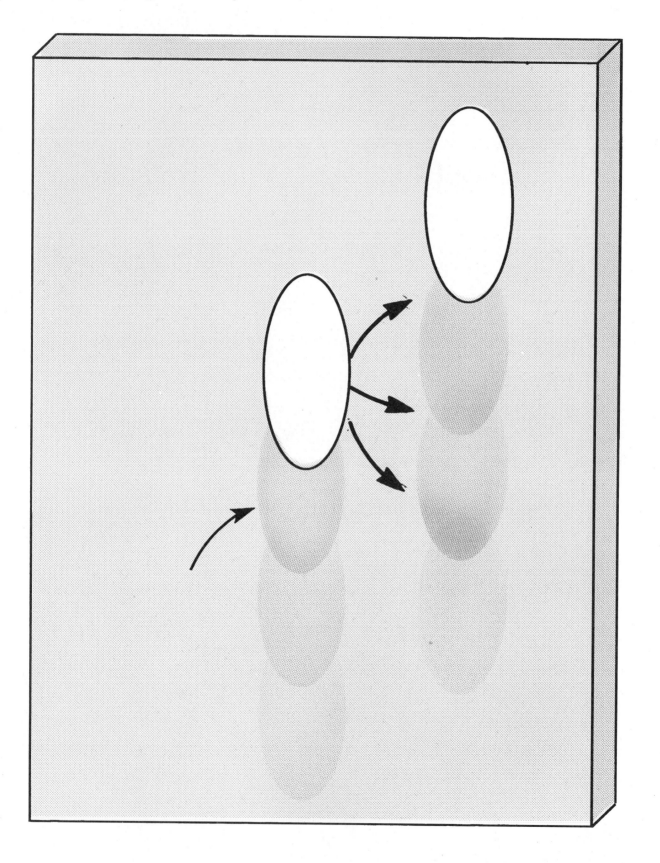

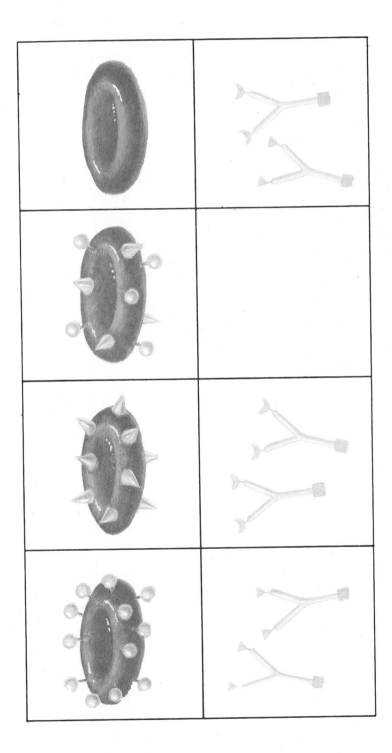

Agglutination Reaction (Fig. 19-11 A & B, p. 623)

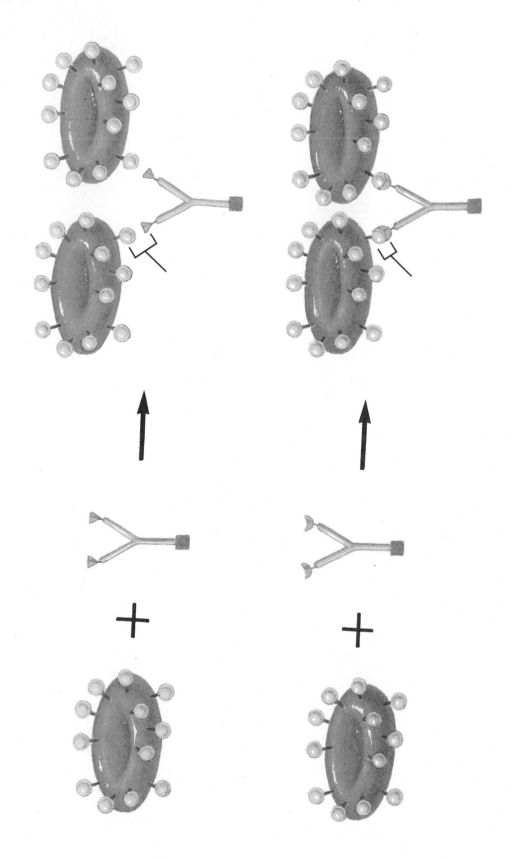

Seeley/Stephens/Tate: Anatomy & Physiology, third edition
© 1995 Mosby–Year Book, Inc.

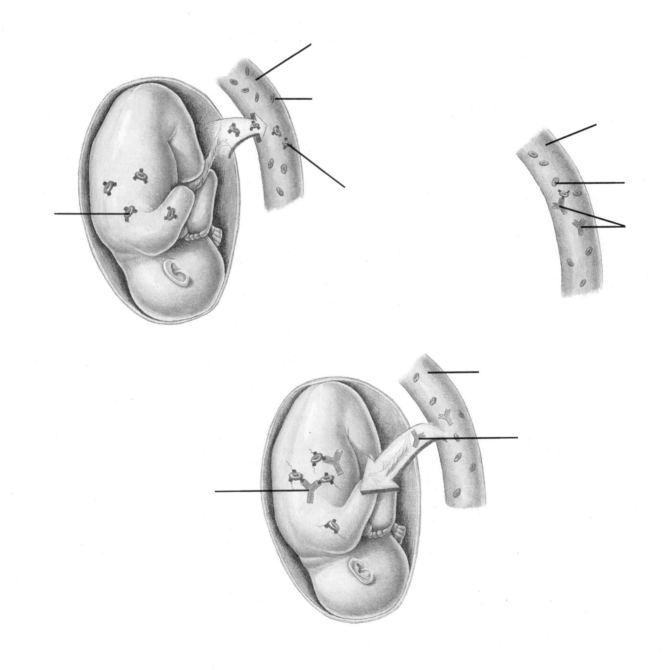

The Systemic and Pulmonary Circulation (Fig. 20-1, p. 632)

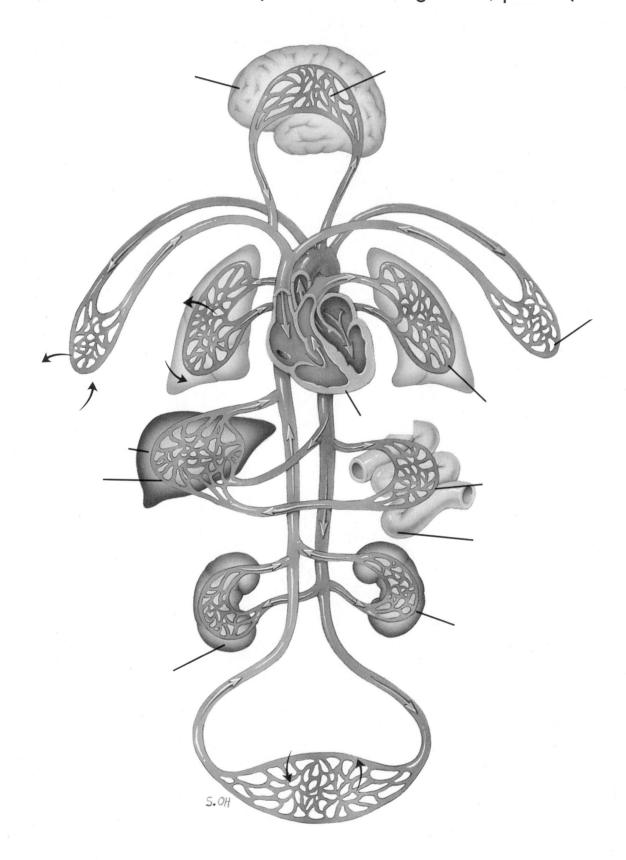

Seeley/Stephens/Tate: Anatomy & Physiology, third edition
© 1995 Mosby–Year Book, Inc.

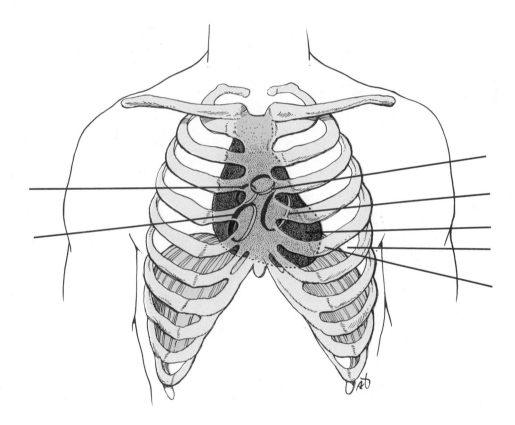

TA 266
Chambers of the Heart (Fig. 20-3, p. 633)

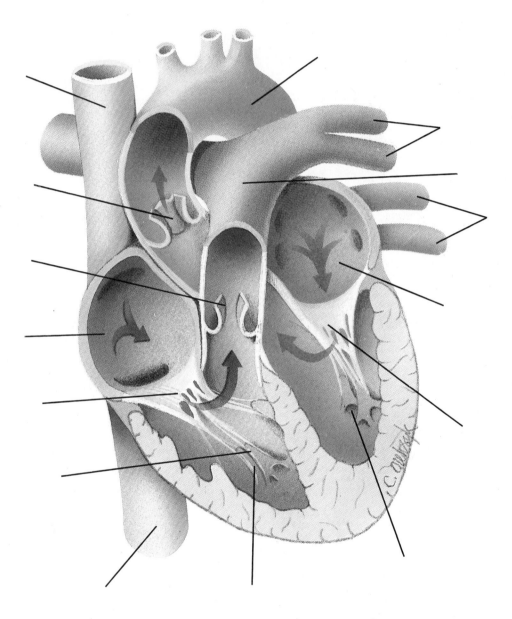

Seeley/Stephens/Tate: Anatomy & Physiology, third edition
© 1995 Mosby–Year Book, Inc.

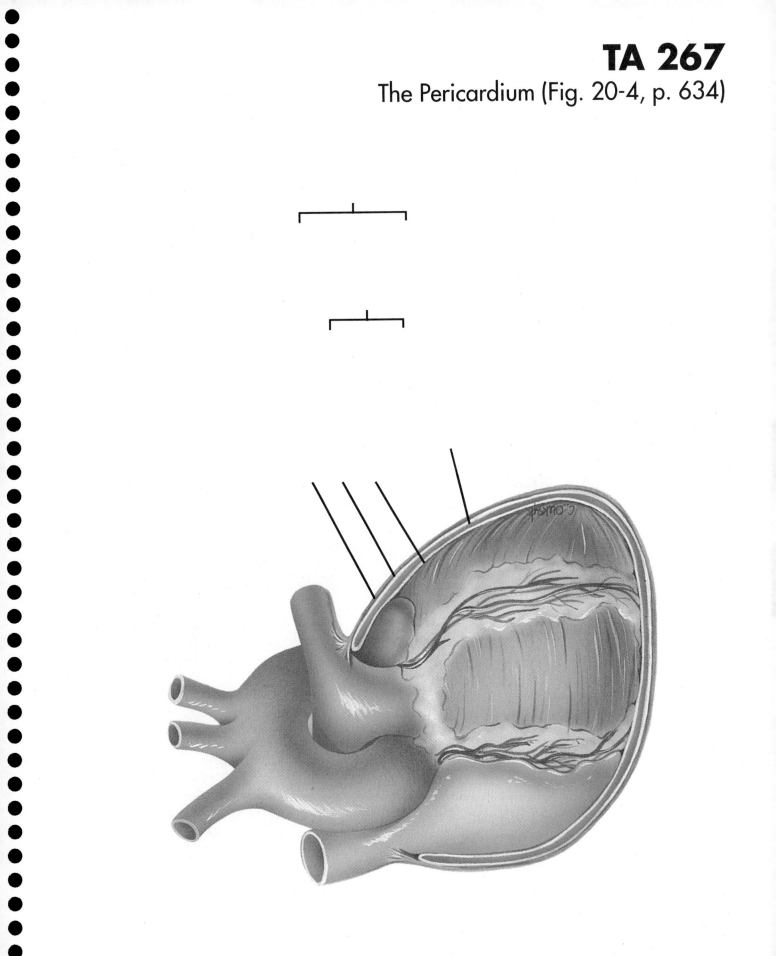

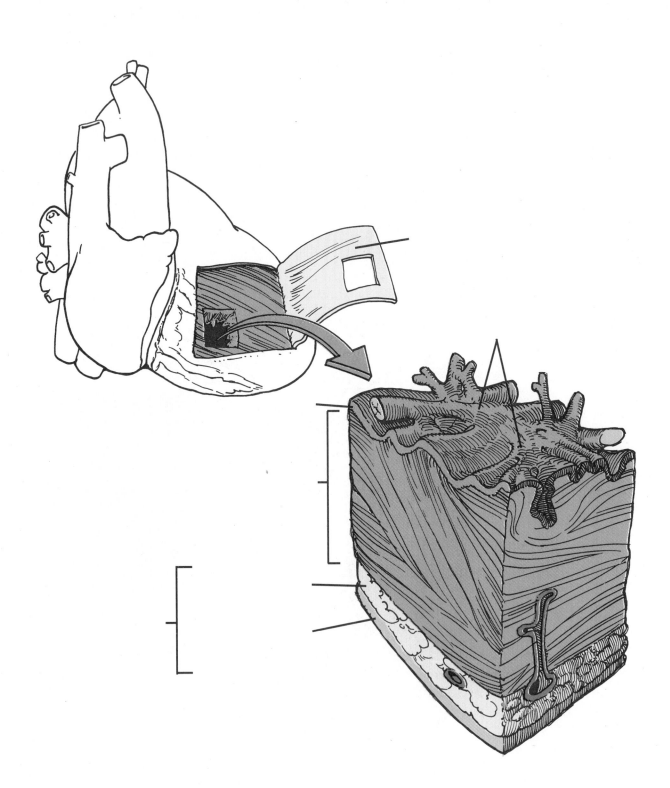

Surface of the Heart (Fig. 20-6 A, C, p. 636, 637)

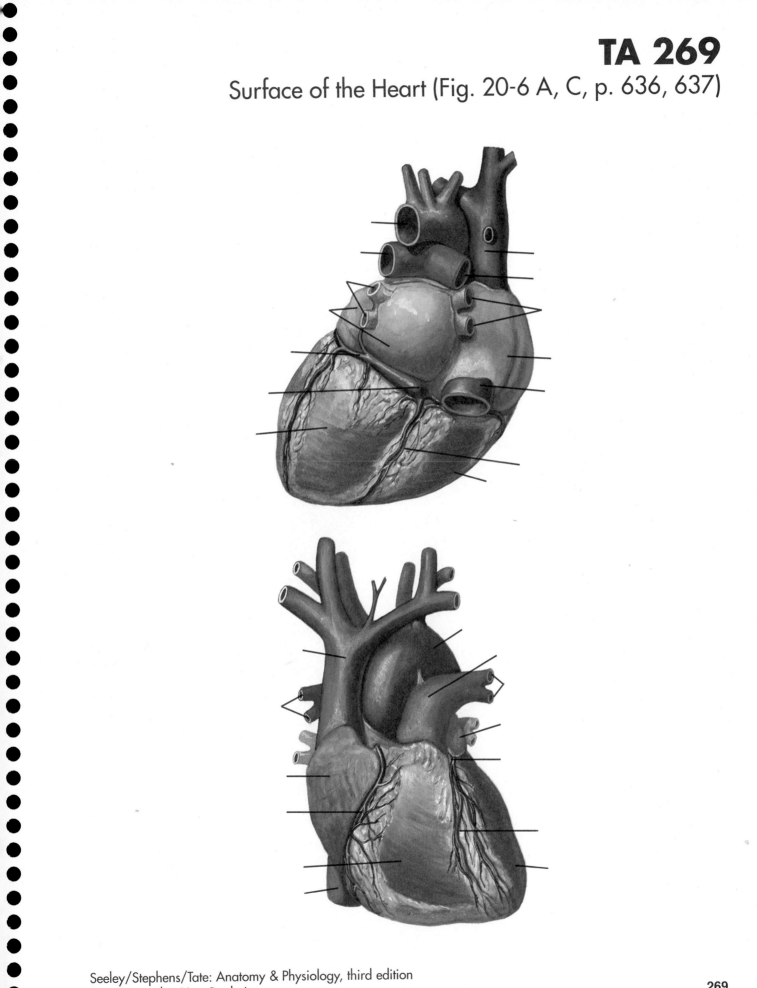

Circulation to the Heart (Fig. 20-7 A & B, p. 637)

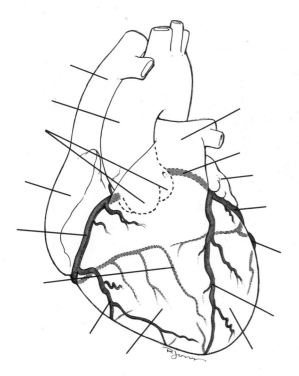

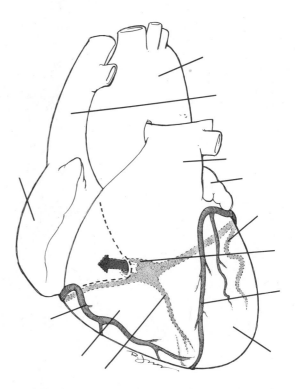

Seeley/Stephens/Tate: Anatomy & Physiology, third edition
© 1995 Mosby—Year Book, Inc.

Histology of the Heart (Fig. 20-11 A & B, p. 642)

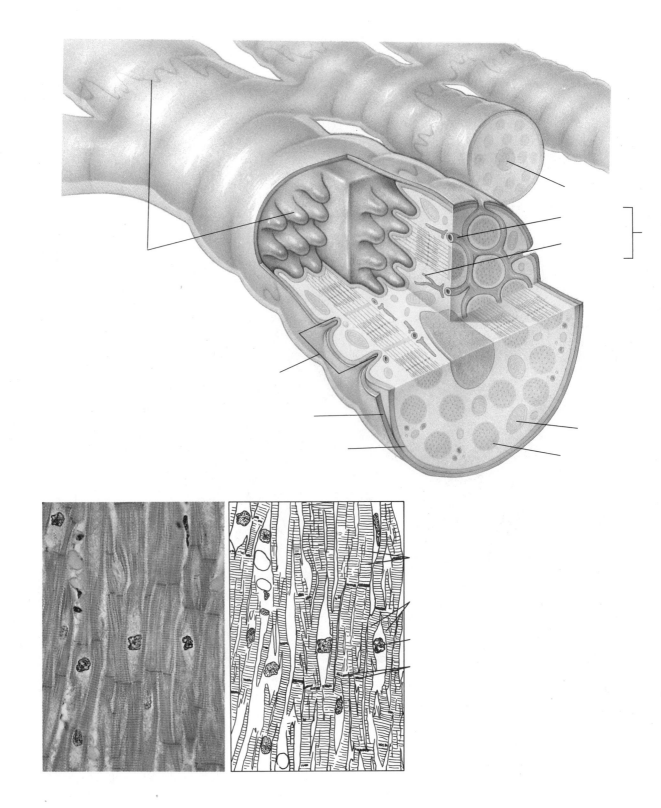

Seeley/Stephens/Tate: Anatomy & Physiology, third edition
© 1995 Mosby–Year Book, Inc.

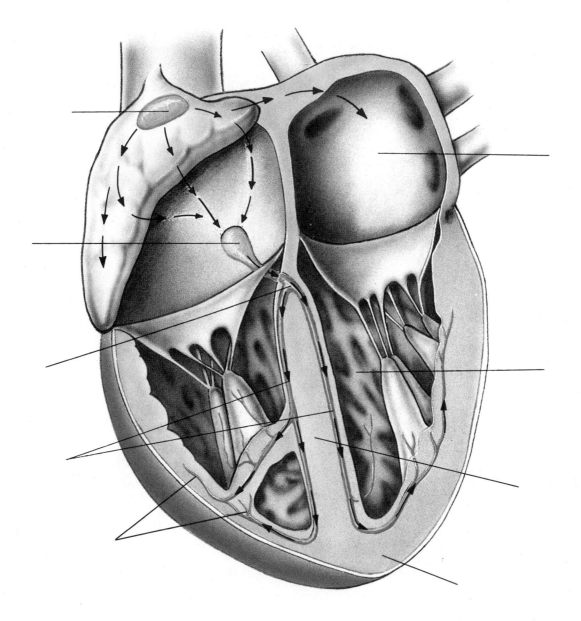

Seeley/Stephens/Tate: Anatomy & Physiology, third edition
© 1995 Mosby–Year Book, Inc.

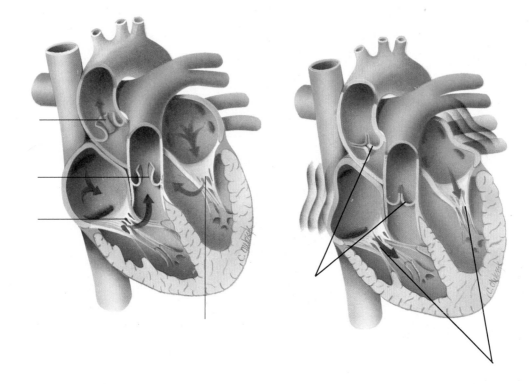

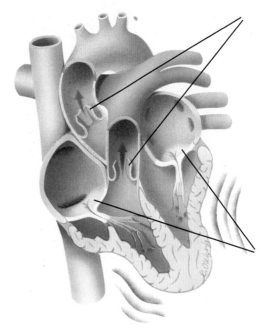

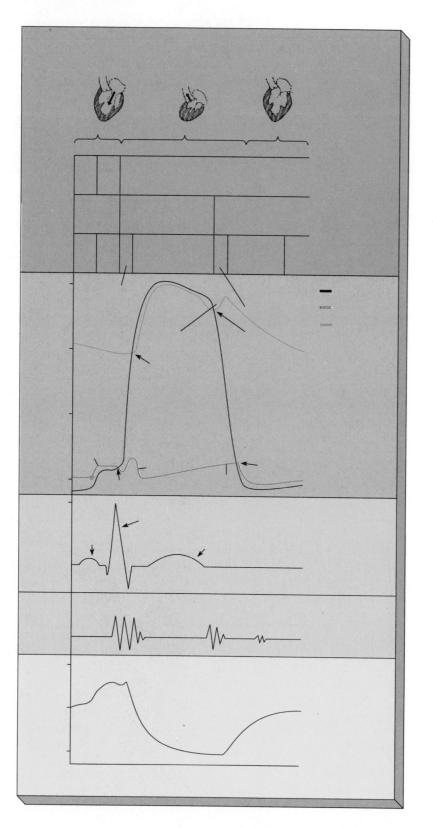

Seeley/Stephens/Tate: Anatomy & Physiology, third edition
© 1995 Mosby–Year Book, Inc.

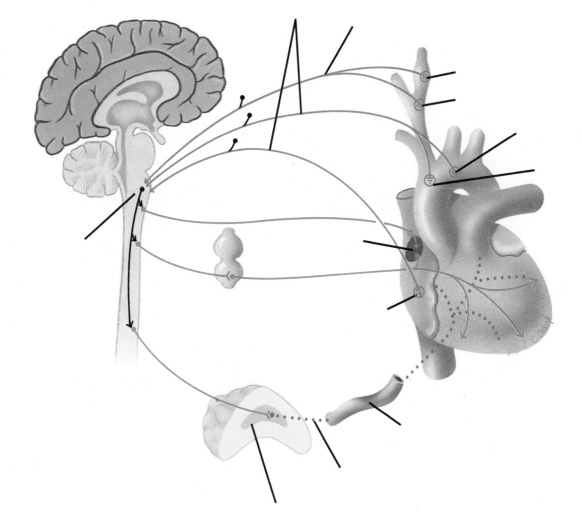

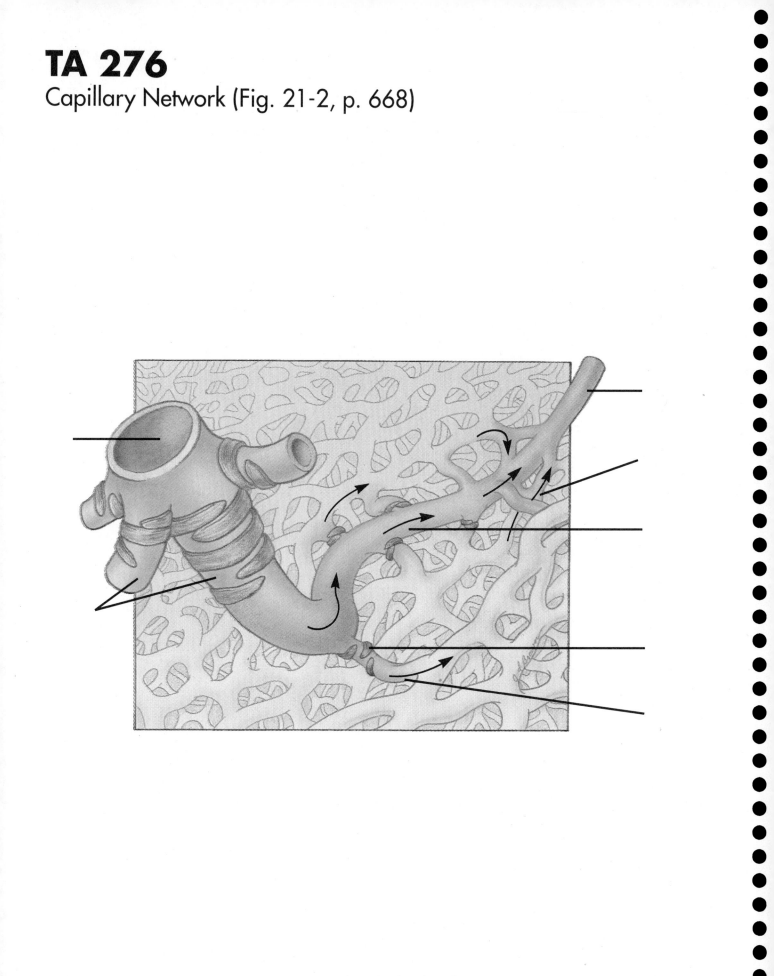

Seeley/Stephens/Tate: Anatomy & Physiology, third edition
© 1995 Mosby–Year Book, Inc.

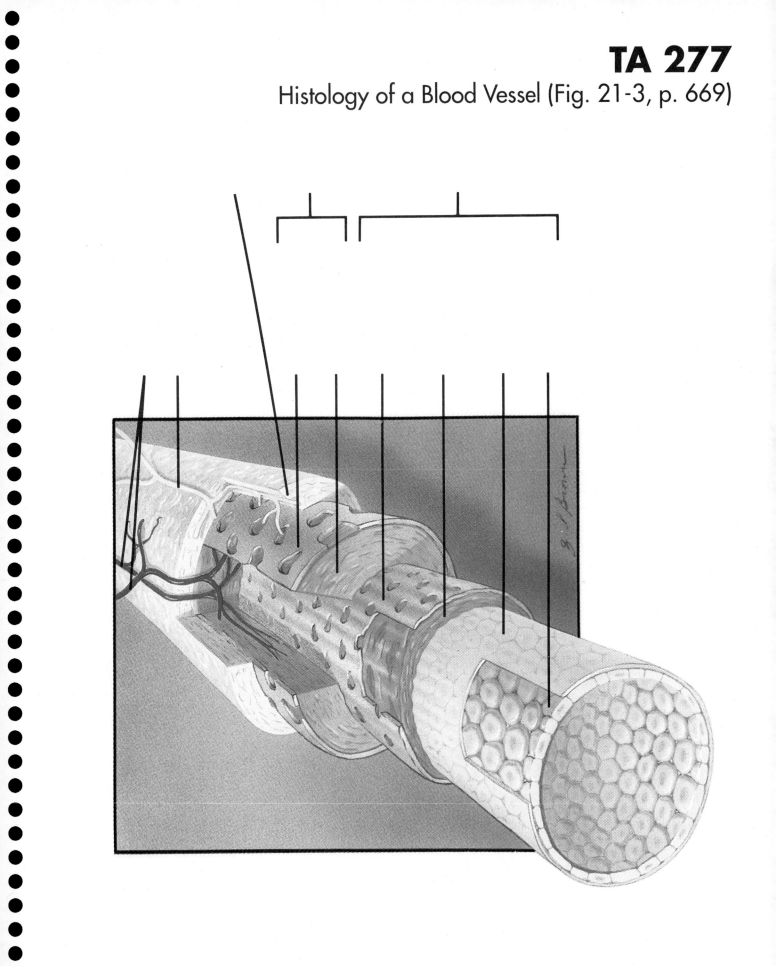

TA 278

Structural Comparison of Blood Vessel Types
(Fig. 21-4 A-D, p. 670)

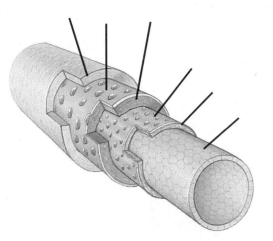

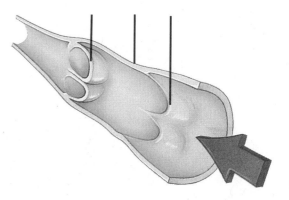

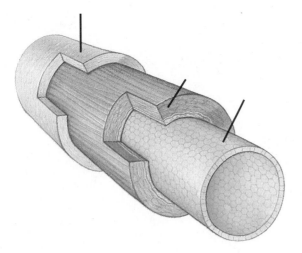

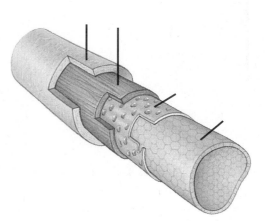

Seeley/Stephens/Tate: Anatomy & Physiology, third edition
© 1995 Mosby–Year Book, Inc.

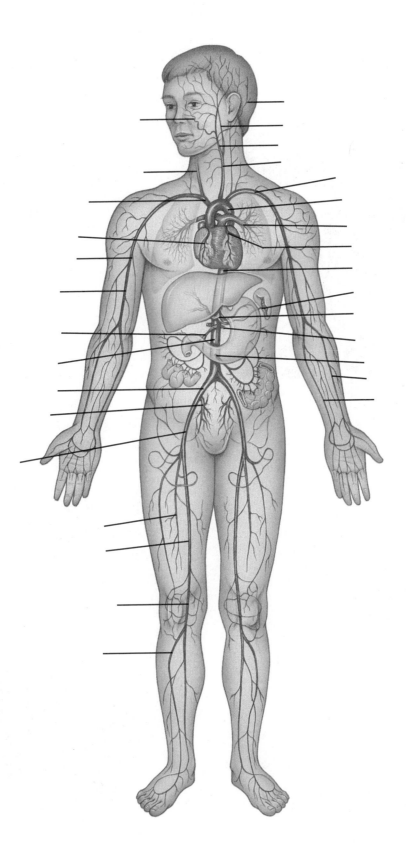

Seeley/Stephens/Tate: Anatomy & Physiology, third edition
© 1995 Mosby–Year Book, Inc.

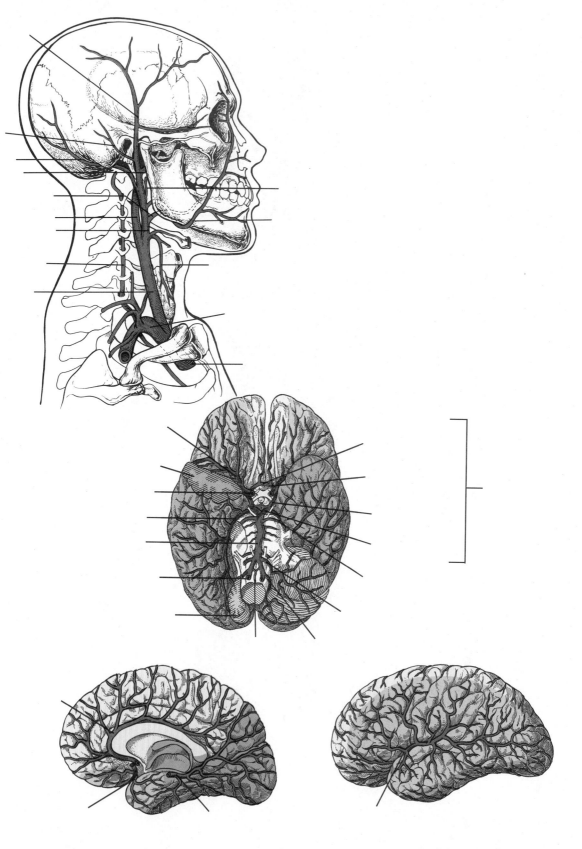

Seeley/Stephens/Tate: Anatomy & Physiology, third edition
© 1995 Mosby–Year Book, Inc.

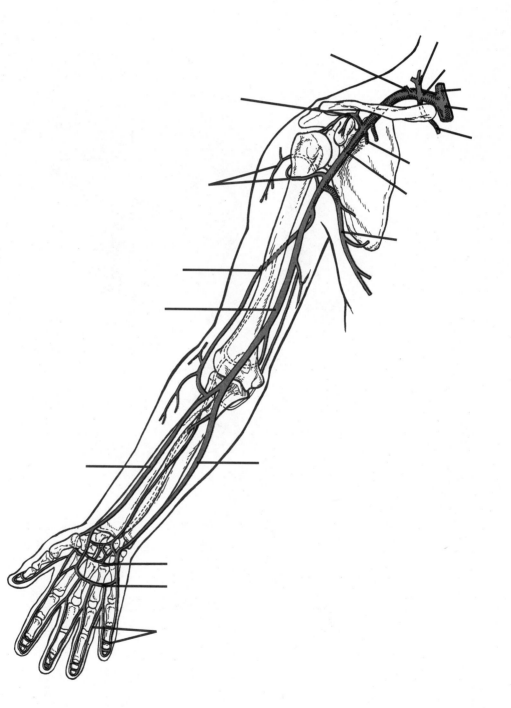

Branches of the Aorta (Fig. 21-9 A, p. 679)

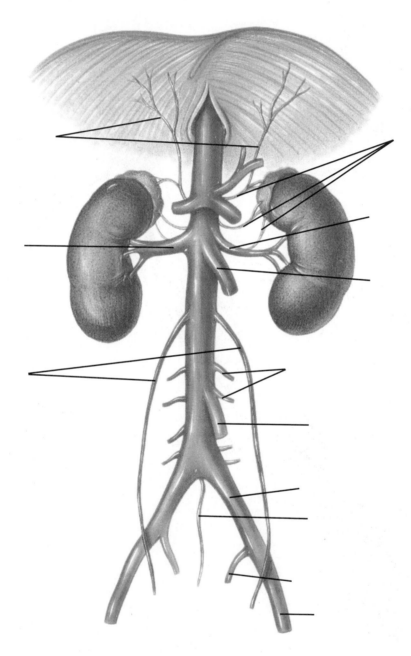

Seeley/Stephens/Tate: Anatomy & Physiology, third edition
© 1995 Mosby–Year Book, Inc.

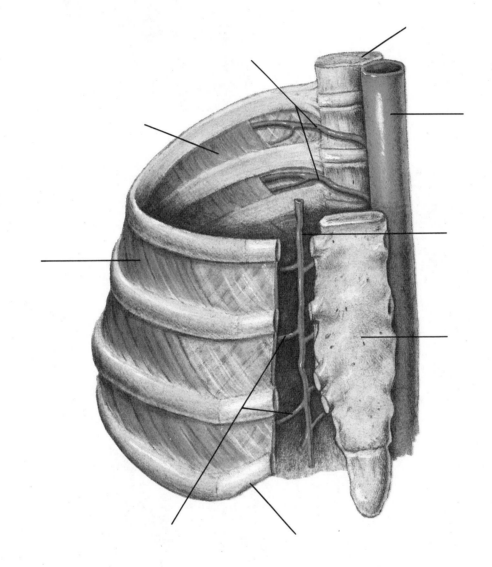

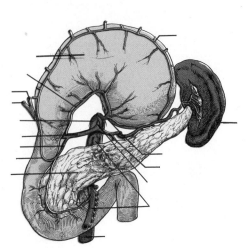

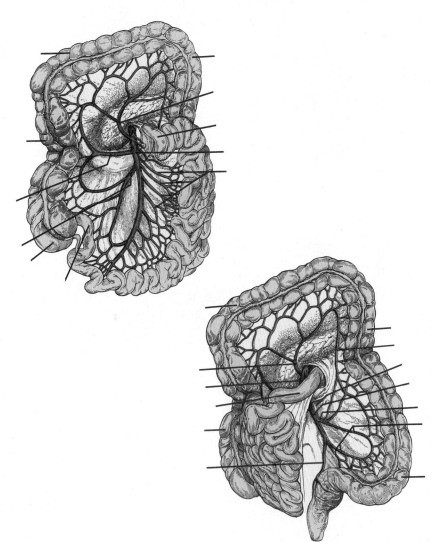

Seeley/Stephens/Tate: Anatomy & Physiology, third edition
© 1995 Mosby–Year Book, Inc.

Arteries of the Pelvis and Lower Limb (Fig. 21-11, p. 682)

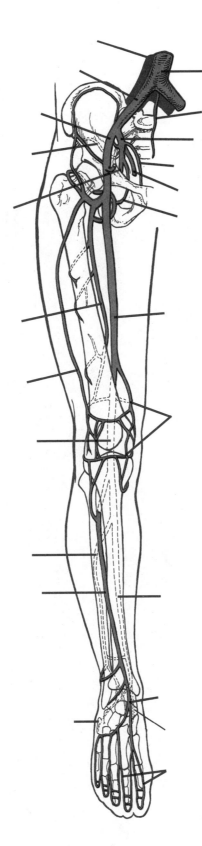

The Major Veins (Fig. 21-12, p. 683)

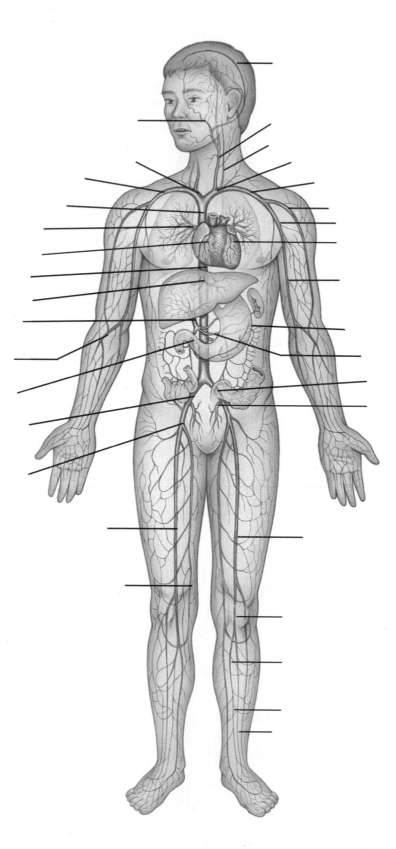

Seeley/Stephens/Tate: Anatomy & Physiology, third edition
© 1995 Mosby–Year Book, Inc.

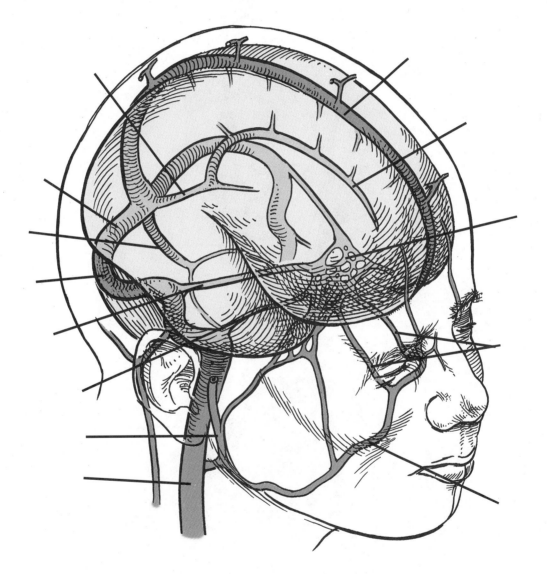

Veins of the Head and Neck (Fig. 21-14, p. 685)

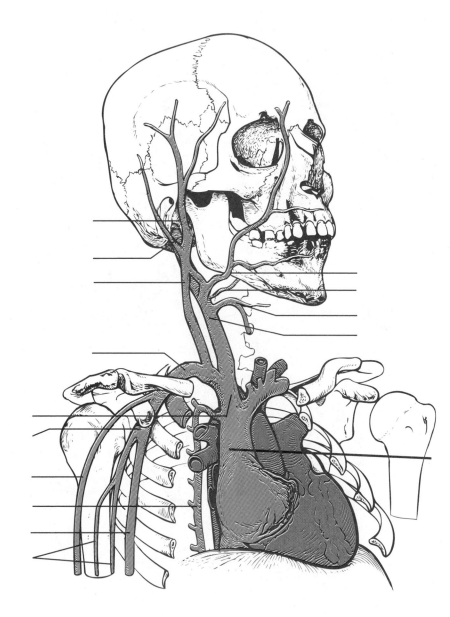

Seeley/Stephens/Tate: Anatomy & Physiology, third edition
© 1995 Mosby–Year Book, Inc.

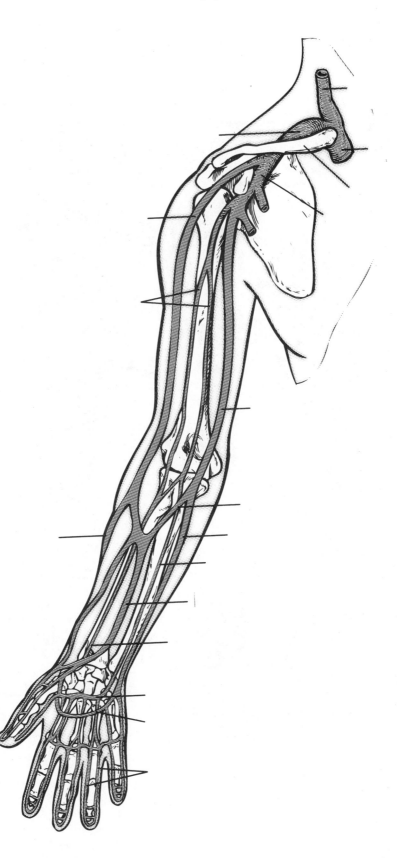

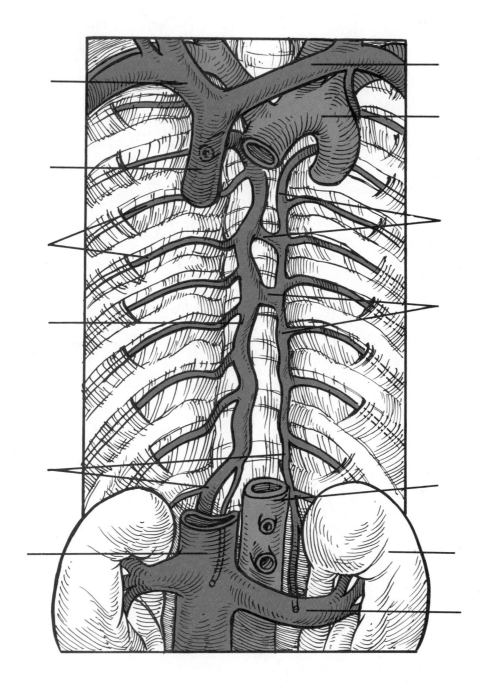

Seeley/Stephens/Tate: Anatomy & Physiology, third edition
© 1995 Mosby–Year Book, Inc.

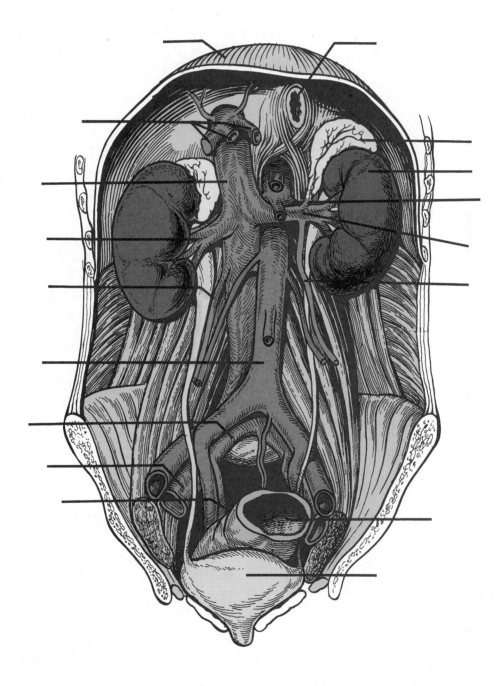

Seeley/Stephens/Tate: Anatomy & Physiology, third edition
© 1995 Mosby–Year Book, Inc.

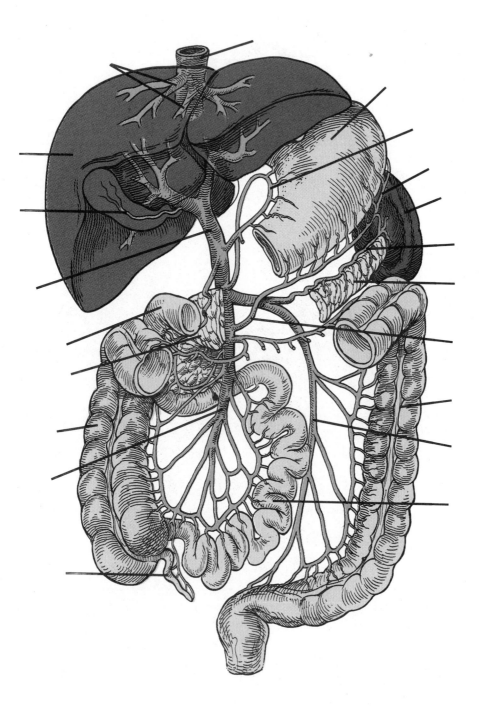

Seeley/Stephens/Tate: Anatomy & Physiology, third edition
© 1995 Mosby—Year Book, Inc.

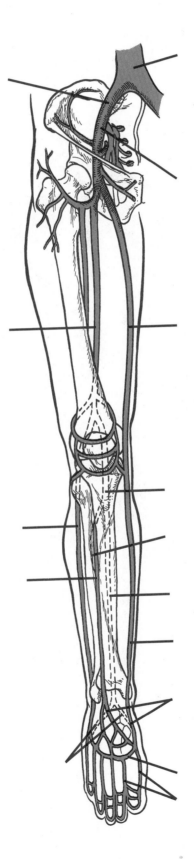

Lymphatic System (Fig. 21-20, p. 690)

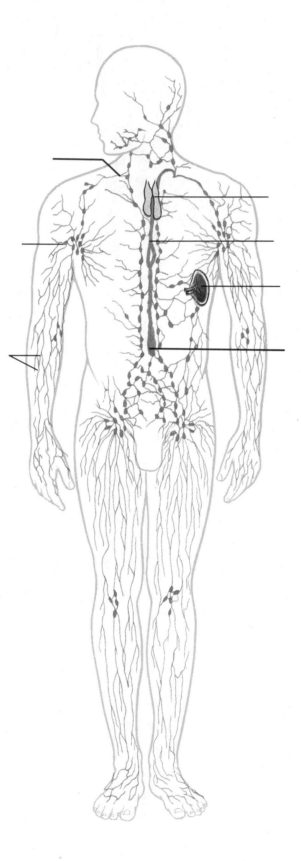

Seeley/Stephens/Tate: Anatomy & Physiology, third edition
© 1995 Mosby–Year Book, Inc.

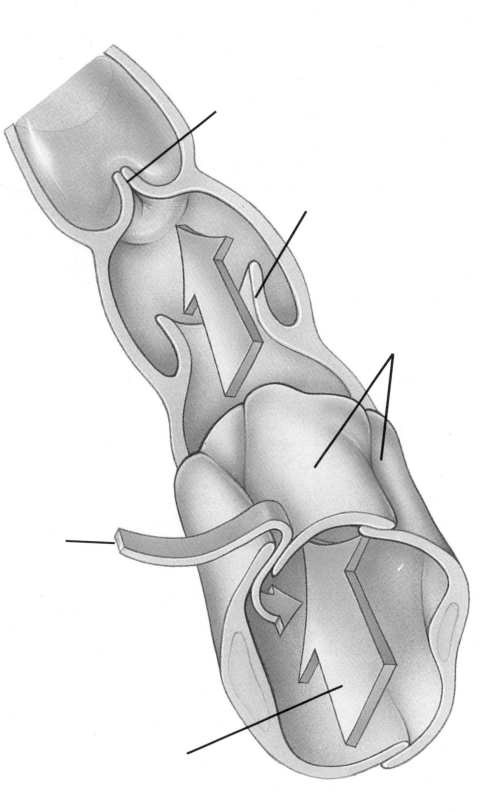

TA 296

Movement of Fluid Between Blood Capillary Wall to Lymphatic Capillaries; Overall Lymphatic Drainage
(Fig. 21-22, 21-23, p. 691)

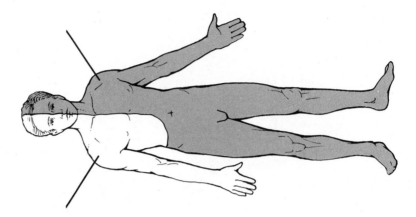

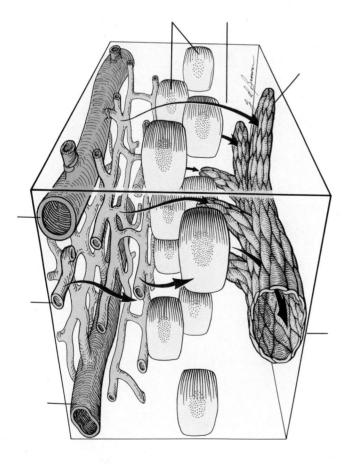

Seeley/Stephens/Tate: Anatomy & Physiology, third edition
© 1995 Mosby–Year Book, Inc.

Laminar and Turbulent Flow (Fig. 21-24 A & B, p. 692)

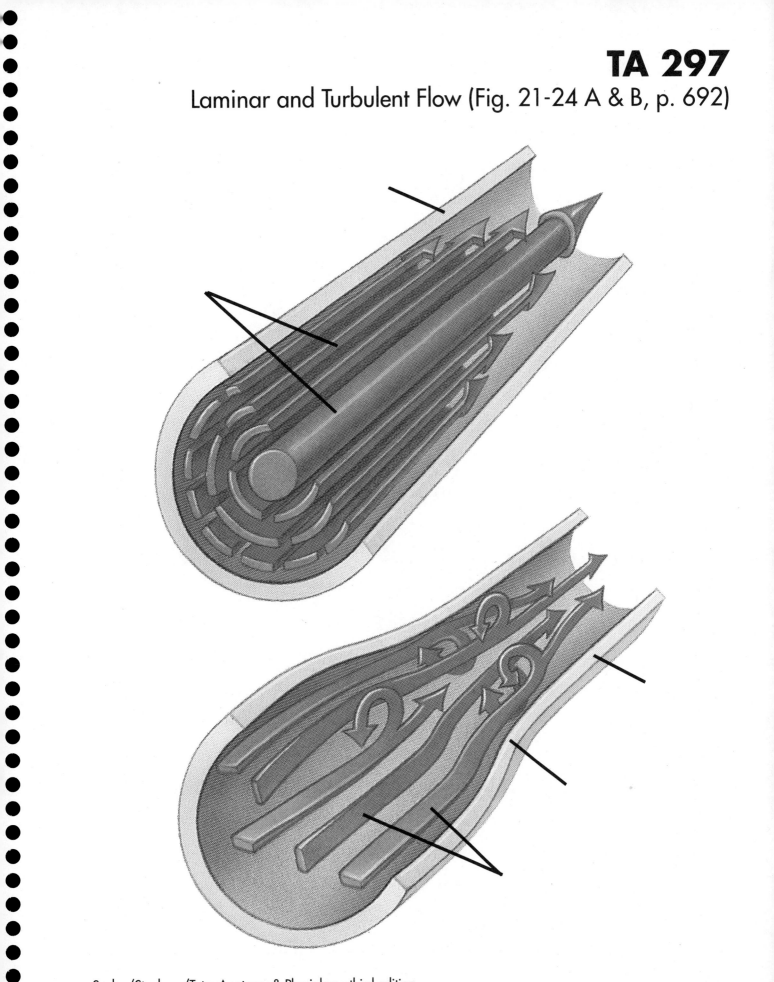

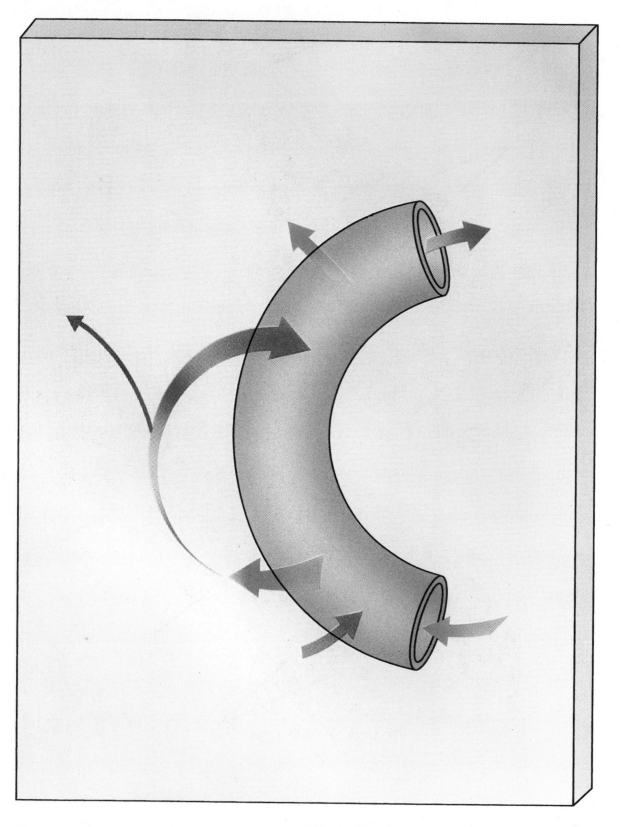

Baroreceptor and Chemoreceptor Reflex
Control of Blood Pressure (Fig. 21-31 A, p. 707)

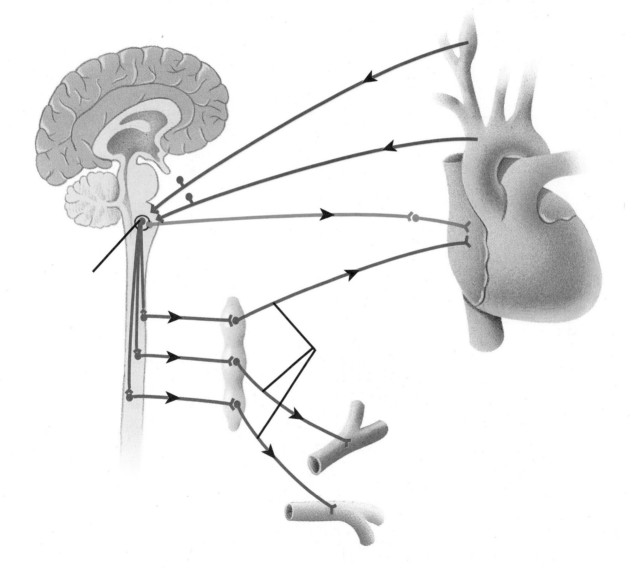

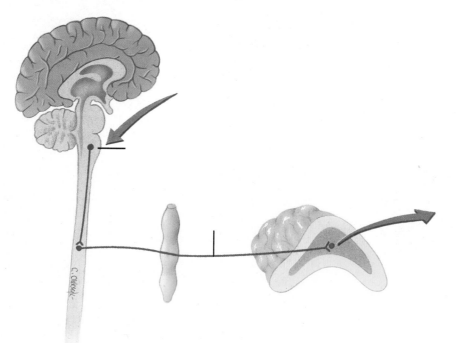

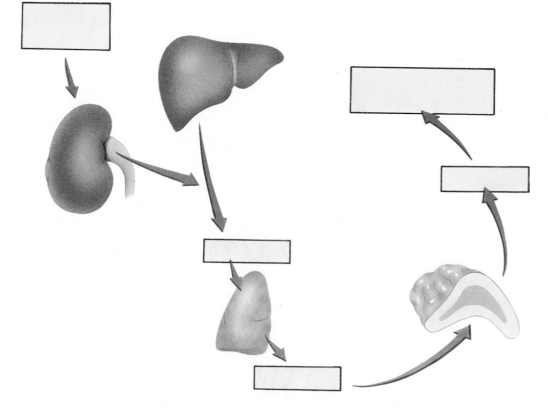

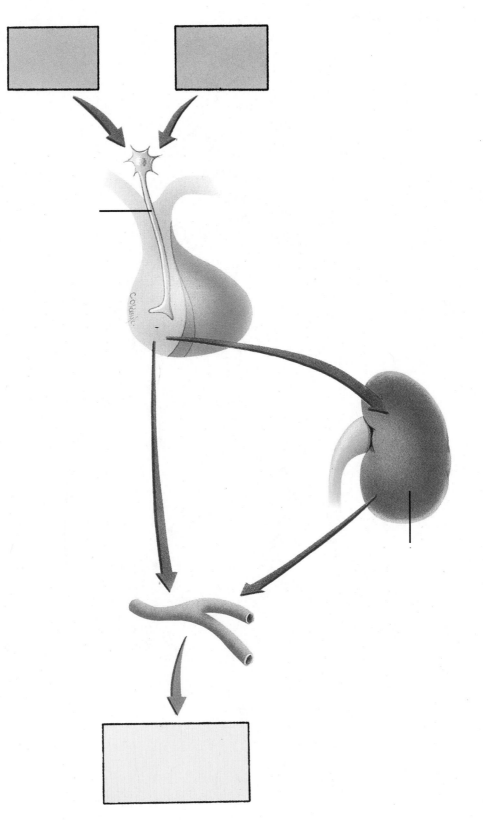

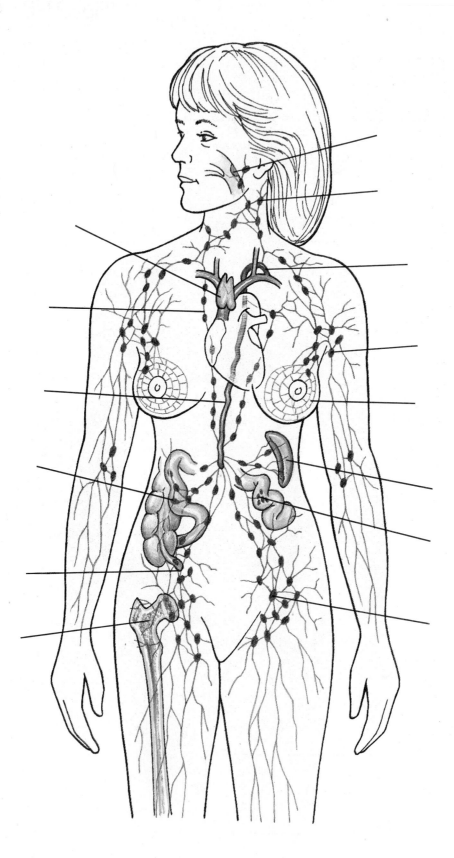

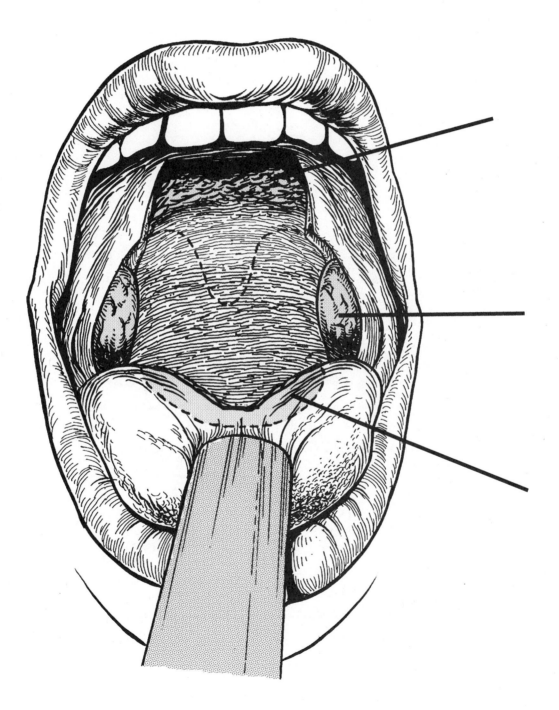

Seeley/Stephens/Tate: Anatomy & Physiology, third edition
© 1995 Mosby–Year Book, Inc.

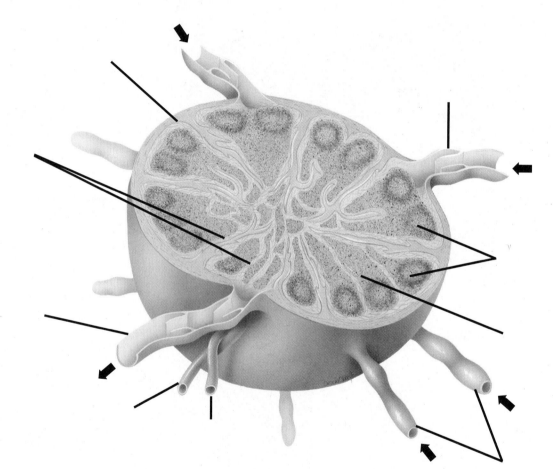

Seeley/Stephens/Tate: Anatomy & Physiology, third edition
© 1995 Mosby–Year Book, Inc.

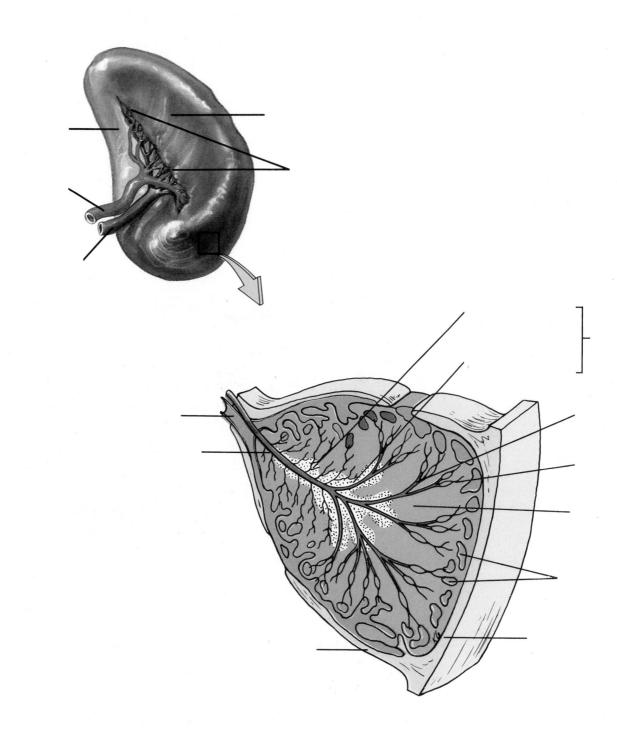

TA 306
Thymus Gland (Fig. 22-6 A & B, p. 726)

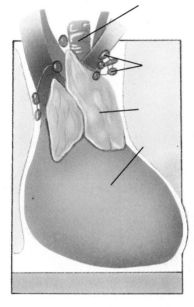

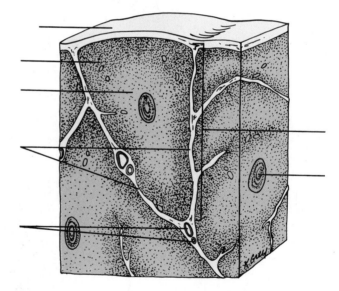

Seeley/Stephens/Tate: Anatomy & Physiology, third edition
© 1995 Mosby–Year Book, Inc.

Origin and Processing of B and T Cells (Fig. 22-9, p. 735)

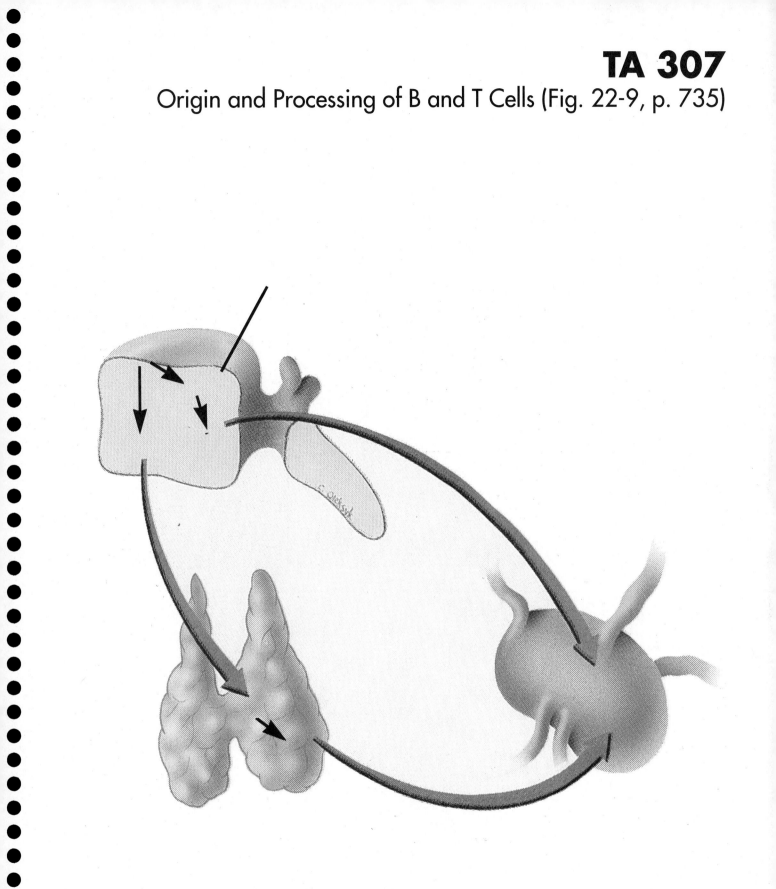

The T Cell Receptor (Fig. 22-10, p. 736)

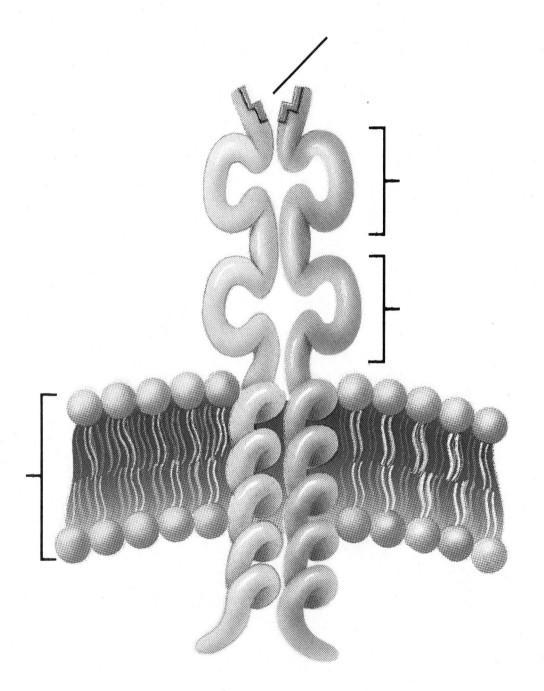

Seeley/Stephens/Tate: *Anatomy & Physiology, third edition*
© 1995 Mosby–Year Book, Inc.

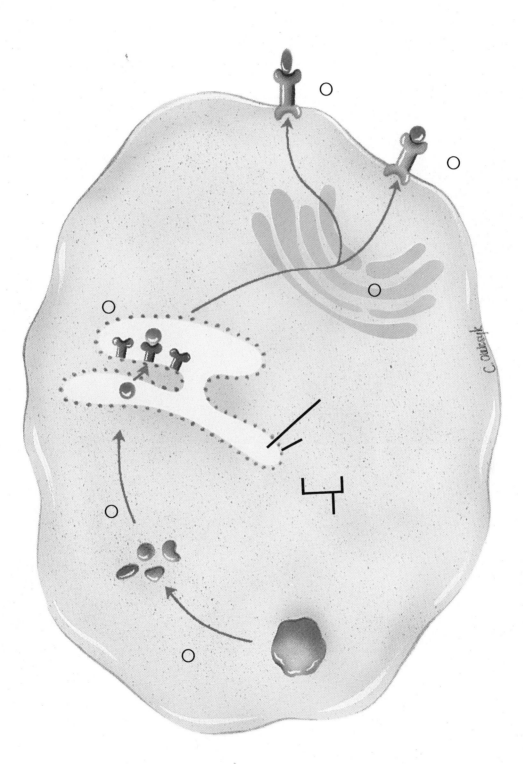

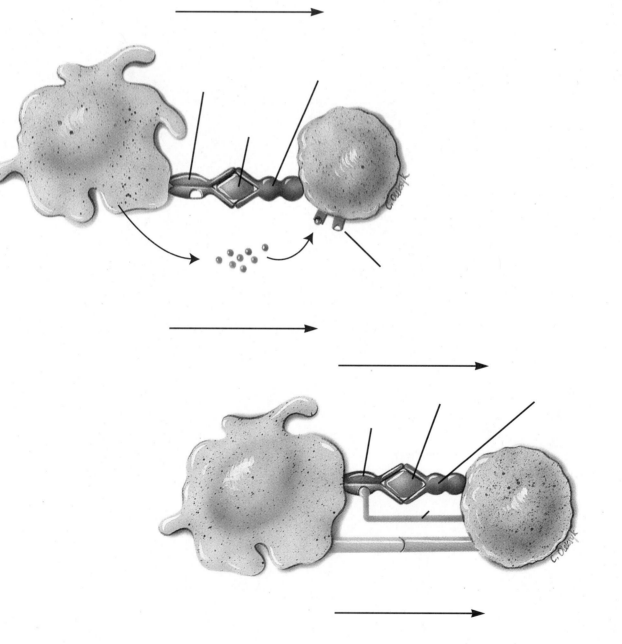

Seeley/Stephens/Tate: Anatomy & Physiology, third edition
© 1995 Mosby–Year Book, Inc.

Proliferation of Helper T Cells (Fig. 22-13, p. 741)

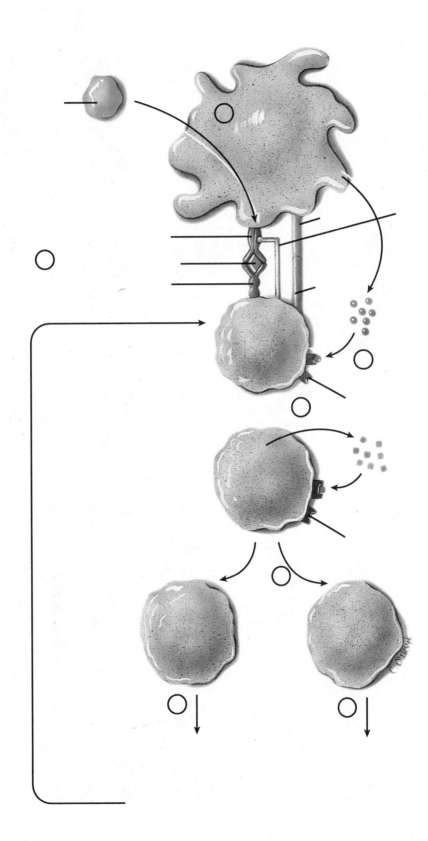

Seeley/Stephens/Tate: Anatomy & Physiology, third edition
© 1995 Mosby–Year Book, Inc.

Proliferation of B Cells (Fig. 22-14, p. 742)

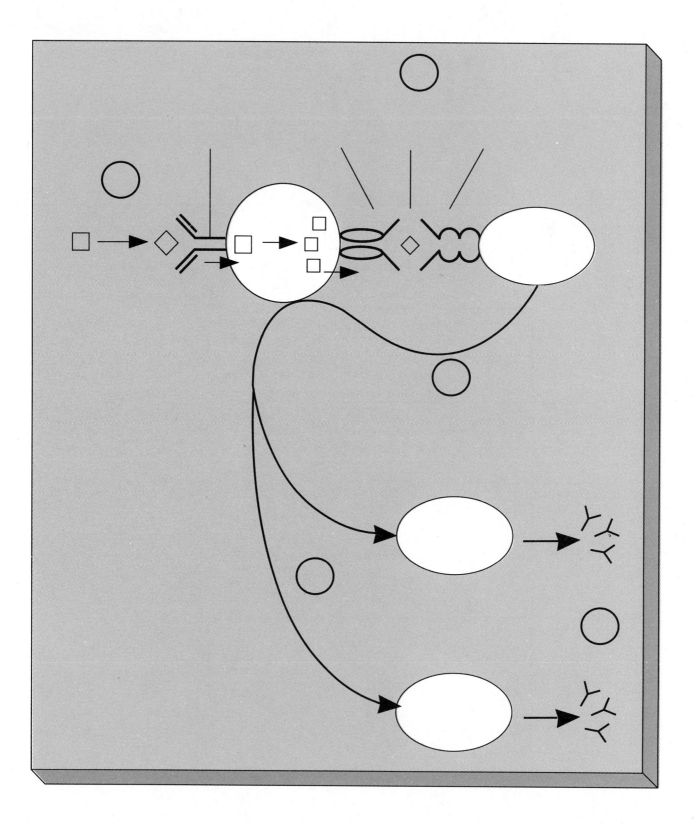

TA 313

Structure of an Antibody (Fig. 22-15, p. 742)

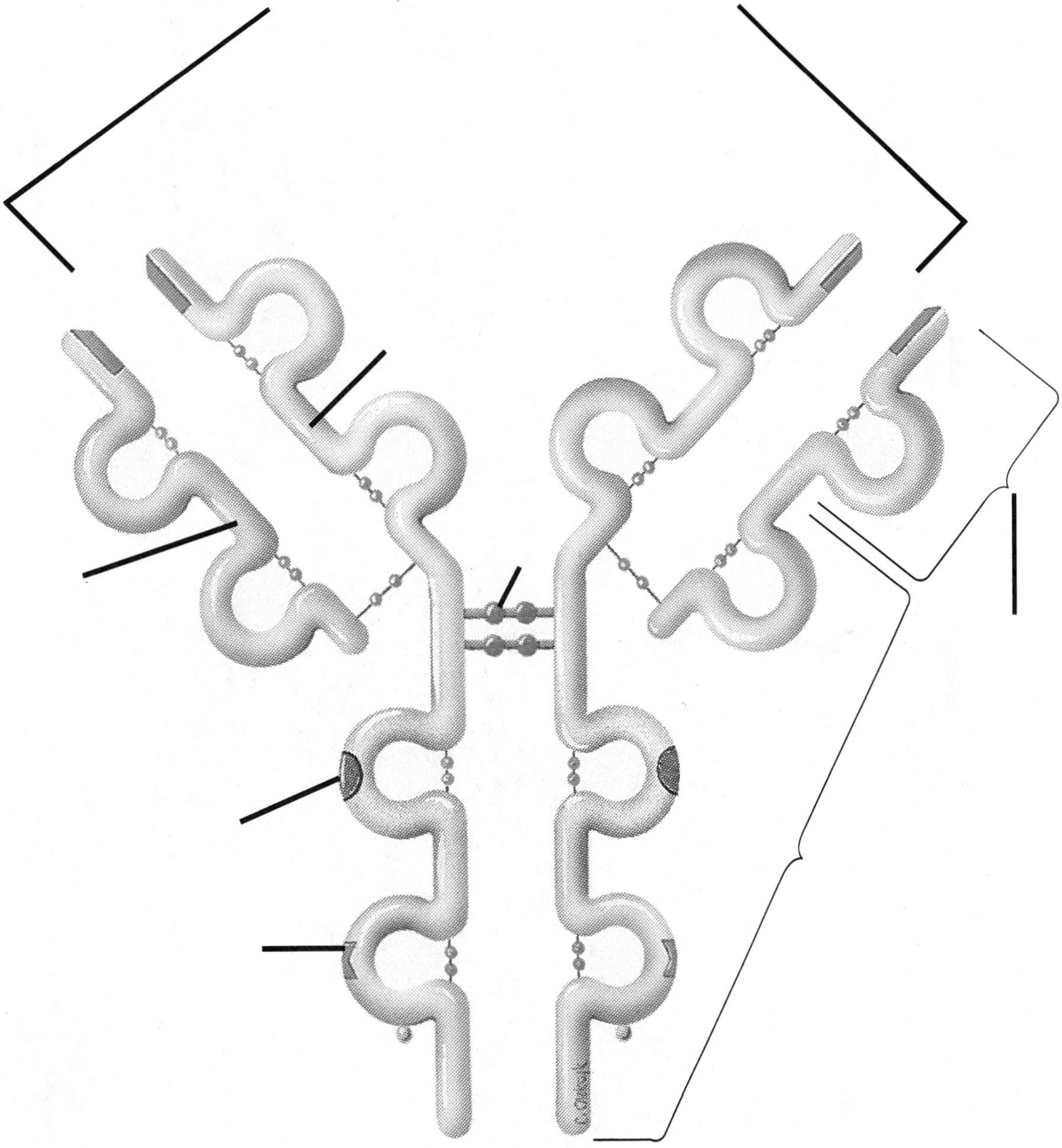

Seeley/Stephens/Tate: Anatomy & Physiology, third edition

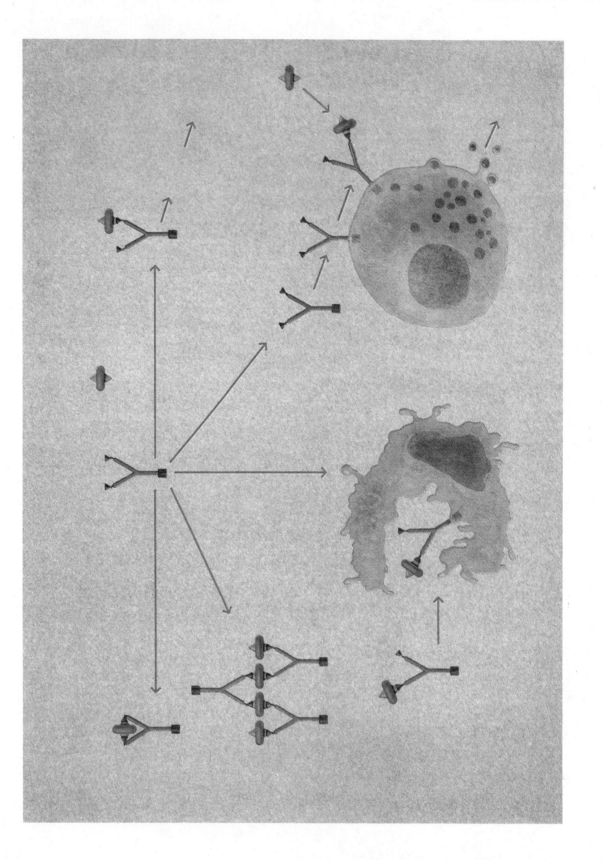

Seeley/Stephens/Tate: Anatomy & Physiology, third edition
© 1995 Mosby–Year Book, Inc.

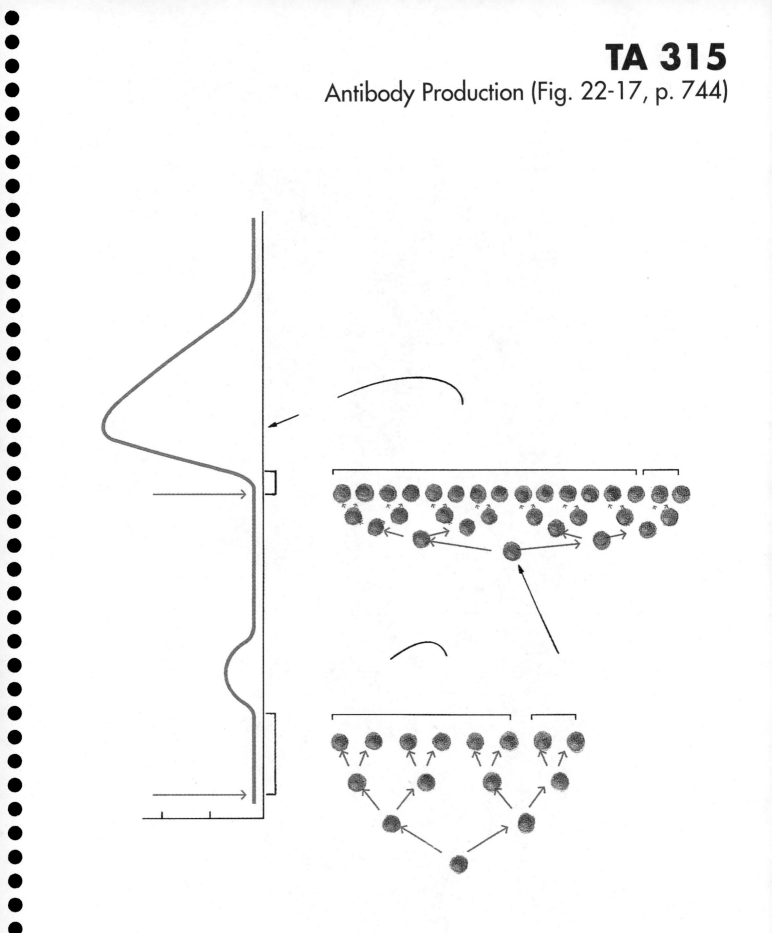

Seeley/Stephens/Tate: Anatomy & Physiology, third edition
© 1995 Mosby–Year Book, Inc.

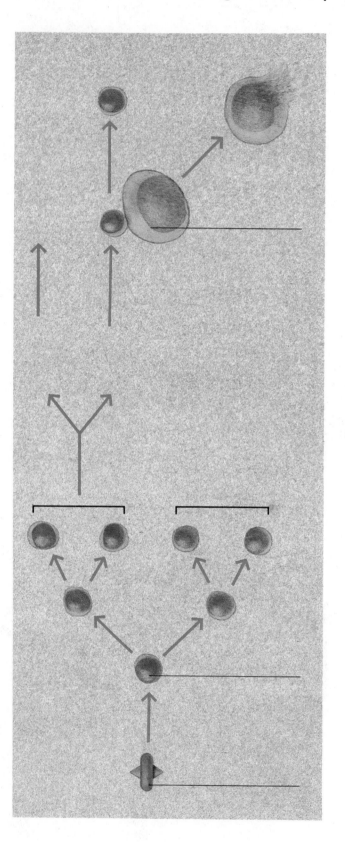

Seeley/Stephens/Tate: Anatomy & Physiology, third edition
© 1995 Mosby–Year Book, Inc.

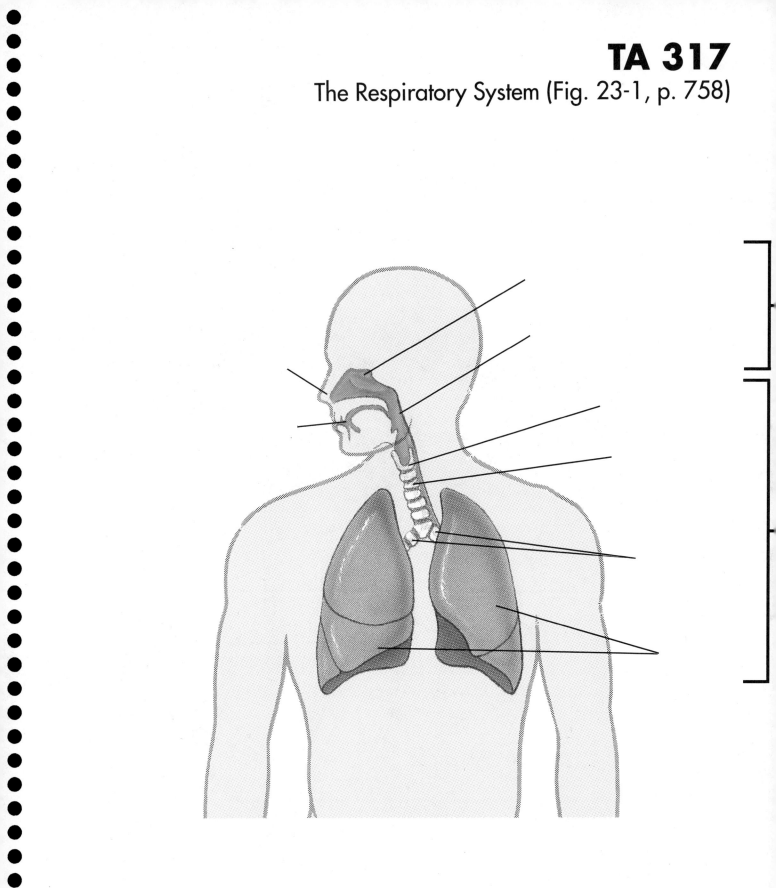

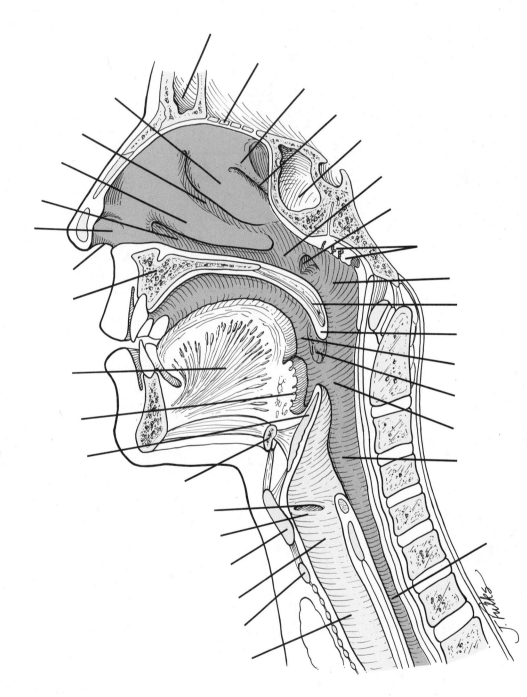

Seeley/Stephens/Tate: Anatomy & Physiology, third edition
© 1995 Mosby–Year Book, Inc.

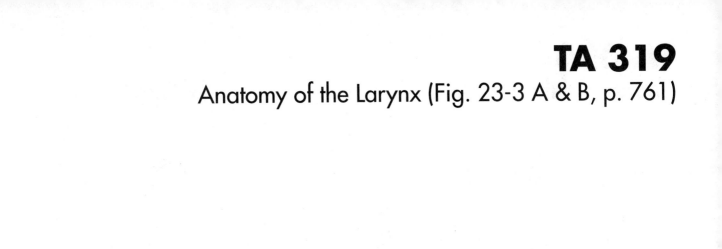

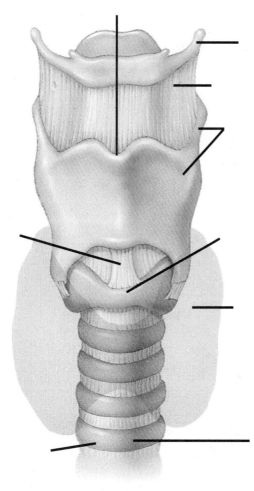

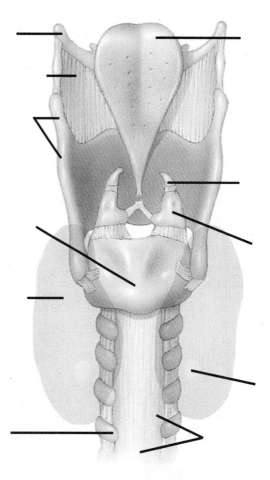

Seeley/Stephens/Tate: Anatomy & Physiology, third edition
© 1995 Mosby–Year Book, Inc.

Anatomy of the Trachea and Lungs (Fig. 23-5 A, p. 762)

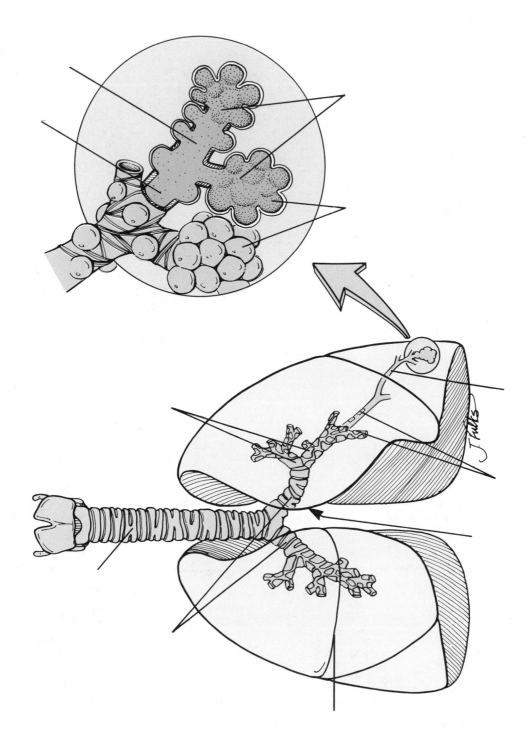

Seeley/Stephens/Tate: Anatomy & Physiology, third edition
© 1995 Mosby–Year Book, Inc.

Pressure Changes During Inspiration and Expiration
(Fig. 23-9 A-D, p. 768)

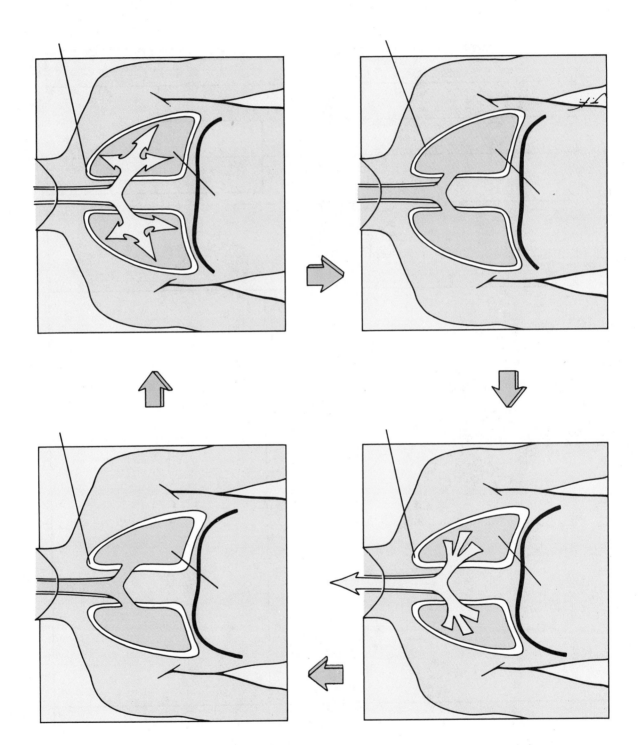

Seeley/Stephens/Tate: Anatomy & Physiology, third edition
© 1995 Mosby–Year Book, Inc.

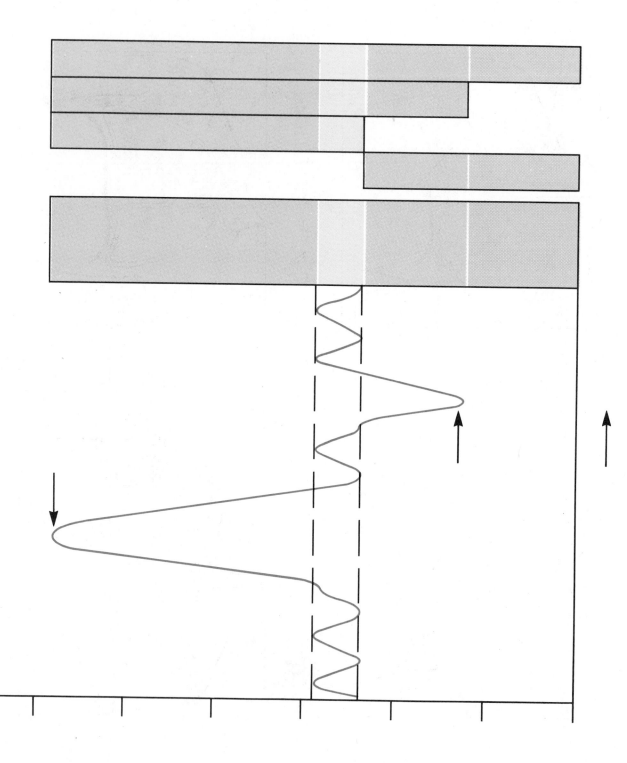

Seeley/Stephens/Tate: Anatomy & Physiology, third edition
© 1995 Mosby–Year Book, Inc.

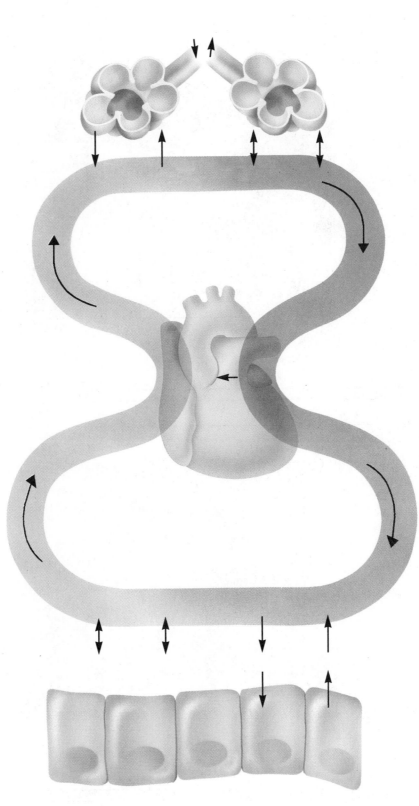

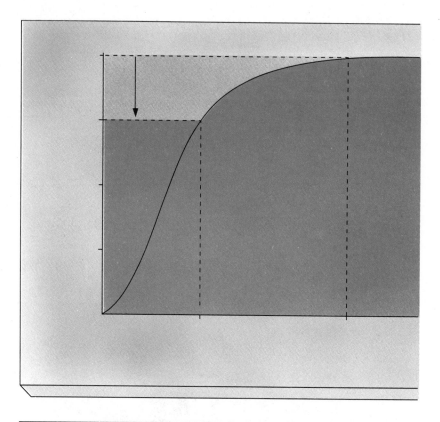

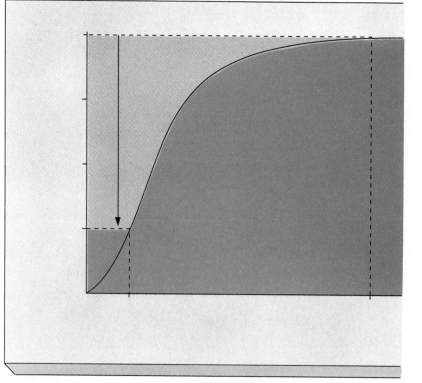

Seeley/Stephens/Tate: Anatomy & Physiology, third edition
© 1995 Mosby–Year Book, Inc.

Effects of Shifting the Oxygen-Hemoglobin Dissociation Curve
(Fig. 23-14 A & B, p. 779)

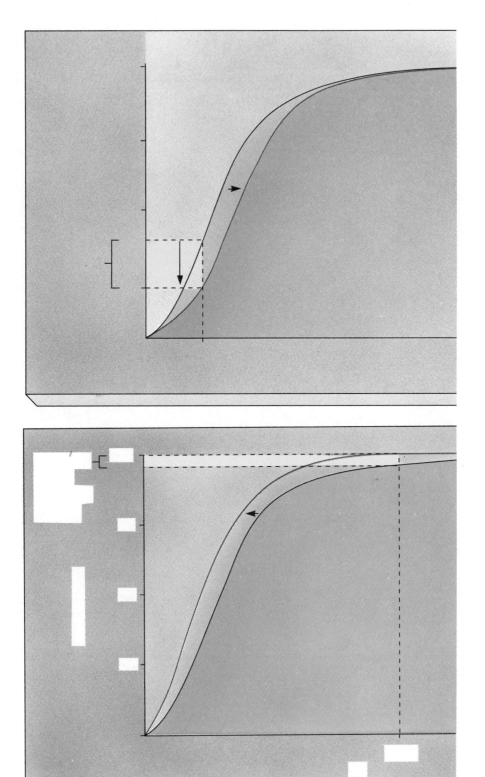

Seeley/Stephens/Tate: Anatomy & Physiology, third edition
© 1995 Mosby–Year Book, Inc.

Chloride Movement (Fig. 23-15 A & B, p. 781)

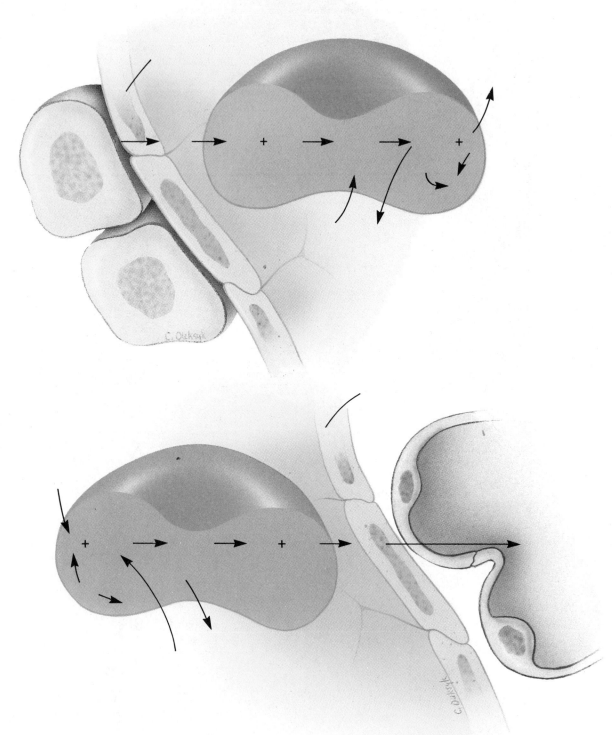

Seeley/Stephens/Tate: Anatomy & Physiology, third edition
© 1995 Mosby–Year Book, Inc.

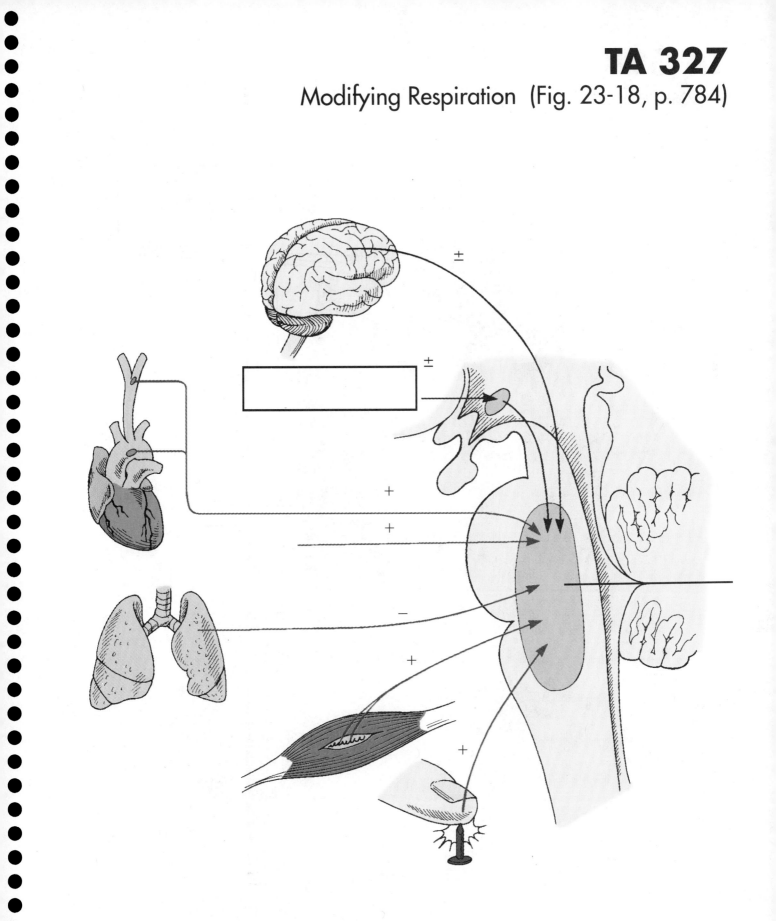

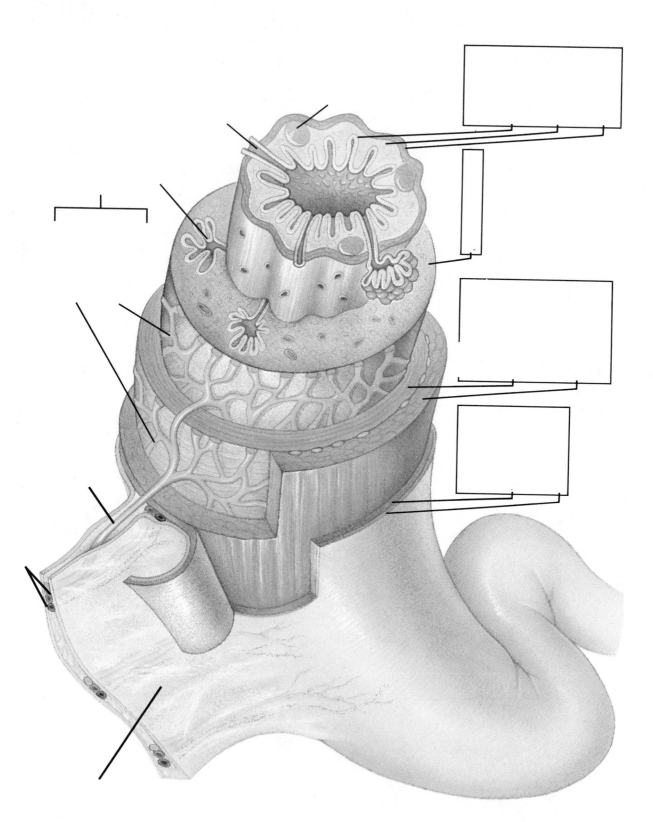

Seeley/Stephens/Tate: Anatomy & Physiology, third edition
© 1995 Mosby–Year Book, Inc.

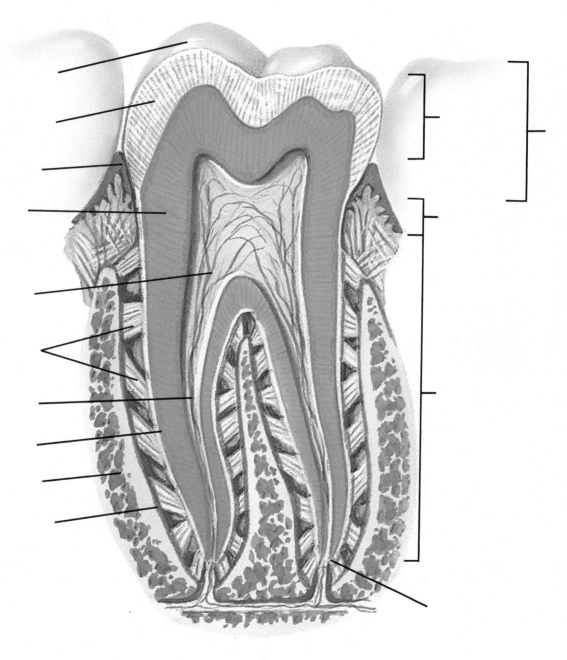

Anatomy and Histology of the Stomach (Fig. 24-8 A, p. 807)

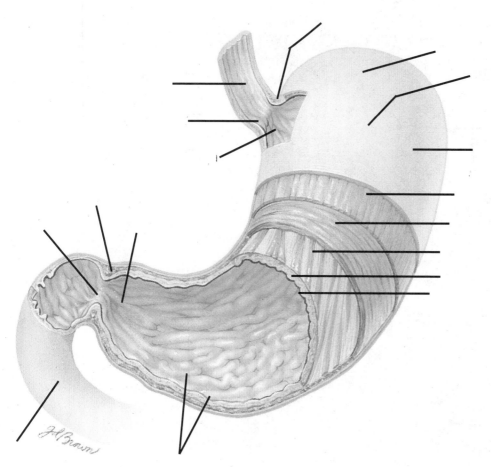

Seeley/Stephens/Tate: Anatomy & Physiology, third edition
© 1995 Mosby–Year Book, Inc.

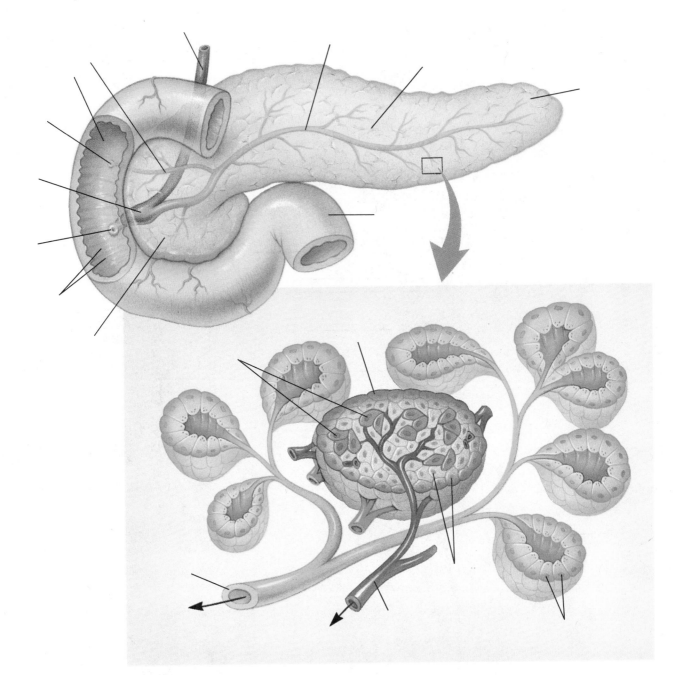

Anatomy and Histology of the Duodenum
(Fig. 24-11A-C, p. 810)

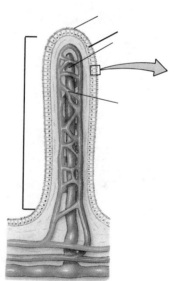

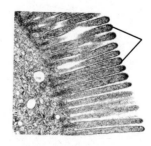

Seeley/Stephens/Tate: Anatomy & Physiology, third edition
© 1995 Mosby–Year Book, Inc.

Anatomy and Histology of the Liver (Fig. 24-12 A-D, p. 811)

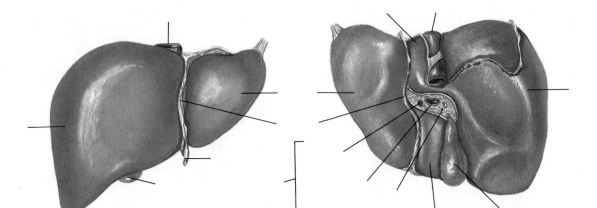

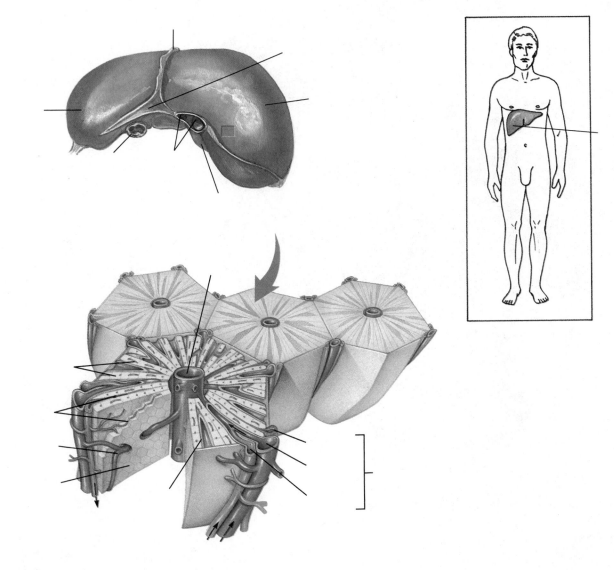

Histology of the Large Intestine (Fig. 24-15 A-C, p. 814)

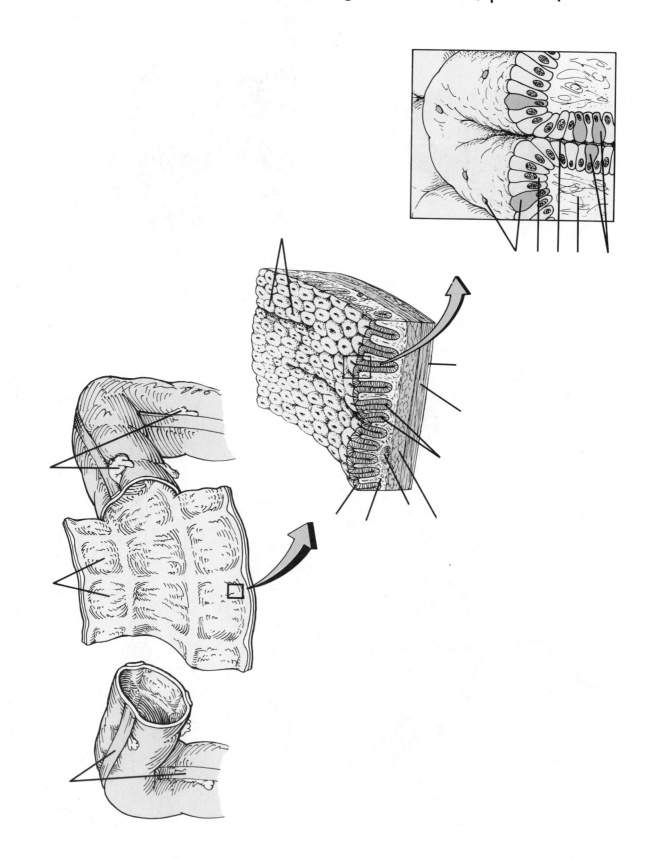

Seeley/Stephens/Tate: Anatomy & Physiology, third edition
© 1995 Mosby–Year Book, Inc.

Three Phases of Gastric Secretion (Fig. 24-19 A-C, p. 823)

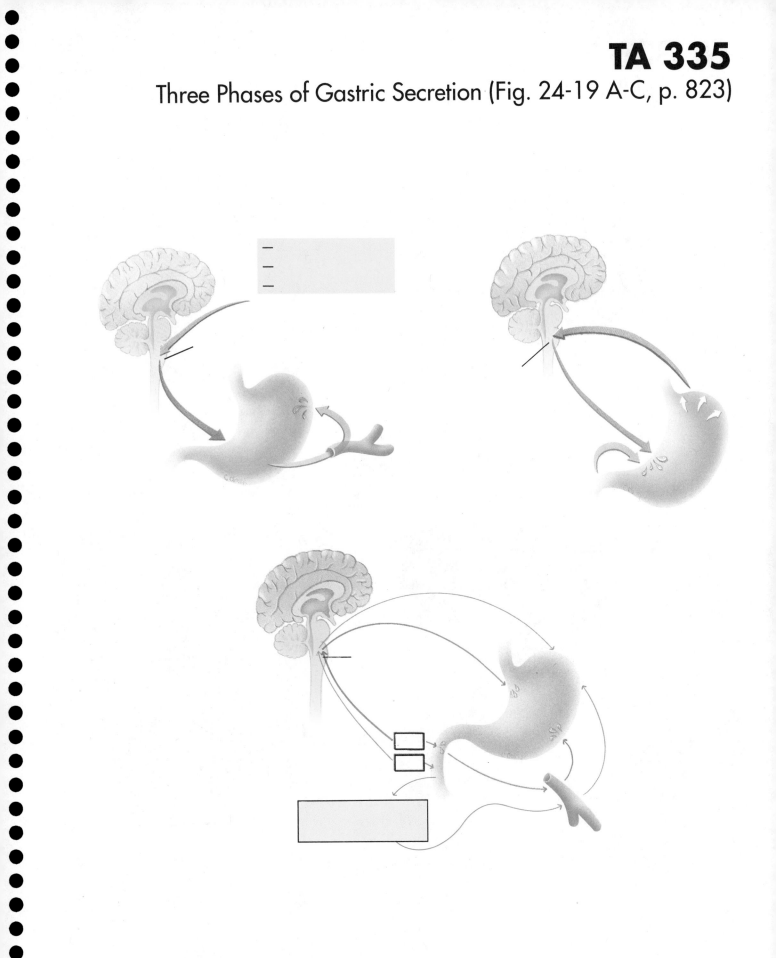

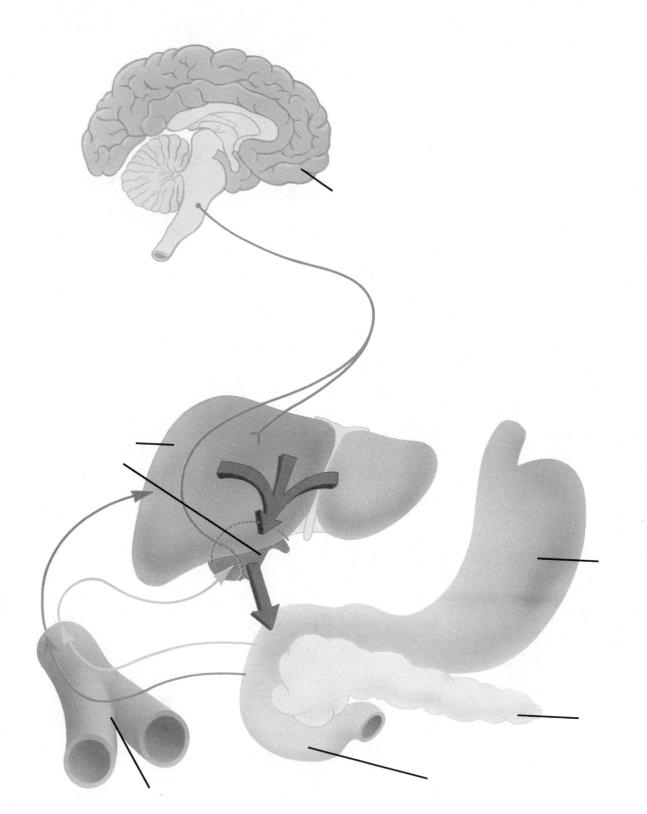

Control of Pancreatic Secretion (Fig. 24-23, p. 831)

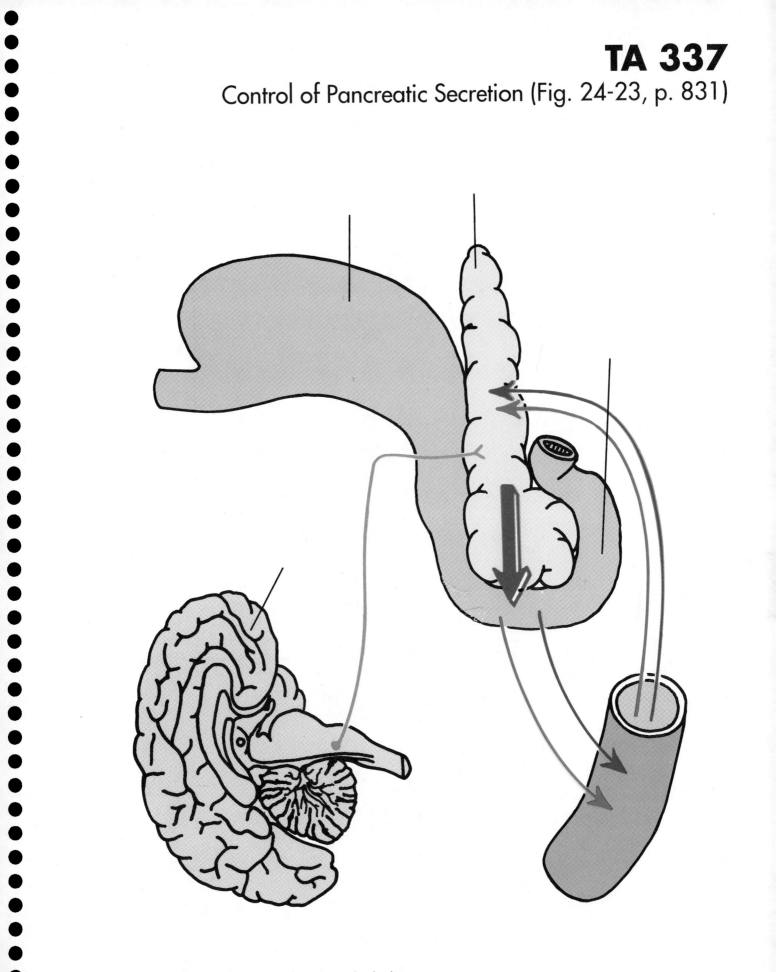

TA 338

Glucose and Galactose Absorption (Fig. 24-25, p. 835)

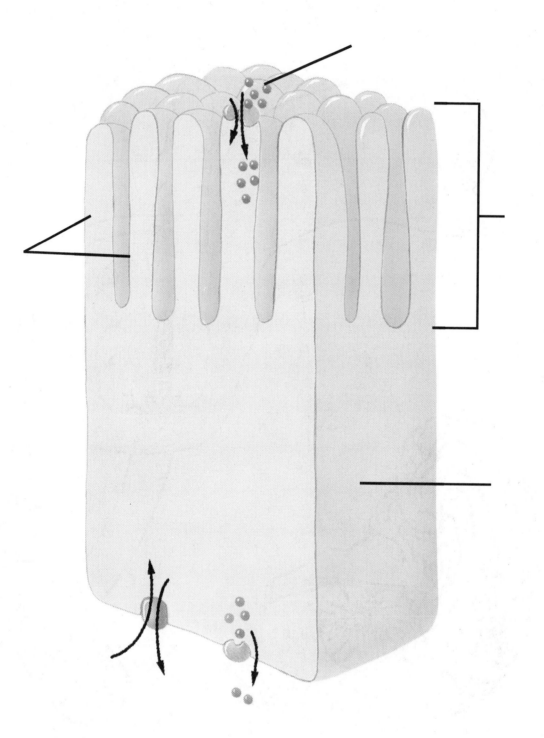

Seeley/Stephens/Tate: Anatomy & Physiology, third edition
© 1995 Mosby–Year Book, Inc.

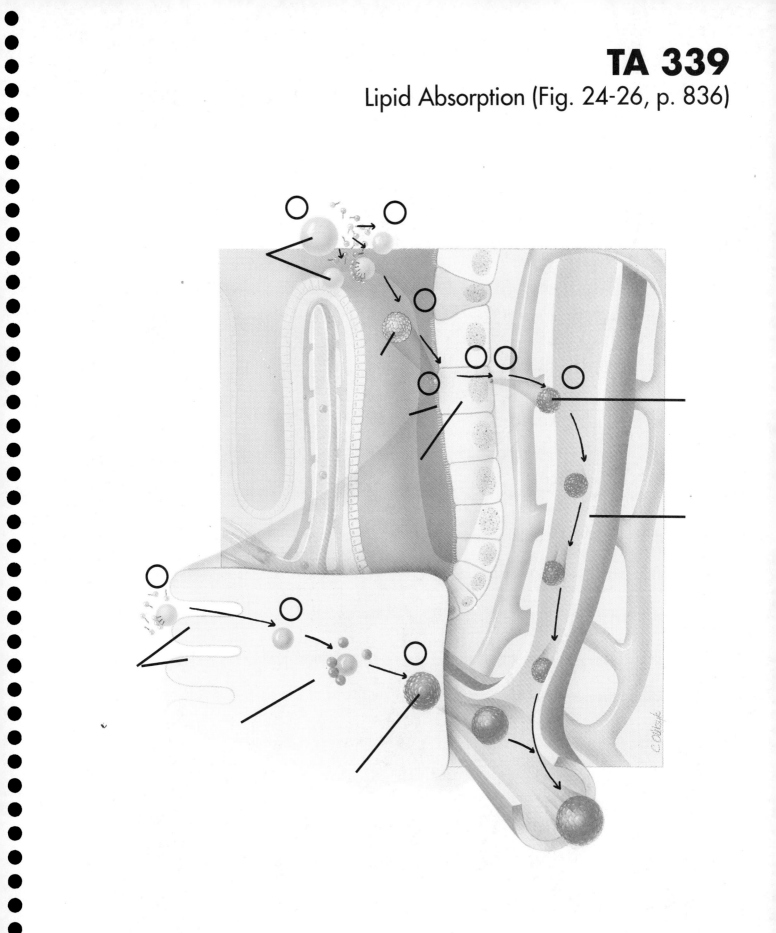

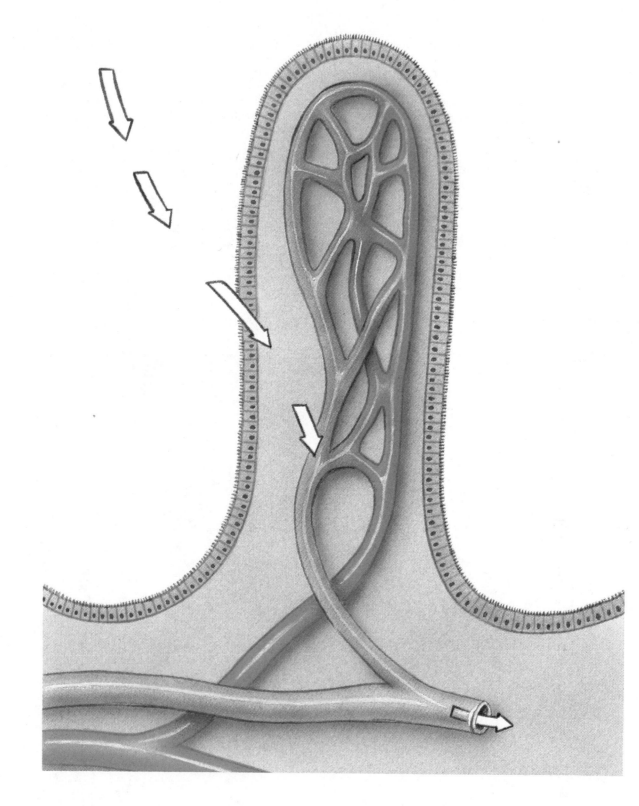

Seeley/Stephens/Tate: Anatomy & Physiology, third edition
© 1995 Mosby–Year Book, Inc.

Cellular Metabolism (Fig. 25-2, p. 855)

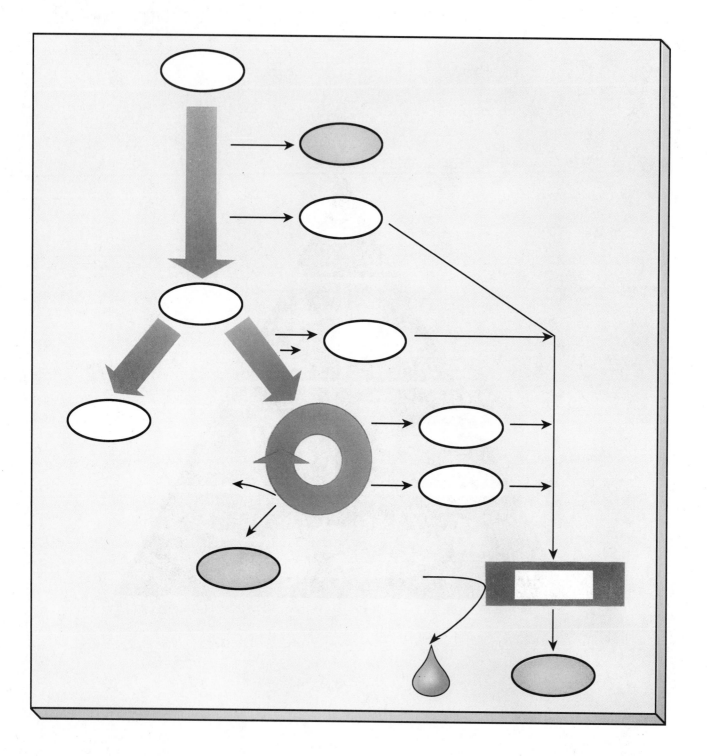

Seeley/Stephens/Tate: Anatomy & Physiology, third edition
© 1995 Mosby–Year Book, Inc.

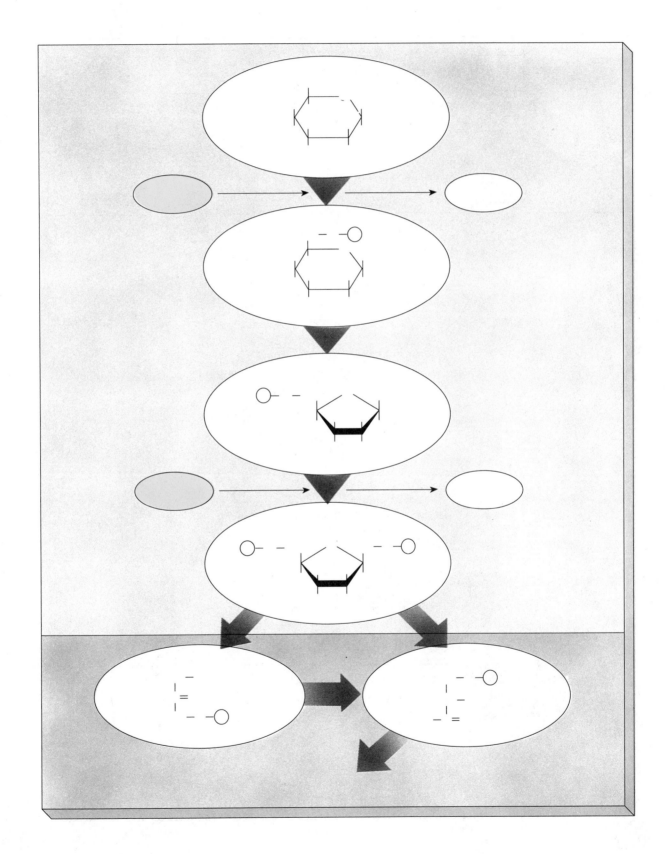

Glycolysis—cont'd (Fig. 25-3 C & D, p. 857)

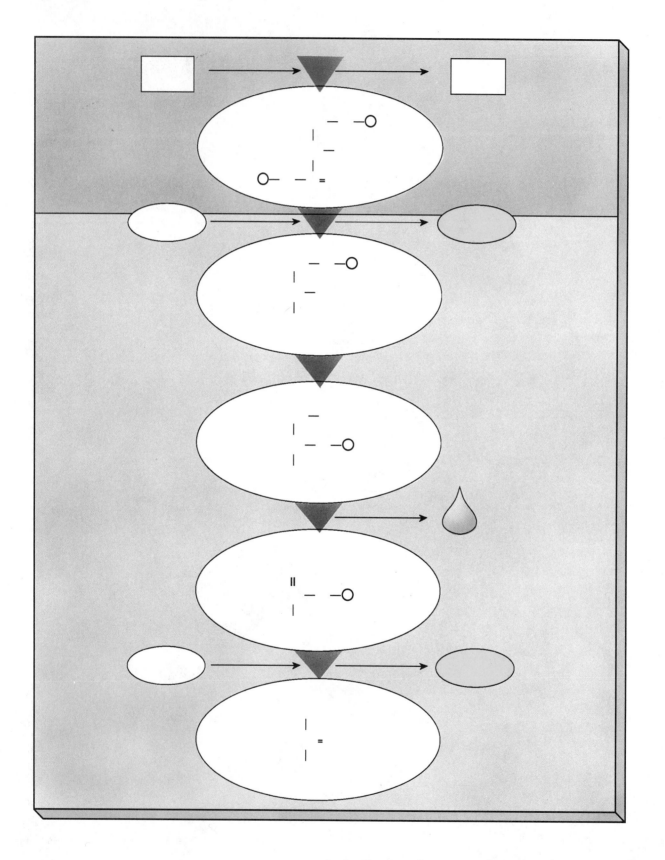

Seeley/Stephens/Tate: Anatomy & Physiology, third edition
© 1995 Mosby–Year Book, Inc.

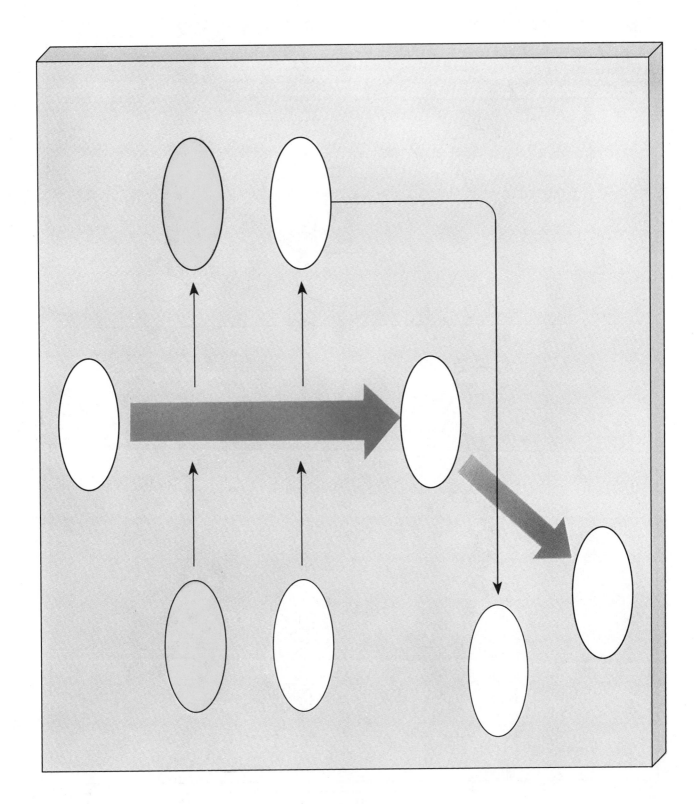

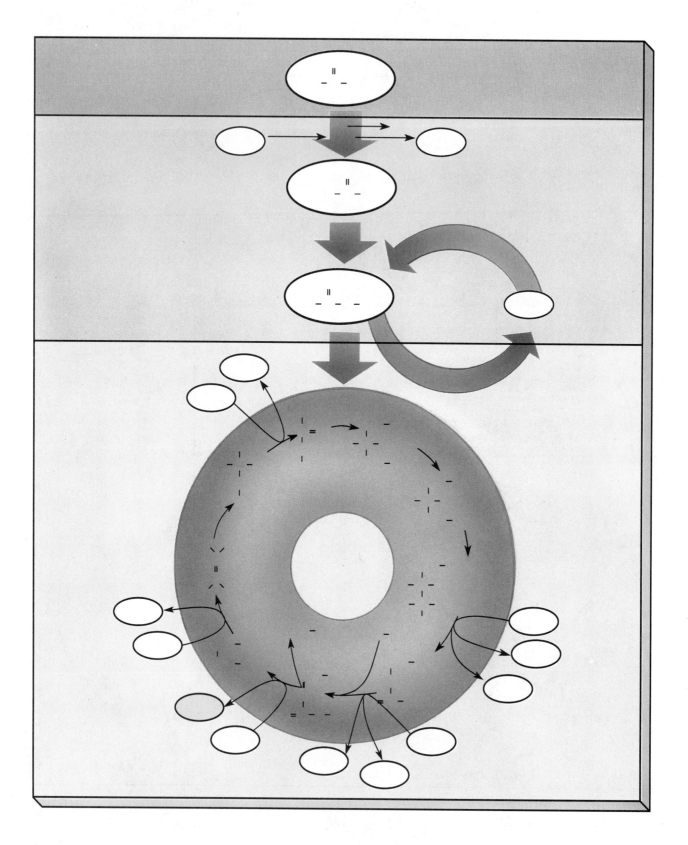

Seeley/Stephens/Tate: Anatomy & Physiology, third edition
© 1995 Mosby–Year Book, Inc.

Electron-Transport Chain (Fig. 25-6, p. 861)

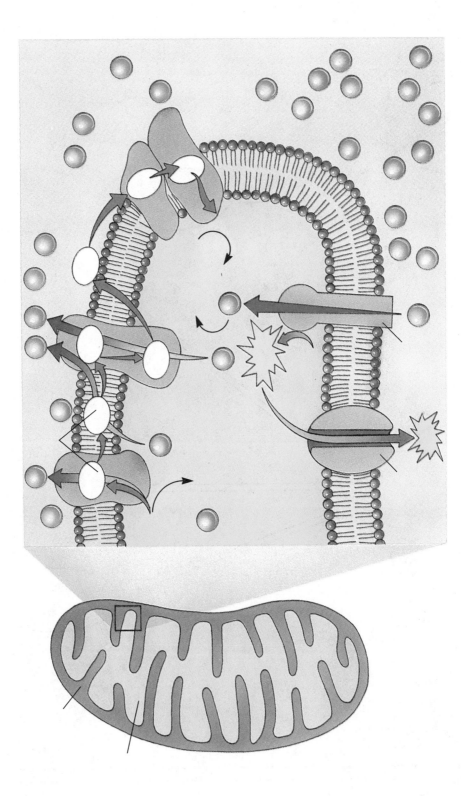

Seeley/Stephens/Tate: Anatomy & Physiology, third edition
© 1995 Mosby–Year Book, Inc.

Lipid Metabolism (Fig. 25-7, p. 863)

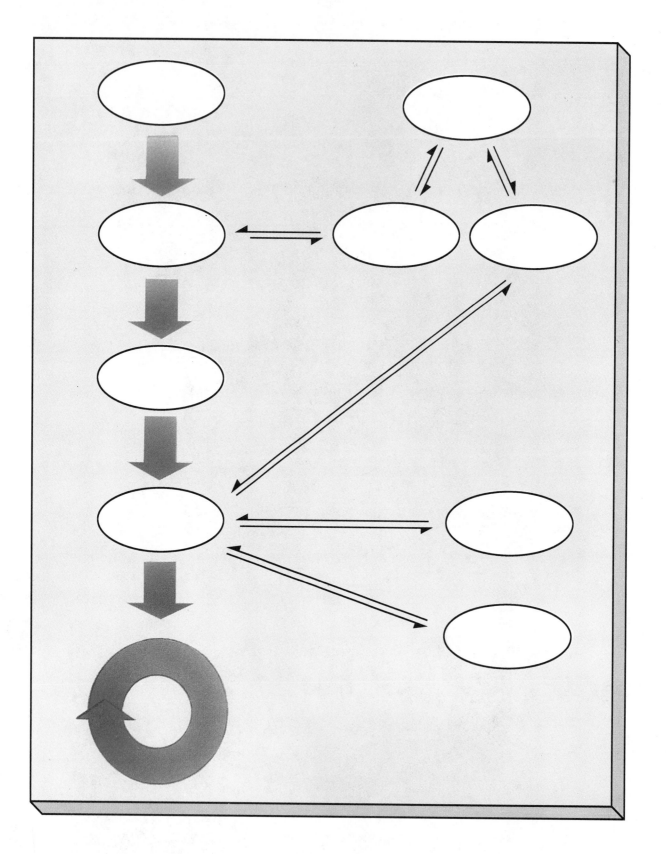

Seeley/Stephens/Tate: Anatomy & Physiology, third edition
© 1995 Mosby–Year Book, Inc.

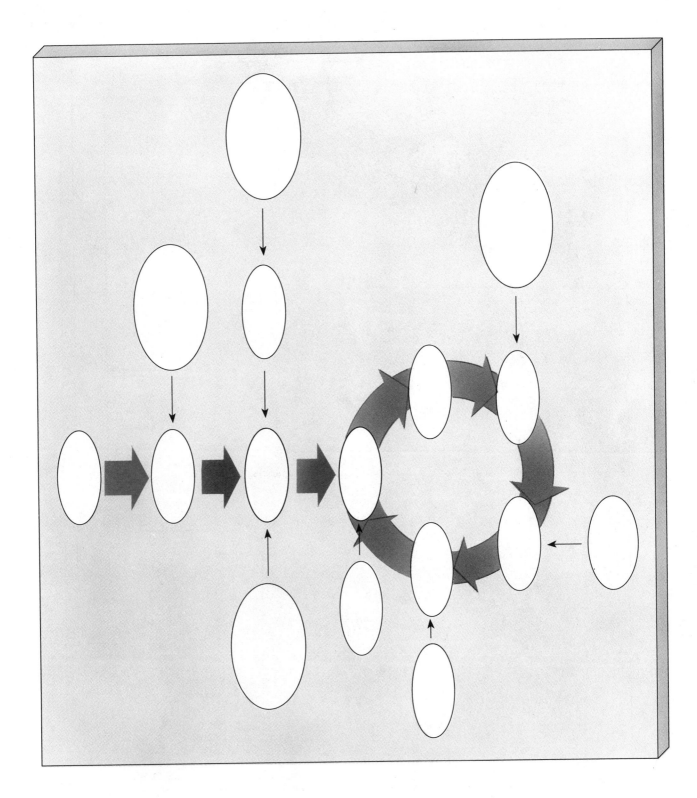

Seeley/Stephens/Tate: Anatomy & Physiology, third edition
© 1995 Mosby–Year Book, Inc.

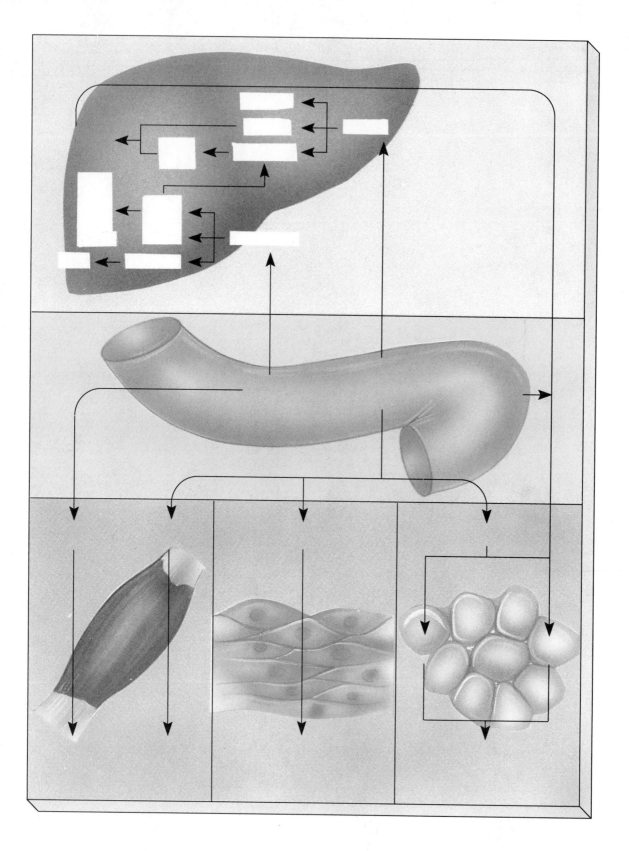

Seeley/Stephens/Tate: Anatomy & Physiology, third edition
© 1995 Mosby–Year Book, Inc.

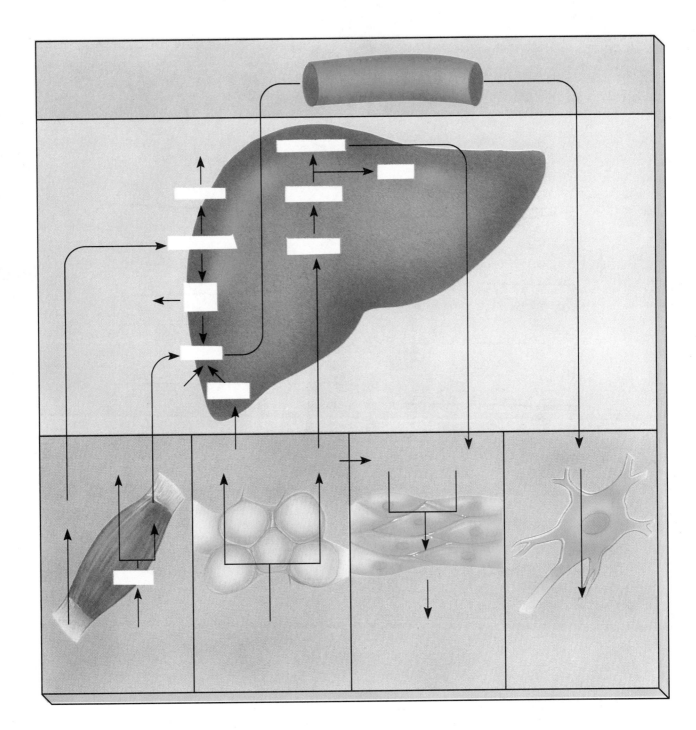

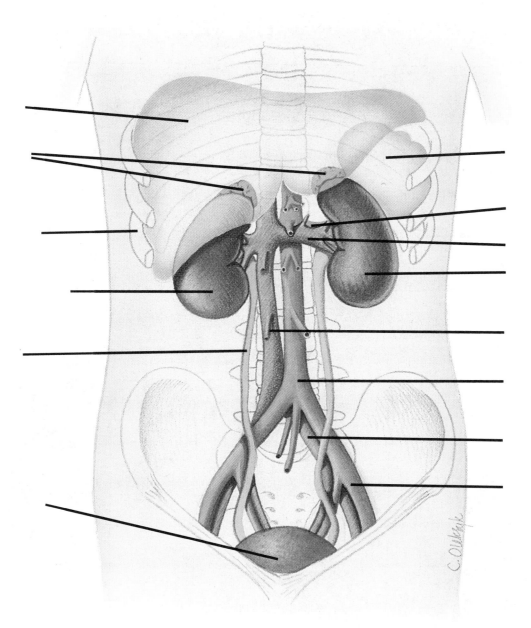

Seeley/Stephens/Tate: Anatomy & Physiology, third edition
© 1995 Mosby–Year Book, Inc.

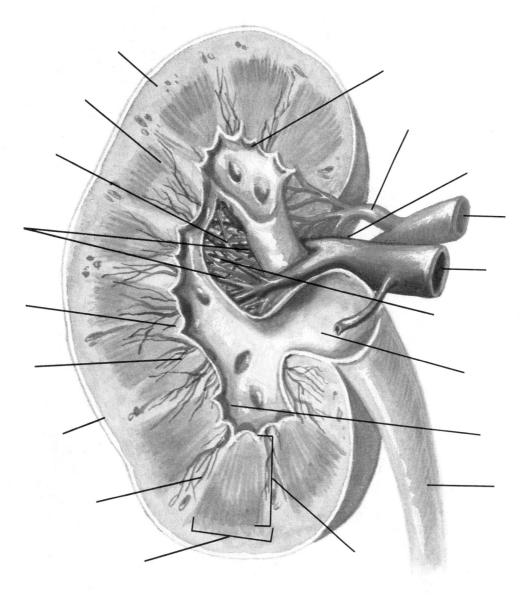

Functional Unit of the Kidney—the Nephron
(Fig. 26-3, p. 882)

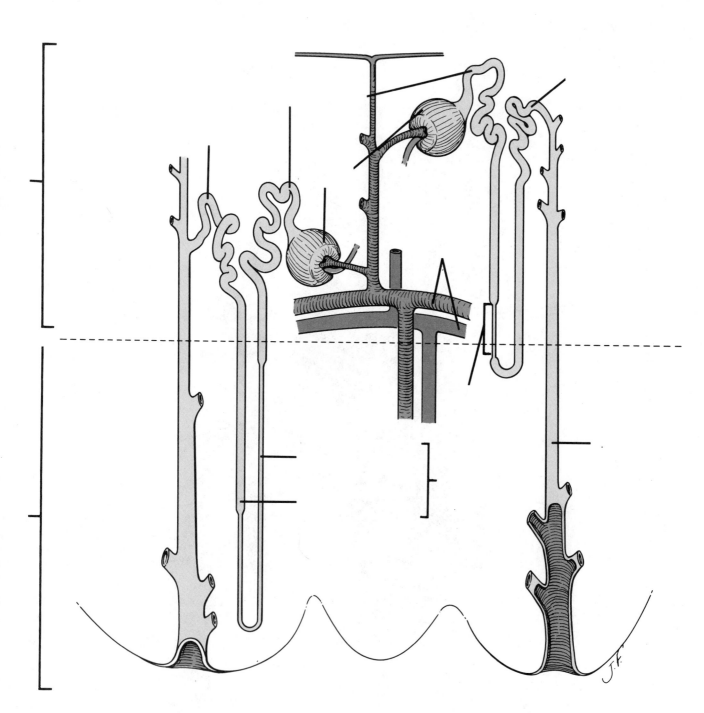

Seeley/Stephens/Tate: Anatomy & Physiology, third edition
© 1995 Mosby—Year Book, Inc.

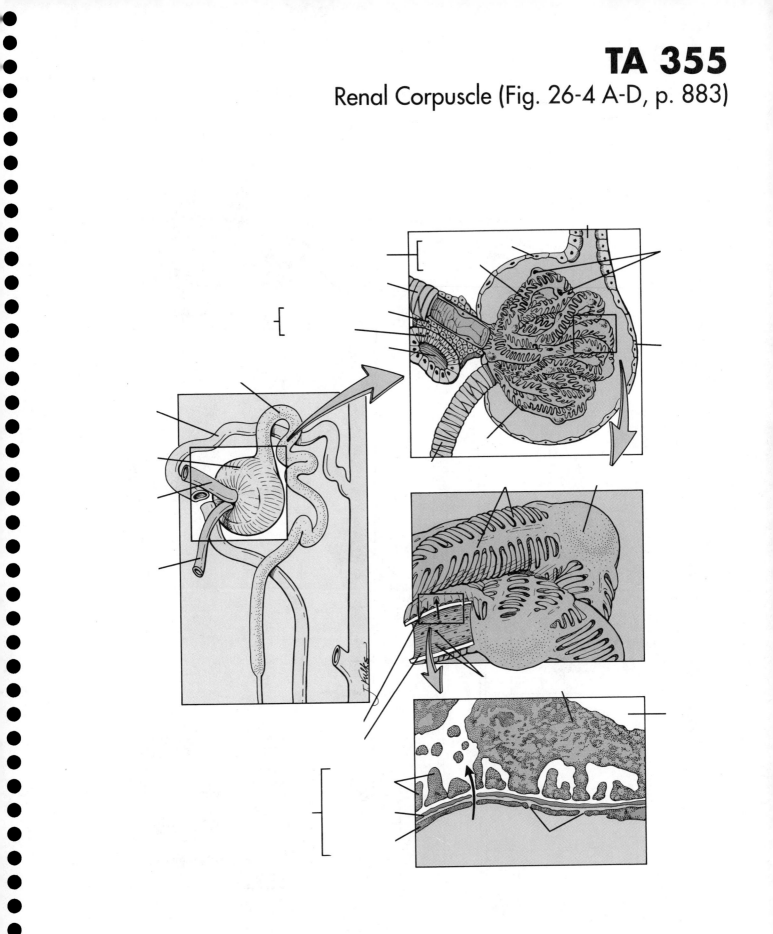

TA 356
Histology of the Nephron (Fig. 26-5 A-E, p. 884)

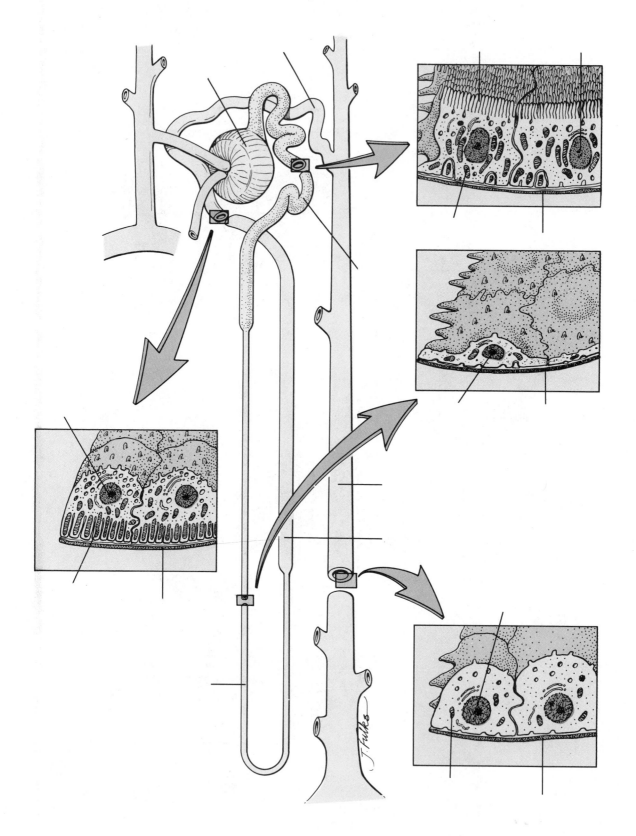

Seeley/Stephens/Tate: Anatomy & Physiology, third edition
© 1995 Mosby—Year Book, Inc.

Blood Flow Through the Kidney (Fig. 26-6 A & B, p. 885)

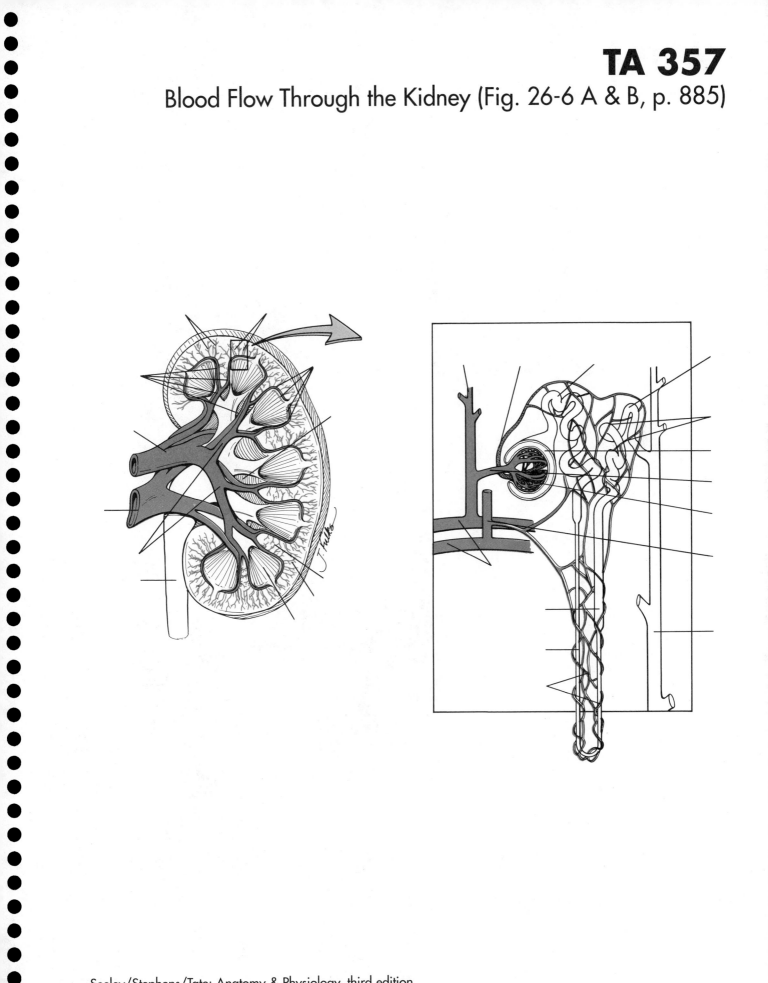

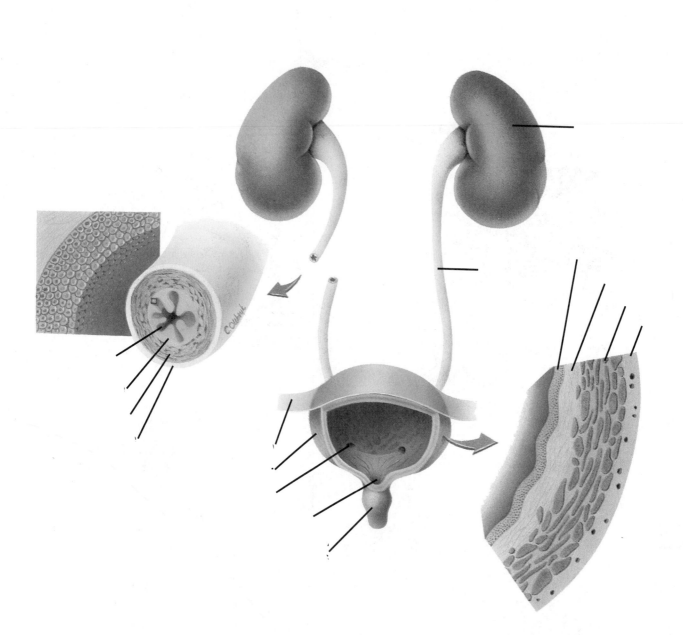

Seeley/Stephens/Tate: Anatomy & Physiology, third edition
© 1995 Mosby–Year Book, Inc.

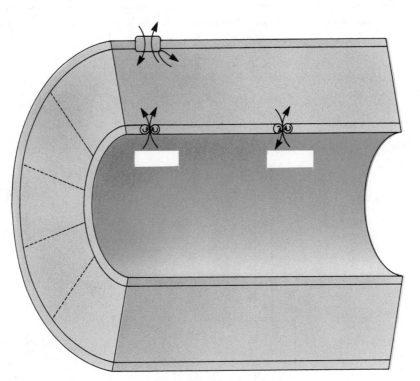

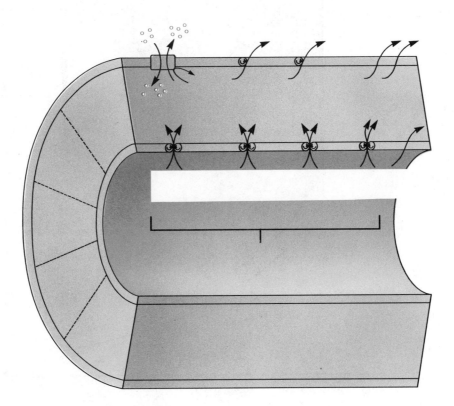

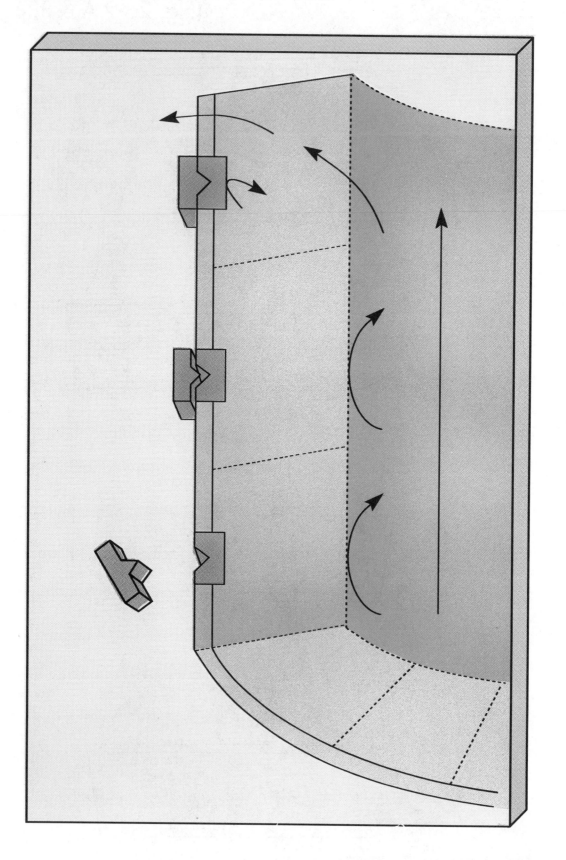

Seeley/Stephens/Tate: Anatomy & Physiology, third edition
© 1995 Mosby—Year Book, Inc.

Urine Concentrating Mechanism (Fig. 26-11, p. 896)

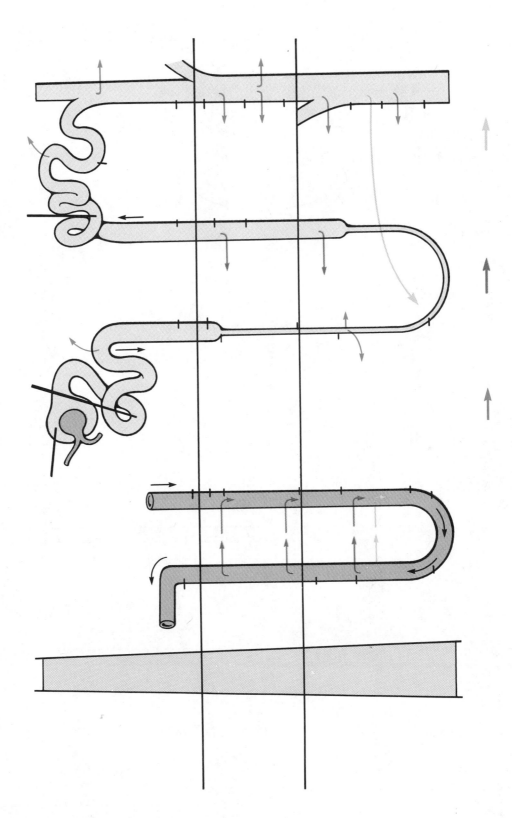

Seeley/Stephens/Tate: Anatomy & Physiology, third edition
© 1995 Mosby–Year Book, Inc.

Effect of Aldosterone on the Distal Convoluted Tubule
(Fig. 26-12, p. 900)

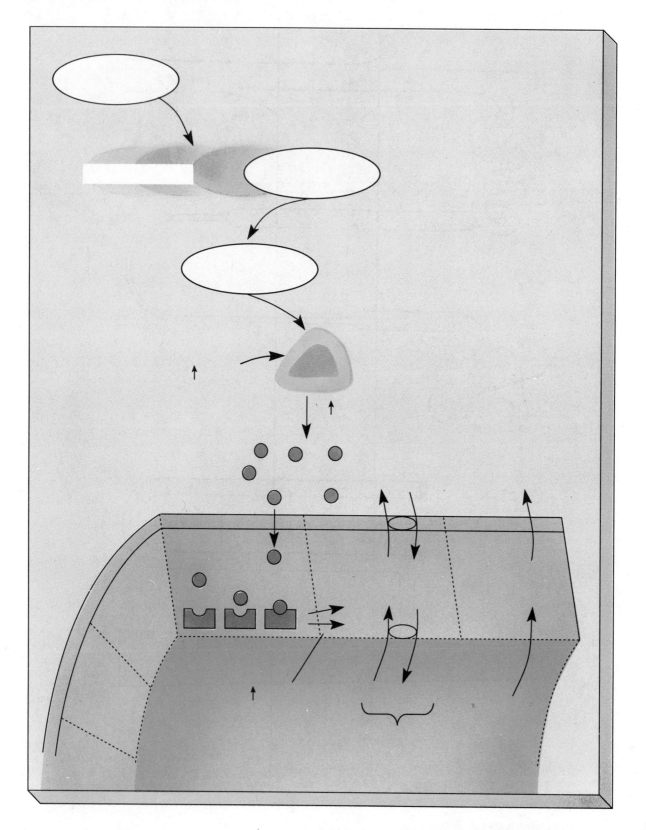

Seeley/Stephens/Tate: Anatomy & Physiology, third edition
© 1995 Mosby–Year Book, Inc.

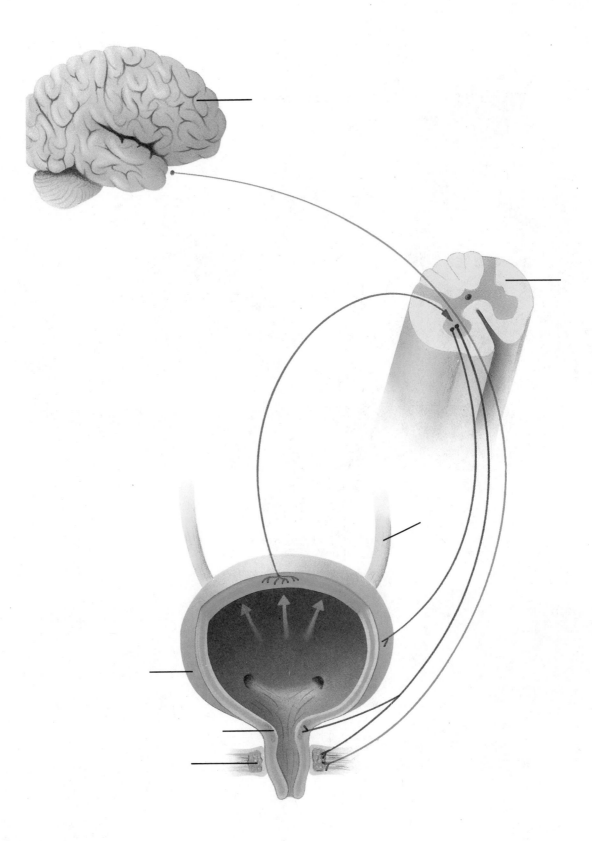

Regulation of Sodium Ion Levels in the Extracellular Fluids
(Fig. 27-2 A-D, p. 918)

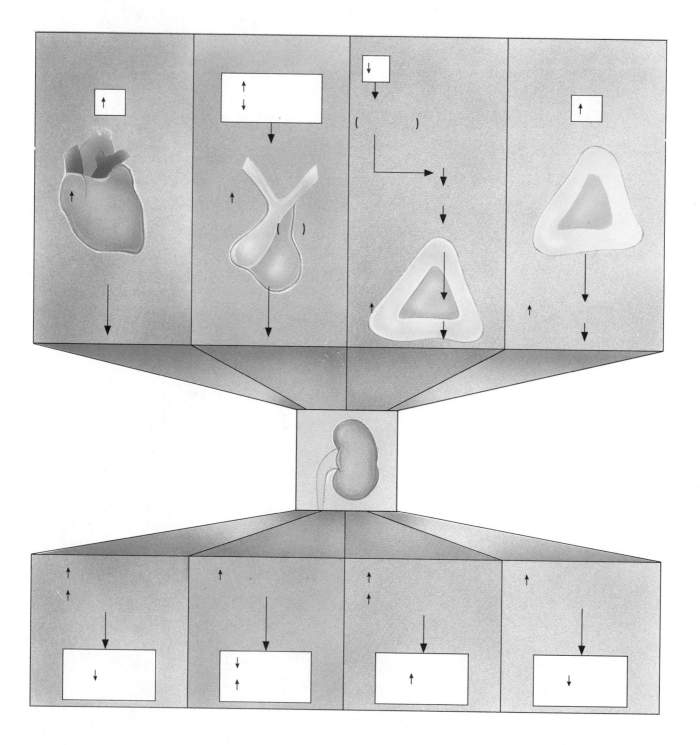

Seeley/Stephens/Tate: Anatomy & Physiology, third edition
© 1995 Mosby–Year Book, Inc.

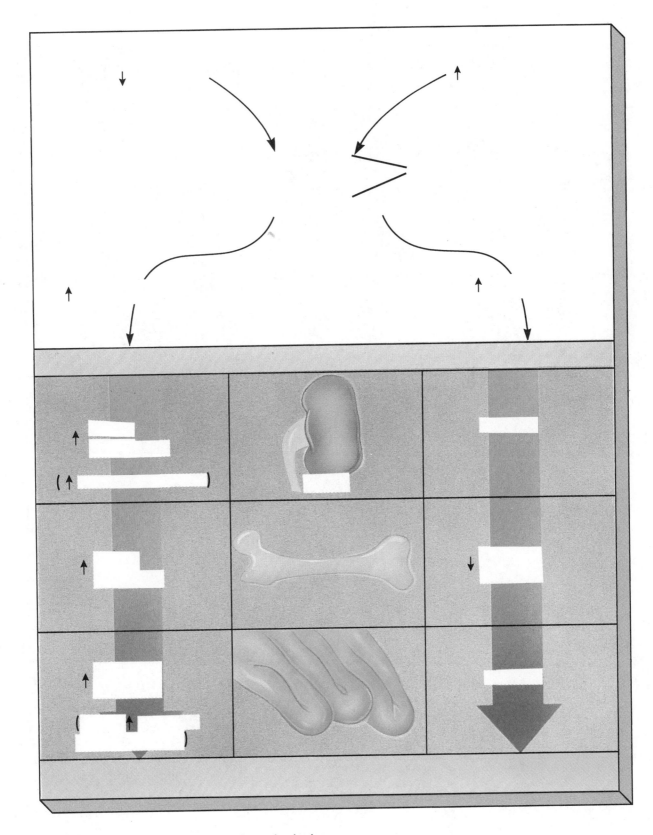

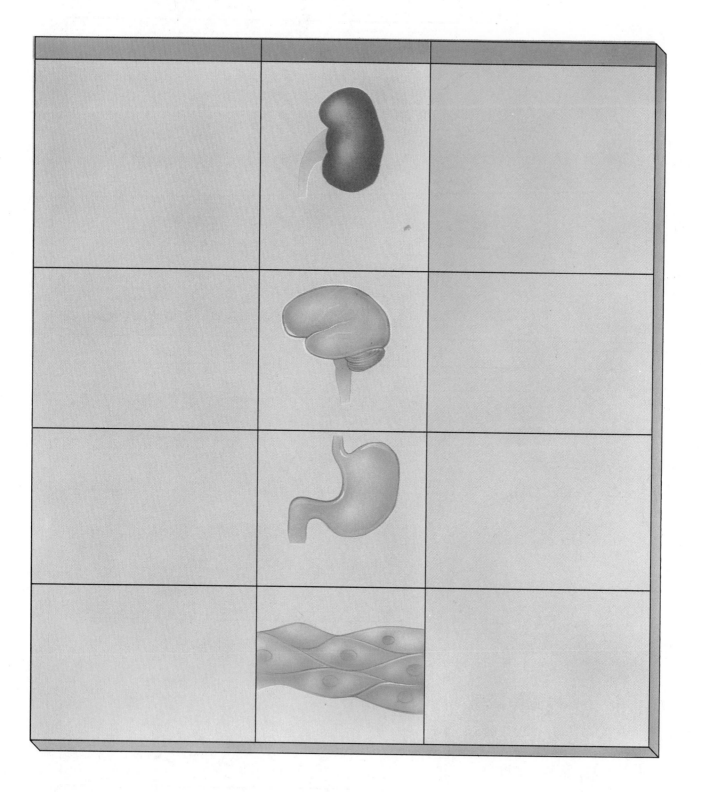

Seeley/Stephens/Tate: Anatomy & Physiology, third edition
© 1995 Mosby–Year Book, Inc.

Carbon Dioxide, Carbonic Acid, Bicarbonate and Hydrogen Ions
(Fig. 27-6, p. 929)

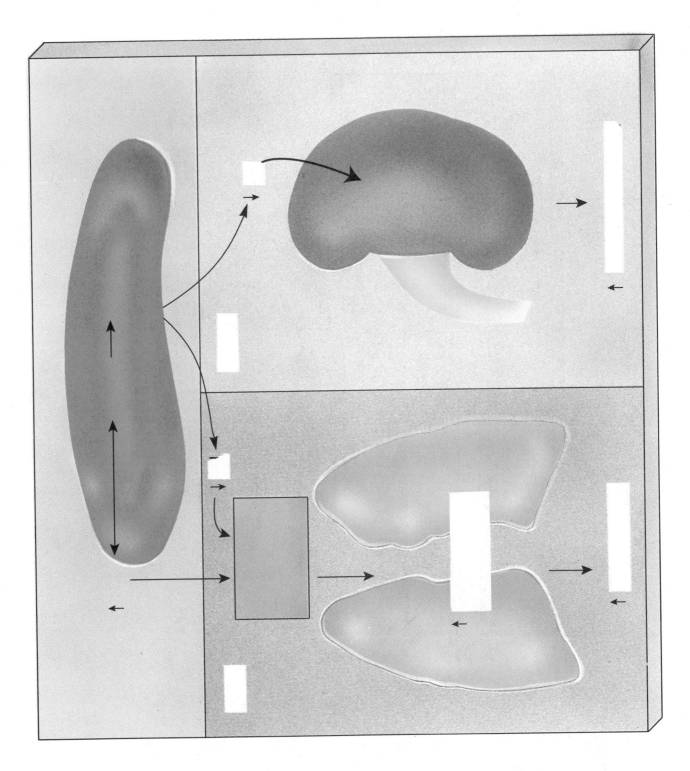

Kidney Regulation of Body Fluid pH (Fig. 27-7, p. 930)

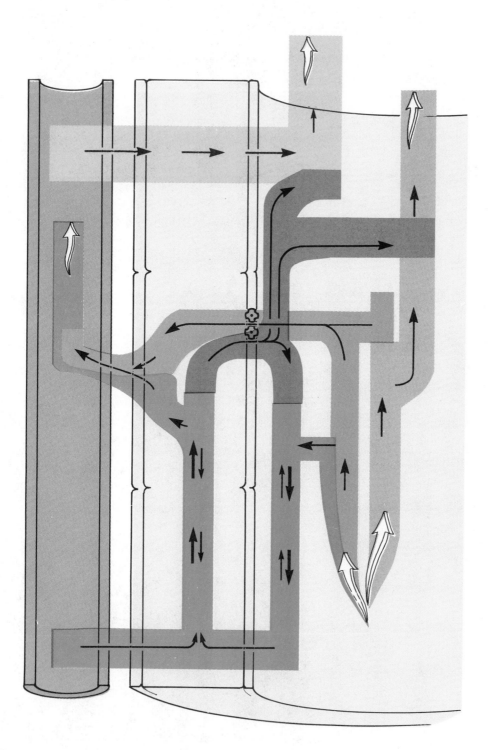

Seeley/Stephens/Tate: Anatomy & Physiology, third edition
© 1995 Mosby–Year Book, Inc.

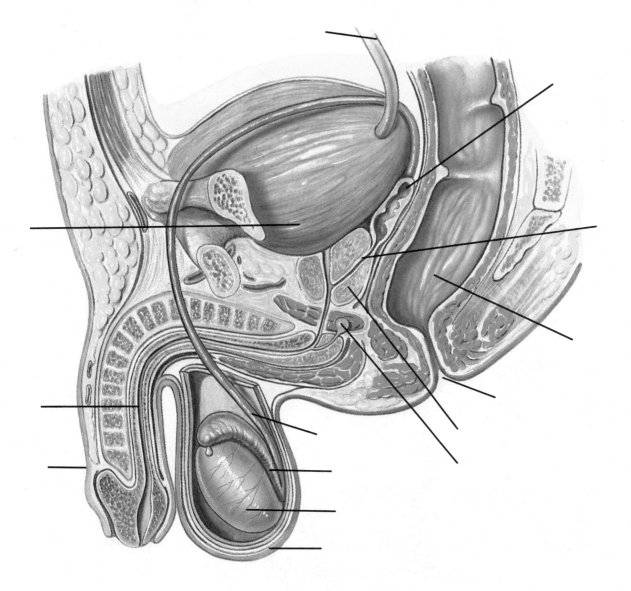

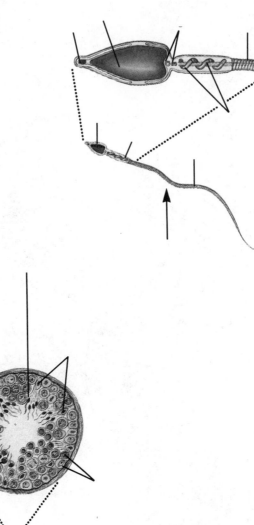

Seeley/Stephens/Tate: Anatomy & Physiology, third edition
© 1995 Mosby–Year Book, Inc.

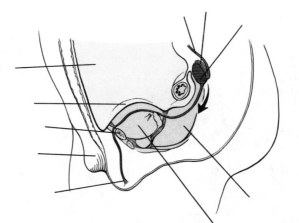

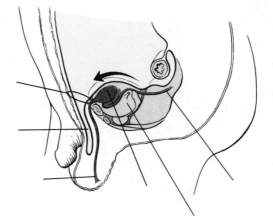

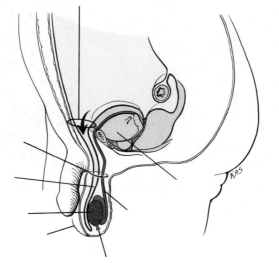

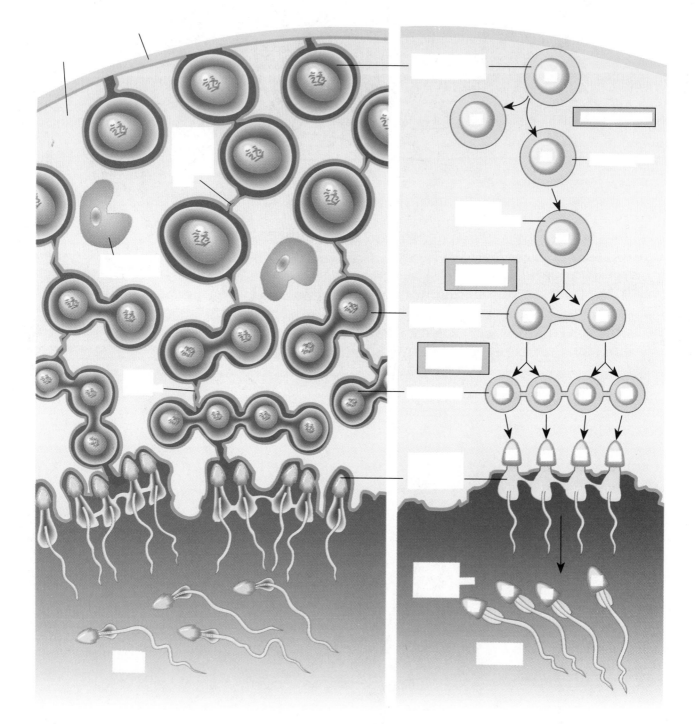

Seeley/Stephens/Tate: Anatomy & Physiology, third edition
© 1995 Mosby—Year Book, Inc.

Male Reproductive Structures (Fig. 28-5, p. 950)

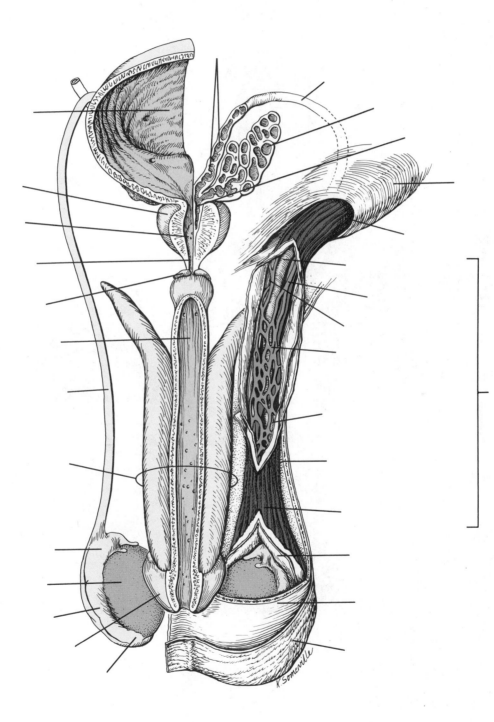

K. Somerville

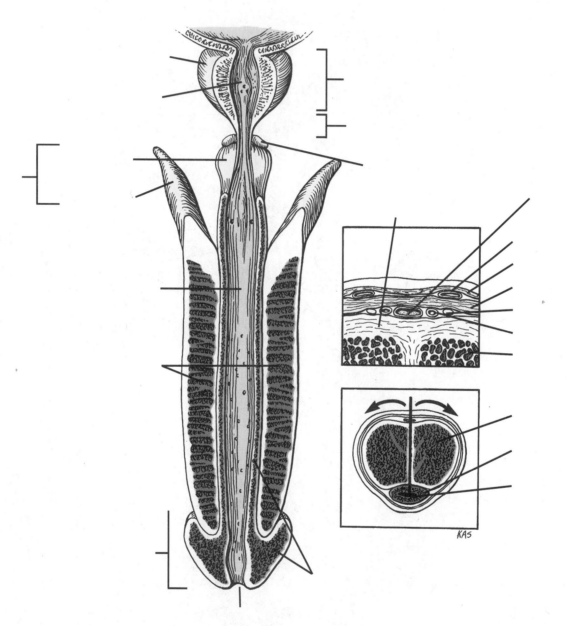

KAS

Seeley/Stephens/Tate: Anatomy & Physiology, third edition
© 1995 Mosby–Year Book, Inc.

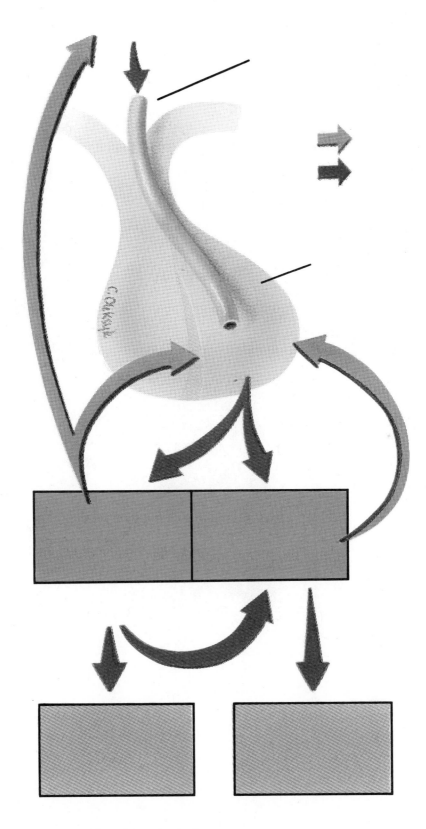

Seeley/Stephens/Tate: Anatomy & Physiology, third edition
© 1995 Mosby–Year Book, Inc.

Uterus, Vagina, Uterine Tubes, Ovaries and Supporting Ligaments
(Fig. 28-9, p. 958)

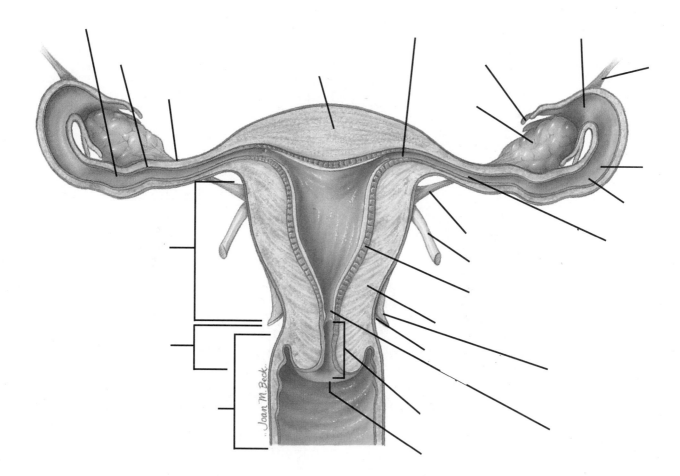

Joan M. Beck.

Seeley/Stephens/Tate: Anatomy & Physiology, third edition
© 1995 Mosby–Year Book, Inc.

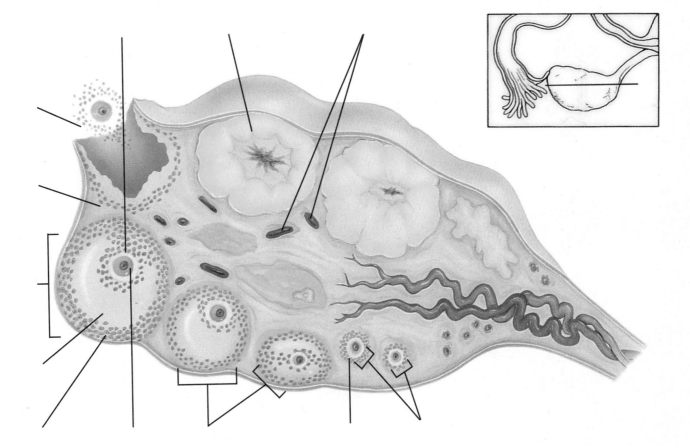

Maturation of the Follicle and Oocyte (Fig. 28-11 A-H, p. 959)

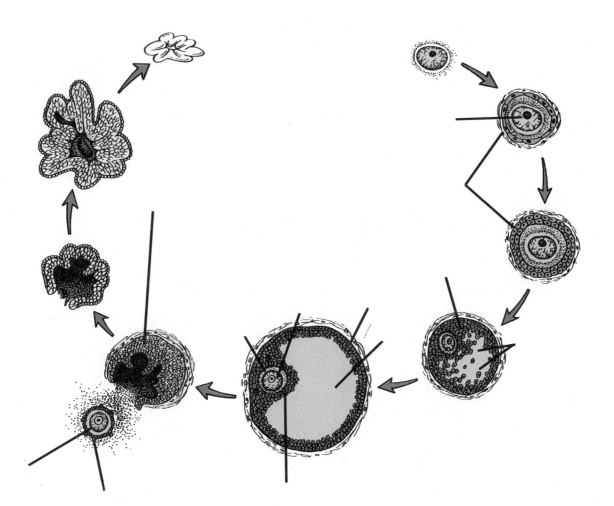

Seeley/Stephens/Tate: Anatomy & Physiology, third edition
© 1995 Mosby–Year Book, Inc.

Maturation and Fertilization of the Oocyte (Fig. 28-12, p. 960)

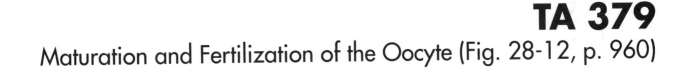

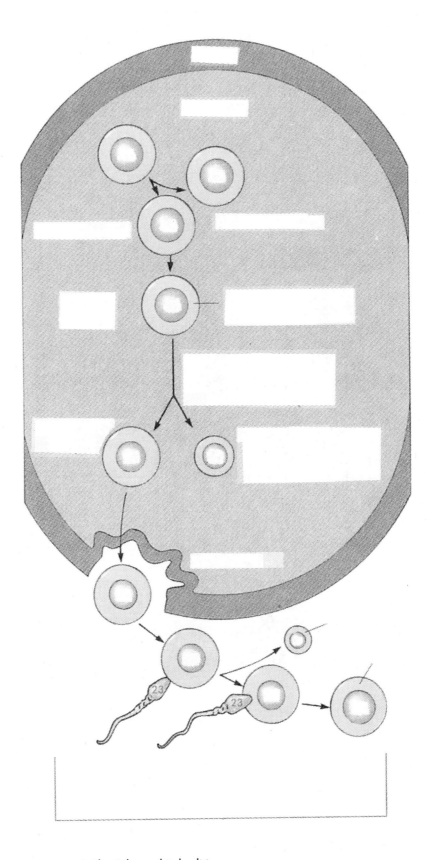

Female External Genitalia (Fig. 28-13, p. 962)

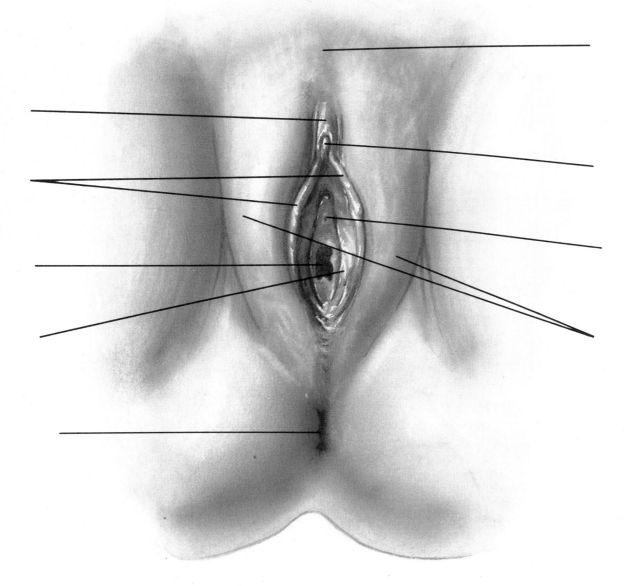

Seeley/Stephens/Tate: Anatomy & Physiology, third edition
© 1995 Mosby–Year Book, Inc.

Inferior View of the Female Perineum (Fig. 28-14, p. 963)

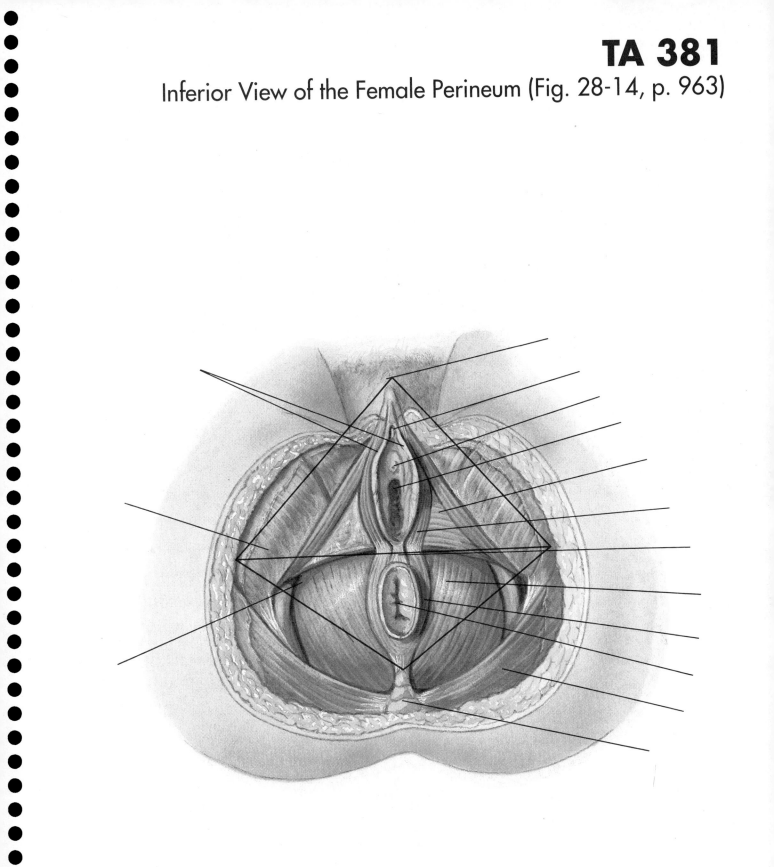

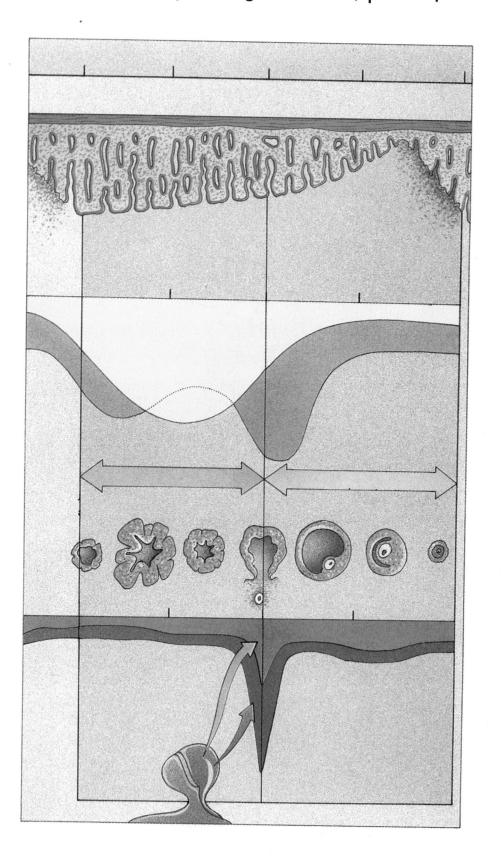

Seeley/Stephens/Tate: Anatomy & Physiology, third edition
© 1995 Mosby–Year Book, Inc.

Changes in Hormone Concentration During Pregnancy
(Fig. 28-18, p. 971)

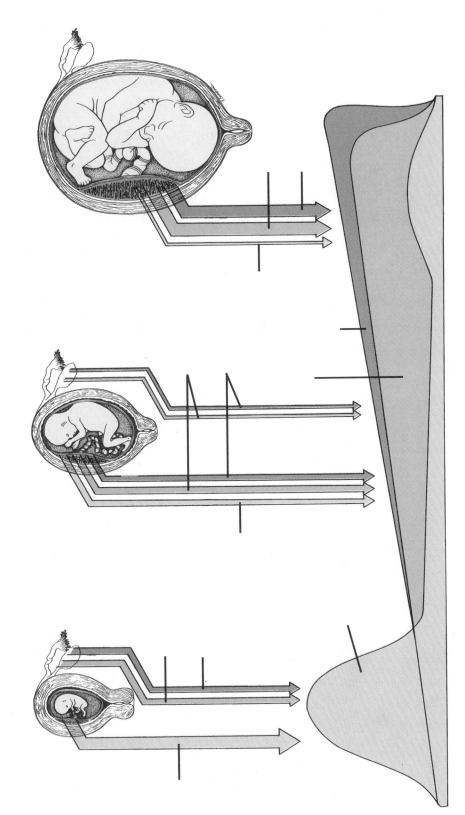

TA 384

Formation of the Placenta (Fig. 29-3 A-C, p. 987)

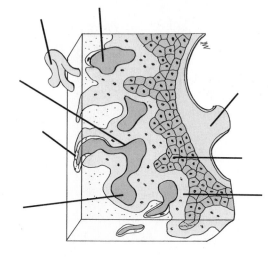

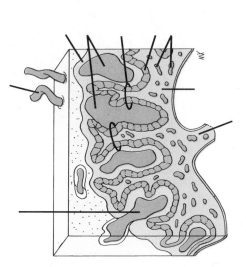

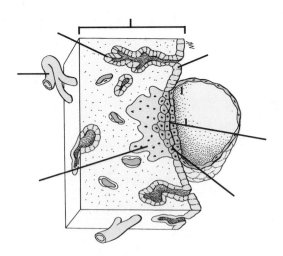

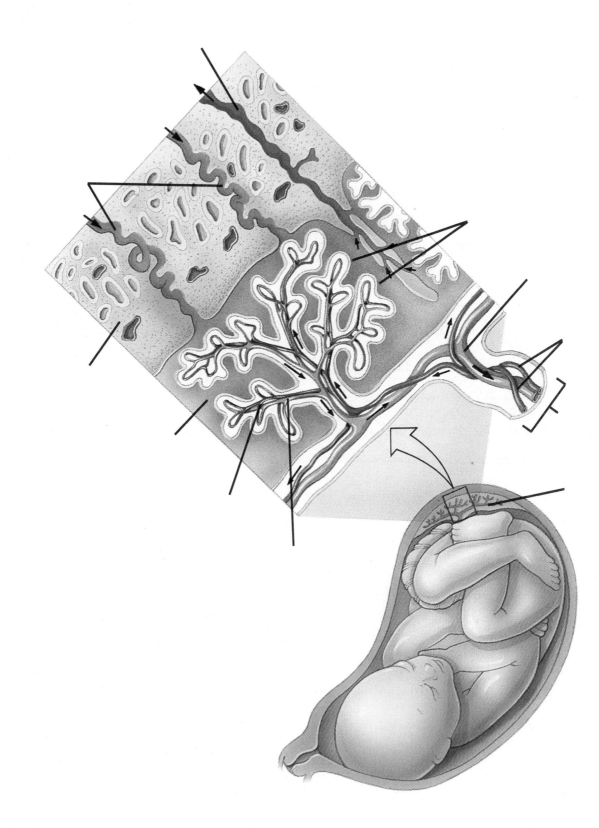

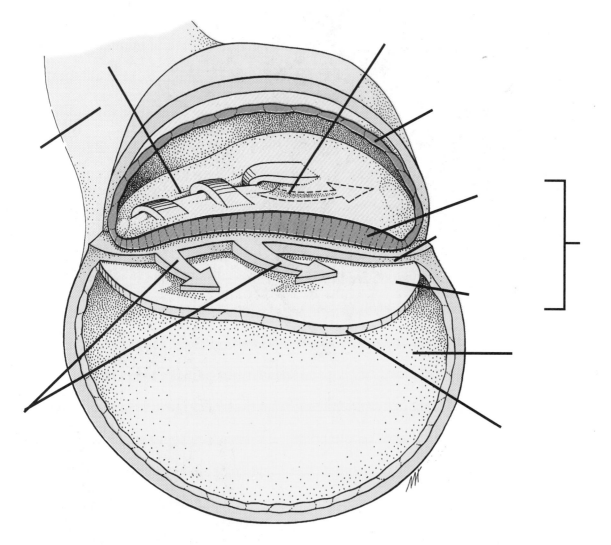

Seeley/Stephens/Tate: Anatomy & Physiology, third edition
© 1995 Mosby–Year Book, Inc.

Formation of the Neural Tube (Fig. 29-7, p. 990)

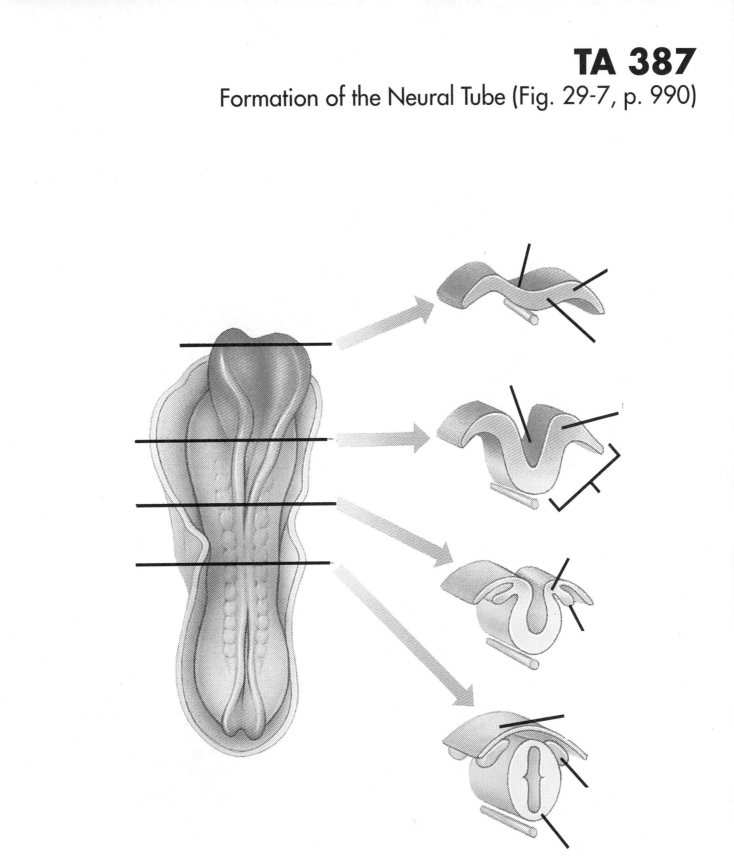

Formation of the Digestive Tract (Fig. 29-8 A-C, p. 992)

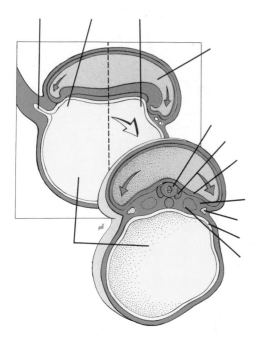

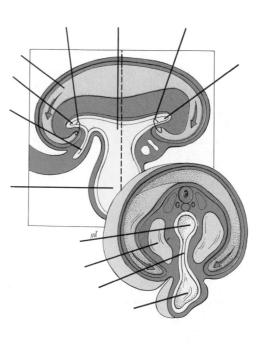

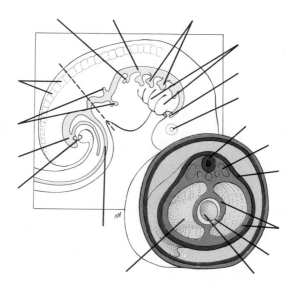

Seeley/Stephens/Tate: Anatomy & Physiology, third edition
© 1995 Mosby–Year Book, Inc.

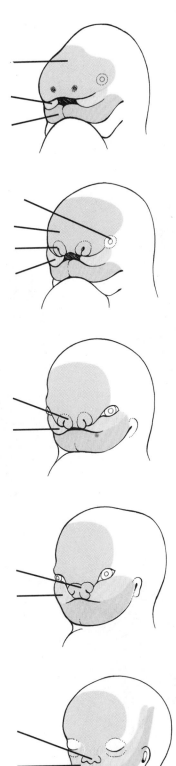

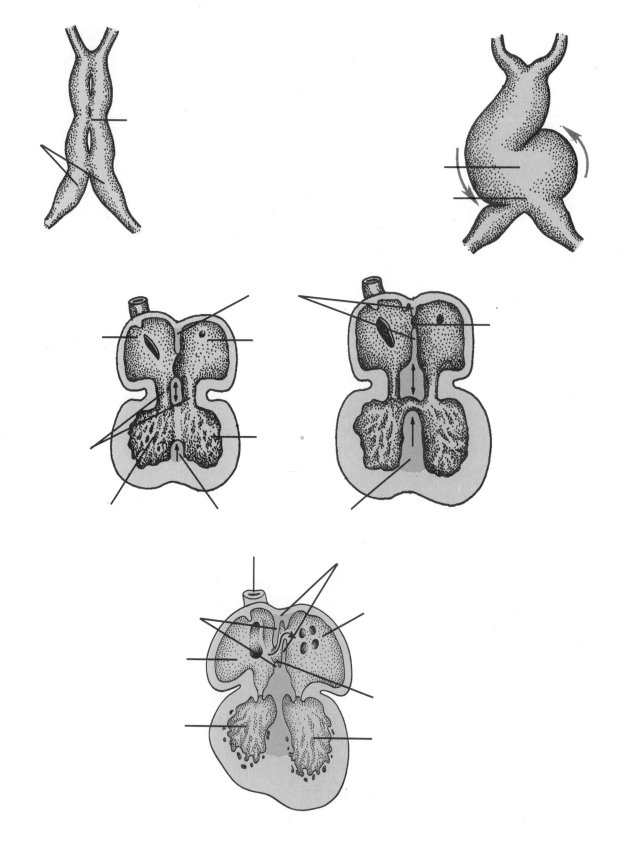

Seeley/Stephens/Tate: Anatomy & Physiology, third edition
© 1995 Mosby–Year Book, Inc.

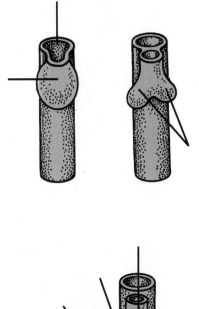

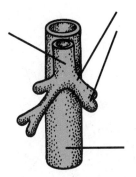

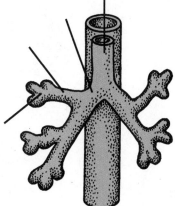

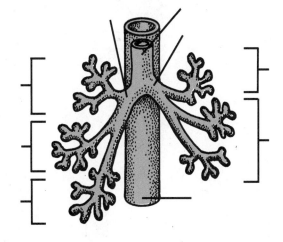

TA 392
Development of the Kidney and Urinary Bladder
(Fig. 29-13 A-D, p. 1000)

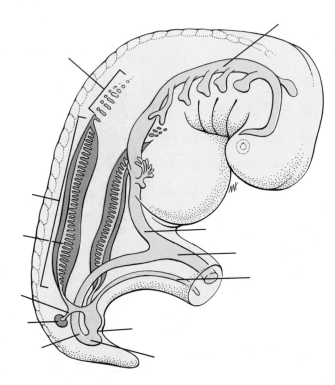

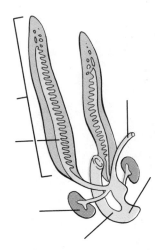

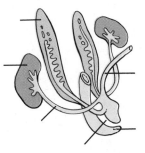

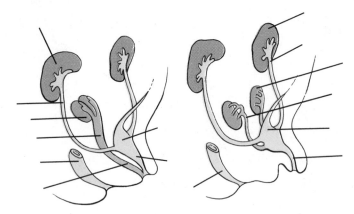

Seeley/Stephens/Tate: Anatomy & Physiology, third edition
© 1995 Mosby–Year Book, Inc.

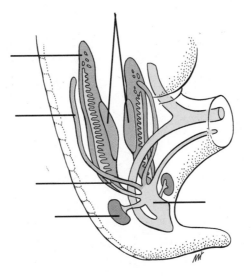

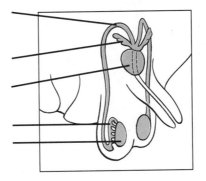

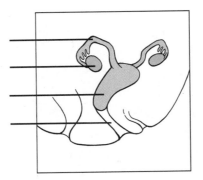

Seeley/Stephens/Tate: Anatomy & Physiology, third edition
© 1995 Mosby—Year Book, Inc.

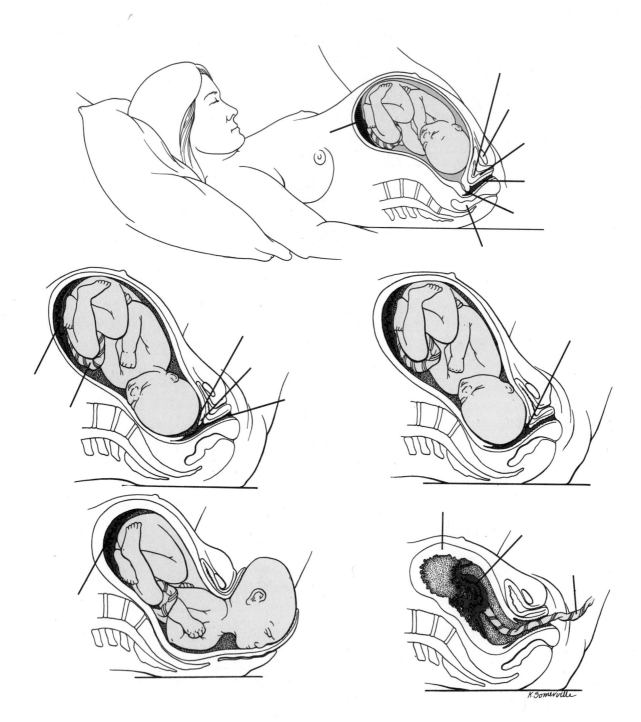

Seeley/Stephens/Tate: Anatomy & Physiology, third edition
© 1995 Mosby—Year Book, Inc.

Factors that Influence the Process of Parturition
(Fig. 29-18, p. 1007)

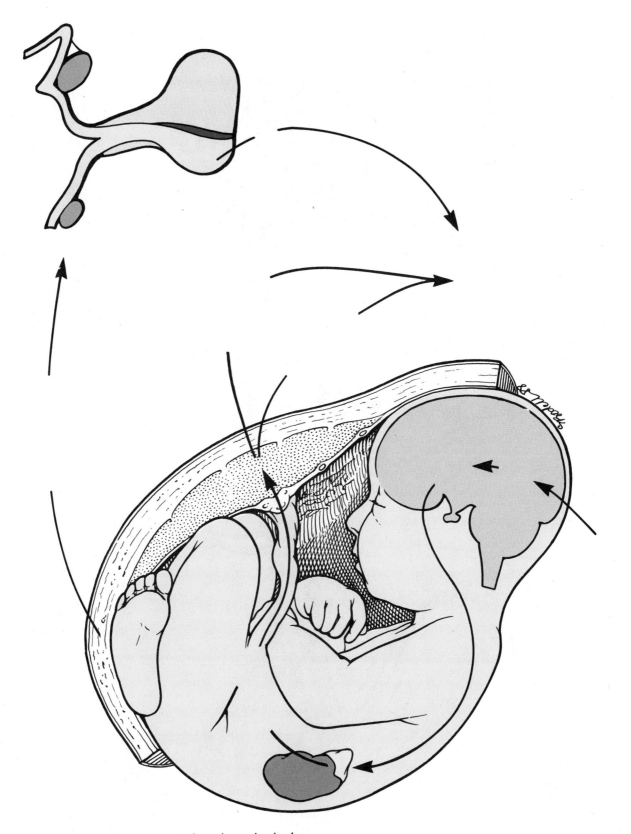

Seeley/Stephens/Tate: Anatomy & Physiology, third edition
© 1995 Mosby–Year Book, Inc.

Circulatory Changes at Birth (Fig. 29-19 A, p. 1008)

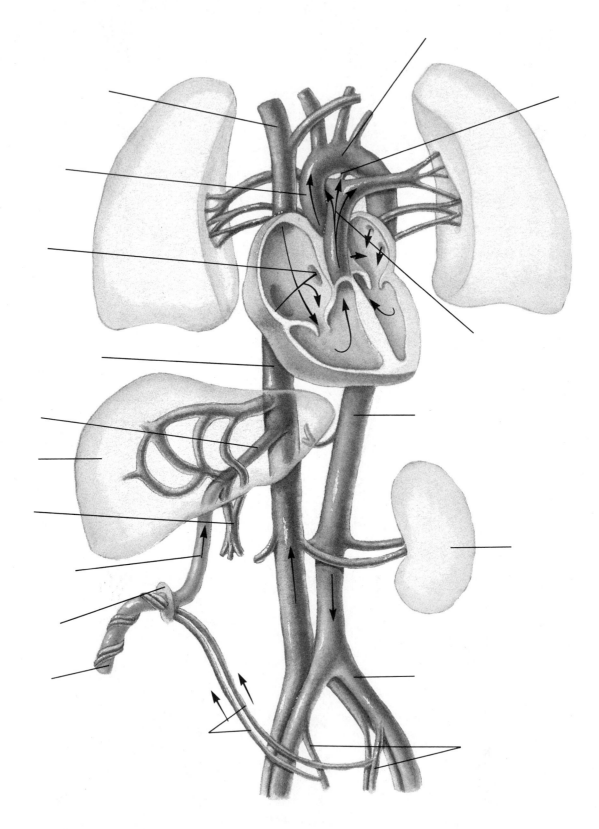

Seeley/Stephens/Tate: Anatomy & Physiology, third edition
© 1995 Mosby-Year Book, Inc.

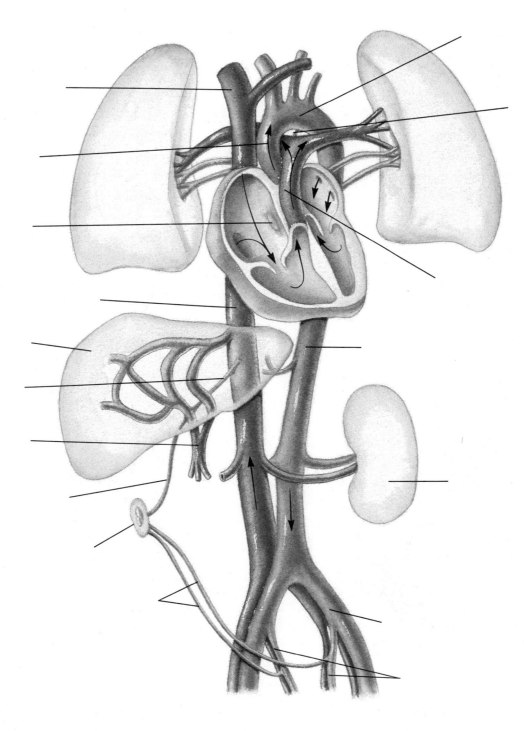

Seeley/Stephens/Tate: Anatomy & Physiology, third edition
© 1995 Mosby–Year Book, Inc.

Hormonal Control of Lactation (Fig. 29-20, p. 1011)

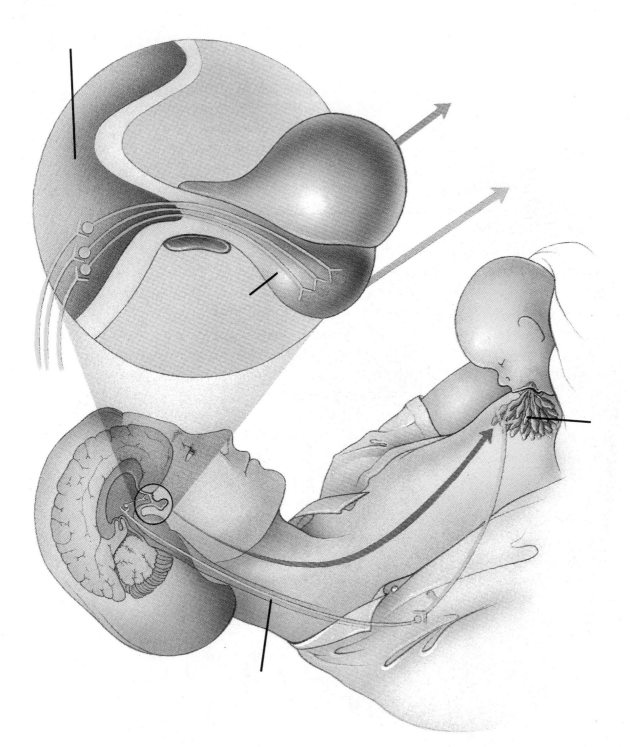

Seeley/Stephens/Tate: *Anatomy & Physiology, third edition*
© 1995 Mosby–Year Book, Inc.

Pedigree of a Simple Dominant Trait (Fig. 29-22, p. 1015)

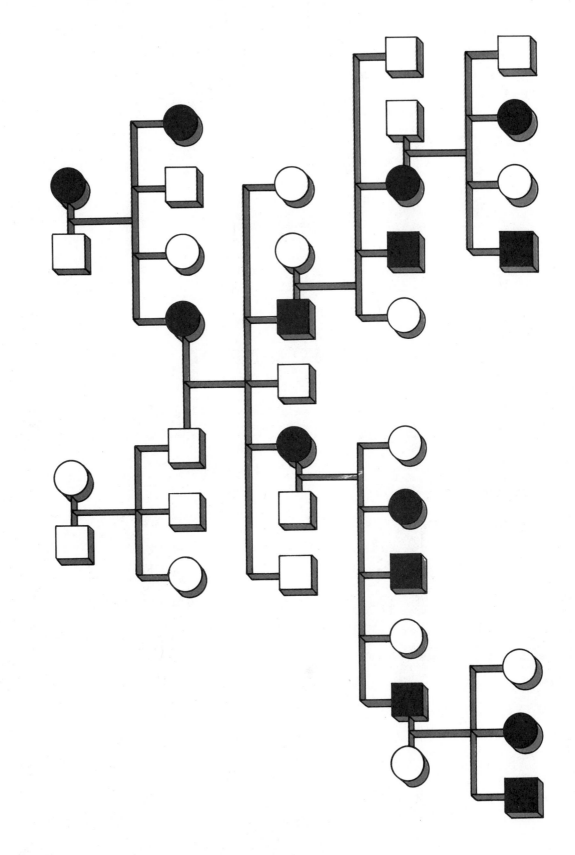

Seeley/Stephens/Tate: Anatomy & Physiology, third edition
© 1995 Mosby–Year Book, Inc.

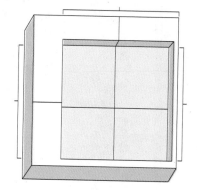

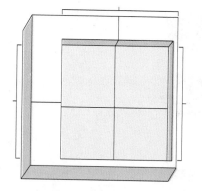

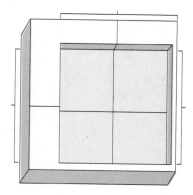